C000115104

Water Wind Art and Debate

How environmental concerns impact on disciplinary research

Edited by Gavin Birch

SYDNEY UNIVERSITY PRESS

Sydney University Press
Published by
SYDNEY UNIVERSITY PRESS
University of Sydney Library
www.sup.usyd.edu.au

© 2007 Sydney University Press

Reproduction and communication for other purposes
Except as permitted under the Act, no part of this edition may be
reproduced, stored in a retrieval system, or communicated in any form
or by any means without prior written permission. All requests for
reproduction or communication should be made to Sydney University
Press at the address below:

Sydney University Press
Fisher Library F03
University of Sydney
NSW 2006 AUSTRALIA
Email: info@sup.usyd.edu.au

ISBN   978-1-920898-65-6

Individual papers are available electronically through the Sydney
eScholarship Repository at:

http://ses.library.usyd.edu.au/handle/2123/2059

Printed in Australia at the University Publishing Service, University of
Sydney

Contents

Foreword

The Australian community has become increasingly concerned about environmental issues, resulting in the Australian Government placing a higher priority on dealing with global warming and climate change. *Water Wind Art and Debate* highlights current research across a variety of humanities and science disciplines.

In August 2006 a new publications initiative to produce books covering multidisciplinary research on topical areas was suggested by Kerrie Legge in the Research Office at the University of Sydney. Extensive collaboration followed between Sydney University Press and the Research Office, resulting in this book. Through this collaboration the University of Sydney hopes to publish a new series of multidisciplinary books highlighting the breadth of new ideas and insights coming from our researchers.

Timothy Stephen's chapter, 'A Slow Burn' critically examines the patchwork of existing legislation having a bearing upon climate change policy in Australia. It also speculates on the future shape and content of Australian climate change law as negotiations on a strengthened international climate regime gather pace.

Stuart Rosewarne's 'Global warming and discourses of uncertainty' exposes some of the fundamental contradictions of and risks associated with the government's procrastination under the guise of a discourse of uncertainty. The Australian Government's longstanding reluctance to accept the science of global warming, or to acknowledge that there is any pressing need to implement policies designed to abate greenhouse gas emissions is discussed.

The chapter of Mladenovic Rosina and Sandra van der Laan, 'State of the Environment Reporting by Local Government' examines Councils' critical role at the micro-level of accountability and reporting processes in activities as diverse as social development through to environmental management, including waste management, land development and use which has consequences for water resources, soil degradation, biodiversity and sewerage. Renewable energy has attracted great attention among governments, industries, academics and societies in the world. In 'Framing Responsibility' John Mikler finds that the institutional basis of capitalist relations in firms' home states is a key determiner of their environmental motivations.

Danielle Spruyt's chapter on the changing status of water suggests that the rights to use water are increasingly linked to the imperative to use water for productive gain, an approach that does not provide a final resolution to the contest between commercial and environmental interests in water use. This shift in policy emphasis challenges us to evaluate our rights to water. Willem Vervoort's 'Management of Water Resources under Uncertainty' reports that forecasting of stream flows and soil moisture balances will be crucial for planning and policy making in agriculture and natural resource management and that a radical rethink of the way simulation models are used to underpin policy and management decisions is needed.

In the chapter 'Energy from Offshore Wind' Dong-Sheng Jeng and Yun Zheng examine the design of offshore wind energy generators and evaluate the selection of potential sites for offshore wind energy in Australia.

Gavin Birch in his chapter, "A short geological and environmental history of the Sydney estuary' traces the recent geological development of Sydney's river system and illustrates how a pristine environment has changed due to human activities. Christopher Dey, Manfred Lenzen and their colleagues report on household environmental pressure from consumption, illustrating the impact of the average Australian's consumption and use of goods and services on the environment. Through detailed census and environmental data, combined with an economy-wide model, they have calculated the total household environmental pressure for over 1300 Australian Statistical Local Areas (SLAs).

Jennifer Barrett's and Phil McManus's chapter on 'Civilising nature: Museums and the environment' considers some of the key discourses in natural history and science museums to reveal a rich legacy of engagement with the environment – arguing that museums shape and reflect environmental attitudes. Catriona Moore's 'Not Just a Pretty Picture: Art as Ecological Communication' traces how the western landscape tradition has been modified by Indigenous concepts of country that combine traditional and inter-disciplinary knowledge within a speculative framework of ecological aesthetics.

The chapter from Gabrielle Higgins, Catherine Maggs, Mathew McKenzie, Eike Christian Meuter, and Erin Semon about the Australian Government's 2006 Nuclear Energy Campaign examines the issue of nuclear energy in Australia from a public relations perspective and within a framework of political communication theory.

The resulting volume provides a unique insight into how concerns about the environment are influencing every facet of life.

Professor Merlin Crossley
Deputy Vice-Chancellor, Research
University of Sydney

Part 1
Legal and political issues

1

A slow burn: the emergence of climate change law in Australia

Tim Stephens

Abstract

Following more than a decade of intransigence on climate change policy, the Australian Government is beginning to yield to sustained pressure from the community and business to enact comprehensive climate change legislation. As the environmental, economic and security implications of global warming are better understood, there are growing calls to place emissions reduction targets within a binding legislative regime that contains both market-based measures (such as emissions trading) and regulatory interventions (such as mandatory efficiency standards). Adding impetus for national climate law reform are initiatives by other governments (including several Australian states) to enshrine emissions reduction targets in law. This chapter critically examines the patchwork of existing legislation having a bearing upon climate change policy in Australia. It also speculates on the future shape and content of Australian climate change law as negotiations on a strengthened international climate regime gather pace.

Introduction

After a decade of opposition to binding national and international measures to address climate change,[1] the Australian Government is

---

[1] See Clive Hamilton, *Scorcher: The dirty politics of climate change* Black Inc, 2007. Hamilton argues that the Howard government has not been content to refuse to take

under sustained pressure to participate constructively in international climate change negotiations and to enact comprehensive national climate change legislation. The pressure points for national law reform have been numerous, and have included better understanding of the threat of climatic change;[2] growing public awareness and concern;[3] business advocacy for investment certainty; fuller appreciation of likely impacts on Australia's environment, economy and security;[4] the rapid increase in Australia's greenhouse gas emissions; and legislative initiatives by the states and territories.[5]

As in many other areas of environmental management, in addressing climate change there appears no substitute for clear and enforceable goals set within a statutory scheme.[6] Indeed the Australian Government now appears to recognise that its voluntary industry and consumer programs have failed to deliver any substantial emissions reductions. In July 2007 the Howard government announced that it would set a long-term 'aspirational' target for reducing Australia's emission in 2008 and would implement a national carbon trading scheme by 2012.[7] For its

---

measures on climate change, but has actively set out to sabotage the Kyoto Protocol. (at p. 221). See also Guy Pearse, *High and dry: John Howard, climate change and the selling of Australia's future* Viking, 2007.

[2] Respected climatologists and other scientists now speak of civilisation being in imminent peril and call for immediate action to be launched in aid of planetary rescue: James Hansen et al, 'Climate change and trace gases', *Philosophical Transactions of the Royal Society*, 2007 (A) pp. 1925–1954. See also James Lovelock, *The revenge of Gaia: why the Earth is fighting back – and how we can still save humanity*, Basic Books, 2006.

[3] One recent poll conducted by World Public Opinion found that Australians were the most likely to favour measures to combat global warming: http://www.worldpublicopinion.org/pipa/articles/home_page/329.php?nid=&id= &pnt=329&lb=hmpg1, viewed 23 March 2007.

[4] See, e.g. Alan Duport & Graeme Pearman, *Heating up the planet: climate change and security*, Lowy Institute, 2006.

[5] See, e.g. *Climate Change and Greenhouse Emissions Reduction Act 2007* (SA) (discussed below) which aims to reduce by 2050 greenhouse gas emissions in South Australia by between 60 and 40 per cent below 1990 levels.

[6] Rosemary Lyster, 'The implications of electricity restructuring for a sustainable energy framework: what's law got to do with it? *Environmental and Planning Law Journal* vol. 20, 2003, pp. 359, 367. See generally Rory Sullivan, *Rethinking voluntary approaches in environmental policy*, Elgar 2005.

[7] Australian Government, *Report of the Prime Ministerial Task Group on Emissions Trading* Commonwealth of Australia, Canberra, 2007; and Australian Government, *Australia's*

part, the federal opposition has committed a Labor government to ratifying the Kyoto Protocol, to emissions cuts of 60 per cent below 2000 levels by 2050, and to establishing, as soon as possible, an internationally-consistent emissions trading scheme.

Against this background, this chapter offers a critical assessment of the limited efforts that have been made to devise and implement an effective Australian climate change law. The first section examines the current state of climate science, the regulatory challenges posed by climate change, and Australia's emissions profile. The achievements of the United Nations Framework Convention on Climate Change (UNFCCC) and the accompanying Kyoto Protocol are discussed, as are the prospects of a new regime post 2012. In the second section, the chapter assesses the value of existing and proposed Australian laws relating to climate change. It is seen that this inchoate Australian climate change law remains a considerable distance from what is required to deal with the existential threat of climate change.

Climate change science and regulation

Climate change science

The 2007 Fourth Assessment Report (AR4) of the Intergovernmental Panel on Climate Change (IPCC) offers the most comprehensive scientific assessment to date of climate change. The four central messages from the AR4 are: that climate change is almost certainly the result of human activity; that substantial increases in temperature this century can be expected; that temperature rises above 2°C will devastate the physical and biological systems upon which humanity depends; and that considerable reduction in carbon emissions is required to stabilise climate systems.

The AR4 reports that emissions of greenhouse gases from human activities are responsible for a rise in global average surface temperatures

---

climate change policy: our economy, our environment, our future, Commonwealth of Australia, Canberra, 2007.

of approximately 0.75°C between 1906 and 2005.[8] The world is now warming at approximately 0.13°C per decade, roughly twice the rate recorded over the previous century. The AR4 projects that temperatures will increase by between 1.1°C and 6.4°C by 2100. As a consequence, sea levels will rise by between 0.18 and 0.59 metres and the oceans will become increasingly acidic. Disturbingly, these projections do not factor in the risk that positive feedback processes may lead to rapid, runaway climate change.

In relation to impacts, the AR4 concludes that climate change has already had a discernable influence on environmental systems.[9] Moreover, the resilience of many ecosystems is likely to be exceeded this century by an unprecedented combination of climate change and other human disturbances. According to the IPCC, Australians can expect water security problems from reduced precipitation and increased evaporation, significant loss in biodiversity, particularly in the ecologically-rich sites of the Great Barrier Reef and Kakadu, and major declines in agricultural productivity. This analysis tends to confirm that Australia is the developed country most at risk from climate change.

The third focus of the IPCC is upon mitigation, that is, the emissions reductions required to avert the worst climate change impacts. Greenhouse gas emissions have risen globally by 70 per cent between 1970 and 2004, and are projected to continue to grow.[10] However, there is substantial economic potential to reduce emissions over the coming decades through the deployment of available technologies, such as renewable modes of energy production. In line with the findings of *The economics of climate change: the Stern review*,[11] commissioned by the British

---

[8] Intergovernmental Panel on Climate Change, *Climate Change 2007: The physical science basis,* summary for policymakers, contribution of Working Group I to the Fourth Assessment Report, 2007.

[9] Intergovernmental Panel on Climate Change, *Climate change 2007: climate change impacts, adaptation and vulnerability,* summary for policymakers, contribution of Working Group II to the Fourth Assessment Report, 2007.

[10] Intergovernmental Panel on Climate Change, *Climate change 2007: mitigation of climate change,* summary for policymakers, contribution of Working Group III to the Fourth Assessment Report, 2007.

[11] Nicholas Stern, *The economics of climate change: the Stern review,* Cambridge University Press, 2007.

Treasury, the economic costs of cutting emissions appear relatively small in the medium to long term (especially in comparison with the high costs of inaction).

The IPCC presents a choice of stabilisation pathways[12] (see Table 1). For instance, to retain concentrations of CO_{2e}[13] at between 445 and 490 parts per million (ppm), and thereby keep temperature increases between 2.0°C and 2.4°C, will require emissions to peak by 2015, and then to be reduced by between 50 and 85 per cent by 2050.[14] A 2°C rise on pre-industrial temperatures is probably the upper limit beyond which we should not step, as it could stimulate irreversible processes, including the melting of the Greenland ice sheet. For this reason the 2°C target has been adopted by the European Union in its climate change strategy.[15]

Table 1.1 Stabilisation Pathways

CO_{2e} concentration (ppm)	Global mean temperature increase (above pre-industrial level) (°C)	Peaking year for CO_2 emissions	CO_2 emissions changes (from 2000 levels) (%)
445–490	2.0–2.4	2000–2015	-85 to -50
490–535	2.4–2.8	2000–2020	-60 to -30
535–590	2.8–3.2	2010–2030	-30 to +5
590–710	3.2–4.0	2020–2060	+10 to +60
710–855	4.0–4.9	2050–2080	+25 to +85
855–1130	4.9–6.1	2060–2090	+90 to +140

Source: Adapted from Intergovernmental Panel on Climate Change, *Climate change 2007: mitigation of climate change*, summary for policymakers, contribution of Working Group III to the Fourth Assessment Report, 2007, p. 23

---

[12] The notion of stabilising greenhouse gas emissions is that a steady concentration can be maintained over time by ensuring that emissions of gases are equal to removals.

[13] A tonne of CO_{2e} (carbon dioxide equivalent) means one metric tonne of CO_2 or a volume of another greenhouse gas with the identical warming effect.

[14] See also Nathan Rive et al 'To what extent can a long-term temperature target guide near term climate change commitments?' *Climatic Change*, vol. 82, 2007, pp. 373–391

[15] Council of the European Union, Information Note 7242/05, 11 March 2005.

Australia's emissions profile

Neither as a matter of law nor policy has Australia committed to the emissions reductions necessary to keep temperatures below 2°C. Indeed, Australia's current and projected greenhouse gas are wholly inconsistent with a pathway of a 50 to 85 per cent reduction in global emissions by 2050 required to meet this temperature target.

Australia shares the dubious distinction of being one of the highest per capita emitters of greenhouse gases. In response to this fact, it is often said that Australia's emissions are small in global terms, at 1.5 per cent. However, in reality Australia is both a major per capita and aggregate emitter. Australia's emissions are equal to those of much larger industrialised countries, such as South Korea and France (both with 1.5%) and only slightly lower than others such as Italy (1.6%) and the United Kingdom (1.9%).[16]

While Australia's emissions increased by only around 2.3 per cent between 1990 and 2004, this was largely because of reduced rates of land clearing. Now that this one-off windfall has been achieved, emissions are beginning to rise rapidly. The government estimates that emissions will reach 109 per cent of 1990 levels by 2008–2012,[17] thereby overshooting the Kyoto Protocol target of a 108 per cent increase over this period. By 2020, emissions are projected to reach 127 per cent of 1990 levels, due mostly to rapid increases in emissions from the stationary energy and transport sectors. This takes into account all abatement measures currently in place at federal and state levels.

The political and regulatory challenges of climate change

Australian climate change policy and law must be made in the context of international efforts to constrain emissions. Improved climate science has clarified the parameters for global policy choices, but it cannot determine what choices should be made.

[16] Baumert KA, Herzog T & Pershing J, *Navigating the numbers: greenhouse gas data and international climate policy*, World Resources Institute, 2006.
[17] Department of the Environment and Heritage, *Tracking to the Kyoto target 2006: Australia's greenhouse emissions trends 1990 to 2008–12 and 2020*, 2006.

Two main choices now confront the international community. The first, and most important, is what global average temperature increase is to be tolerated. As has been seen, 2°C appears the most scientifically defensible target if the more serious effects of climate change are to be avoided, which in turn implies a global goal for reducing emissions of between 50 and 85 per cent on 1990 levels by 2050. This then leads to a second and more difficult decision: how is the burden of reducing emissions to be distributed fairly among nations? The fairest approach is that of 'contraction and convergence', under which total global emissions are reduced over time (contraction), while per capita emissions are gradually equalised among nations in the North and South (convergence). However, this approach stands at odds with the national interests of Australia and other fossil-fuel reliant economies, and is therefore in competition with a range of other models posited as a replacement for the Kyoto Protocol which pay greater deference to national circumstances.

Coupled with these difficult geopolitical choices are equally challenging regulatory challenges. Anthropogenic climate change is unlike any environmental problem that has been subject to national or international regulation, for four main reasons. First, climate change is a global process of environmental change driven by emissions from activities central to human livelihoods and industries across the planet. To ensure effective reductions and avoid free-riding, global coordination to reduce emissions is indispensable. Second, climate change is a phenomenon driven by activities across almost all economic sectors. As a consequence, climate change calls for an expansive regulatory regime that encompasses all sources of greenhouse gas emissions. The third special feature of the problem is the time lag between the causes and effects of climate change. While some change has already taken place, the most serious impacts are yet to be felt, and their magnitude will be directly determined by the policy choices governments make today. Fourth, there remains considerable uncertainty as to how serious will be the impacts of climate change. Although there is good scientific evidence that climate change is the most serious threat to the planet's biodiversity (rivalling, or exceeding deforestation),[18] when it comes to impacts upon human civilisation there is considerable uncertainty as to which societies will bear the most serious effects of change, and whether they will be able to adapt to a radically altered climate.[19]

International climate change law

The existing international legal framework does not establish anything like a comprehensive system to deal with the political and regulatory challenges of climate change. Nonetheless, it does set out important parameters and principles that form the foundations for an effective international climate change law.

The building blocks for an international climate change law

The UNFCCC was agreed at the 1992 Rio Conference on Environment and Development, and now has almost universal membership with 189 parties, including Australia. The provisions of the UNFCCC have been well documented,[20] and for the purposes of this chapter only several key features need be noted. The foremost of these is the overarching goal to stabilise emissions at a level that will prevent dangerous anthropogenic interference with the climate system.[21] Second, the UNFCCC introduces the notion of common, but differentiated responsibilities. This is the concept that while all states have a shared duty to combat climate change, industrialised nations responsible for most carbon wastes emitted to the atmosphere are to take the lead in cutting emissions, with developing countries to contribute according to their capacity to do so. Third, the UNFCCC emphasises that the precautionary approach is to structure the global response to climate change, so that scientific uncertainty should not justify inaction. Finally, while all parties took on a commitment to reduce emissions, industrialised states are encouraged,

---

[18] Malcolm JR, et al 'Global warming and extinctions of endemic species from biodiversity hotspots' *Conservation Biology*, vol. 20, no. 2, 2006, pp. 538–548, 545.

[19] Arrow KJ, 'Global climate change: a challenge to policy' *The Economists' Voice*, June 2007, p. 1.

[20] See, e.g. Bodansky D, 'The United Nations Framework Convention on Climate Change: A Commentary' (1993) 18 *Yale Journal of International Law* 451.

[21] UNFCCC, Article 2.

but not required,[22] to limit their greenhouse gas emissions to 1990 levels by 2000.

In the face of rapidly rising greenhouse gas concentrations in the atmosphere, it was the task of the Kyoto Protocol to give concrete effect to the broad objectives of the UNFCCC by setting binding emission reduction targets. Although agreed in 1997, it was not until February 2005 that the Kyoto Protocol attracted the required ratifications from industrialised countries to enter into force. As with the UNFCCC, it is now a very widely supported agreement, with 172 parties ranging from the most highly developed to least developed nations.

The Kyoto Protocol operationalises the central bargain agreed in the UNFCCC, namely that developed countries would take on legally-binding emissions reduction or limitation targets and, in providing technological and other assistance to developing countries would help these countries to develop less carbon-intensive economies. As with the Montreal Protocol on Substances that Deplete the Ozone Layer, the expectation was that once developed countries had demonstrated real progress in reducing emissions in several commitment periods, developing countries would begin to assume similar obligations.

This bargain was repudiated by the United States and Australia, the only industrialised nations not to join the Kyoto Protocol. Both of these states maintain that they will not participate in an internationally-binding framework until key developing countries, such as China and India, have committed to do so. Australia's refusal to ratify Kyoto is perplexing in a number of respects. Australia won major concessions in the 1997 negotiations, namely the so-called 'Australia clause' that permitted countries with net emissions from land use change and forestry in 1990 to include net land use change emissions in their 1990 baseline, and an emissions increase (to 108% of 1990 levels) rather than the reduction that most other states were required to implement (such as the 92% of 1990 levels required of the European Union). Moreover, despite refusing to ratify the Kyoto Protocol, the government has consistently argued that it is working towards meeting the emissions limitation target set for

---

[22] Gillespie A, *Climate change, ozone depletion and air pollution,* 2006, p. 181.

Australia. This sits at odds with the government's claim that to join Kyoto would destroy the Australian economy.

The future climate change regime

Whereas the UNFCCC set out important governing principles, the Kyoto Protocol laid much of the institutional groundwork for international action on climate change. This is particularly through the so-called 'flexible mechanisms' of joint-implementation, clean-development mechanism, and emissions trading.[23] However, the emissions reductions agreed in 1997 are not a comprehensive climate change solution. Even if fully implemented, they will produce global emissions reductions of around one per cent, a fraction of the 50 to 85 per cent cuts that are required. As a consequence, there is a need to build a new international consensus on emissions reduction targets.

The first phase of the Kyoto Protocol will conclude in 2012 when the end of the 'first commitment period' is reached. The essential choice facing the international community is whether to rollover Kyoto and adopt a follow-up framework that sets new emissions targets and that includes a wider range of emitters with greater stringency, or whether to discard Kyoto and adopt a new regime altogether. Given the international commitment to Kyoto and its long and difficult gestation, it is naïve in the extreme to think that a new agreement can be concluded quickly. As Hamilton has noted, the Kyoto Protocol represents 'the most complex and ambitious international treaty process ever attempted'.[24]

Although it has been subject to considerable criticism by the Howard government, the Kyoto Protocol is in fact a remarkably pliable agreement, and can accommodate a whole range of modifications consistent with the basic principles of the UNFCCC. For instance, a second commitment period could include binding targets for developed countries, and for developing countries binding policy commitments (e.g. obligations to reduce deforestation rates) and

---

[23] See, in particular, Stokke OS, Hovi J & Ufstein G (eds), *Implementing the climate regime: international compliance*, Earthscan, 2005.

[24] Clive Hamilton, 'Building on Kyoto', *New Left Review*, vol. 45, 2007, pp. 91, 96.

binding sectoral commitments (e.g. obligations to reduce emissions in a certain economic sector).[25]

Such issues are already being floated in negotiations on a post-2012 framework. In 2005 the parties to the Kyoto Protocol established an Ad Hoc Working Group to consider future emissions reductions. As a non-party to Kyoto, Australia has no formal voice in this process. However, parallel with the Kyoto-track negotiations have been a more general dialogue under the UNFCCC in which Australia has participated. Both processes come to a head in December 2007 when the parties to UNFCCC and Kyoto meet in Bali to discuss the future of international climate change law. The Bali meeting has been given particular impetus following the declaration of the G8 at the 2007 Heiligendamm summit. The G8 declaration acknowledges that "the UN climate process is the appropriate forum for negotiating future global action on climate change", that "further action should be based on the UNFCCC principles of common, but differentiated responsibilities and respective capabilities", and that a global agreement "under the UNFCCC" should be agreed by 2009. [26]

The Howard government has sent mixed messages concerning the importance of the United Nations as a venue for determining global climate policy. As with the Bush Administration in the United States, it was initially highly critical of any UN-led process for establishing a new post 2012 consensus. Instead it has championed alternative arrangements, such as the non-binding 2006 Asia Pacific Partnership on Clean Development and Climate. AP6, as it is known, comprises the United States, China, India, Japan, Korea and Australia, which together emit 50 per cent of global emissions. AP6 sets no targets, timeframes or benchmarks for emissions reductions, but places its faith in promoting technological innovation through direct government subsidy.[27]

---

[25] Claussen E & Diringer E, 'A new climate treaty: US leadership after Kyoto', *Harvard International Review*, vol. 29, no. 1, 2007, p. 80.
[26] G8 Summit Heiligendamm 2007, *Growth and responsibility in the world economy: summit declaration*, http://www.g-8.de/Content/EN/Artikel/__g8-summit/anlagen/2007-06-07-gipfeldokument-wirtschaft-eng,property=publicationFile.pdf, viewed 27 June 2007.
[27] See http://www.asiapacificpartnership.org/, viewed 27 June 2007.

Unfortunately, it appears unlikely to deliver any substantial emissions reductions, according to recent economic modelling by the Australian Bureau of Agricultural and Resource Economics.[28]

The meagre achievements of the voluntary AP6 stand in stark contrast to the mandatory approach taken in Europe through the European Union Emissions Trading Scheme (EU ETS) that is effectively harnessing market forces to reduce emissions across the EU within a Kyoto-compatible framework.[29] The EU ETS forms the basic mechanism for pricing carbon in European economies and will be an important tool for achieving the binding 20 per cent by 2020 emissions reduction target agreed by European heads of government in early March 2007.[30]

In light of recent statements by the G8, the Howard government now appears to accept that the United Nations remains the central forum when it comes to climate negotiations. Hence, in the Australian Government's Climate Change Policy, released in July 2007, it is said that Australia "will pursue an effective international framework through all available avenues, including the United Nations Framework Convention on Climate Change."[31]

---

[28] Fisher B et al *Technological development and economic growth:* ABARE research report 06.1, Australian Bureau of Agricultural and Resource Economics, 2006, p. 34. See also Clive Hamilton 'The political economy of climate change', Milthorpe Lecture, Macquarie University, June 2006, http://www.tai.org.au, viewed 27 June 2007.

[29] The EU ETS was designed to assist in achieving the EU's eight per cent emissions reduction target under the *Kyoto Protocol.* Its coverage includes energy production, and metals, minerals, pulp and paper production industries. It establishes a cap and trade system under which eligible companies are given an emissions allocation (calculated on the basis of the member state's emissions reduction target). They may purchase additional allocations or sell surplus allocations on the EU market. See http://ec.europa.eu/environment/climate/emmission.htm, viewed 27 June 2007.

[30] See http://europa.eu/rapid/pressReleasesAction.do?reference=PRES/06/58& language=en, viewed 27 June 2007.

[31] op cit.

Australian climate change law

It is against the backdrop of uncertain international agreement that Australia and other states must make regulatory decisions concerning their emissions levels. The announcement that a national emissions trading system will be established signals some willingness on the part of the Australian Government to promulgate a national climate change law. However, there is no sense of urgency in this law reform agenda. The emissions trading system will not be in place for another five years, and legislation on relatively minor energy efficiency measures, such as the phasing-out of incandescent light globes, has not even been introduced in the parliament.[32]

This exceptionally sluggish legal response places Australia at odds with many other jurisdictions where the pace of climate law reform is quickening. 'Climate change law' is a new and burgeoning field of practical action and scholarly inquiry as attempts are made to grapple with the legal dimensions of global warming. In the courts, governments and civil society actors are litigating climate change cases.[33] In parliaments throughout the world, legislators are beginning to debate and pass climate change laws. The breakneck speed of developments in some jurisdictions is astonishing, including in the United States where several bipartisan bills currently being debated in Congress would require emission cuts of 60 to 80 per cent by 2050.[34]

Federal climate change law

In deciding not to ratify the Kyoto Protocol, the Howard government asserted its opposition to the main pillars of the agreement, and argued

---

[32] The Hon Malcolm Turnbull, 'World First! Australia slashes greenhouse gas emissions from inefficient lighting', Media Release, Parliament House, Canberra, 20 February 2007, http://www.environment.gov.au/minister/env/2007/pubs/mr20 feb07.pdf, viewed 27 June 2007.

[33] See Peel J, 'The role of climate change litigation in Australia's response to global warming' *Environmental and Planning Law Journal*, vol. 24, 2007, p. 90.

[34] See the discussion in Lyster R, 'Chasing sown the climate change footprint of the private and public sectors: forces converge', *Environmental and Planning Law Journal*, vol. 24, 2007, p. 281.

instead that Australia would meet its Kyoto Protocol target on a 'no regrets' basis. This preference for a voluntary approach to emissions reduction internationally has been closely tracked by a similar fondness for voluntary schemes at the domestic level. The argument has been that no legal regulation of emissions is required, as optional schemes for business and consumers, government spending programs and research funding can produce sufficient emissions reductions without damaging the economy.[35]

Commonwealth funding for climate mitigation

In pursuit of its voluntarist climate policy, the government has unveiled a collection of administrative and funding packages in the area of climate change since 1996.[36] Key programs were announced in 1997 in Safeguarding the Future: Australia's Response to Climate Change and in 1999 in Measures for a Better Environment with a total value of $1.8 billion. Among other things, these two packages established Greenhouse Challenge (a voluntary industry program to cut emissions) and the Greenhouse Gas Abatement Program (financial support for activities likely to result in emissions reduction). Subsequently, in 2004, the Prime Minister released a white paper on energy and climate, Securing Australia's Energy Future, which included additional funding programs.[37] These included the Low Emissions Technology Demonstration Fund (to support commercial demonstration of low carbon energy production technologies), and the Solar Cities Program (to demonstrate use of solar power and energy efficiency measures in urban locations). More recently, in July 2007, the government announced a $200 million Global Initiative on Forests and Climate, $336 million Green Vouchers for Schools Programme (to fund installation of solar hot water systems and rainwater tanks in schools), and a $252 million Solar Hot Water Rebate scheme (to provide rebates to households replacing electric hot water systems with solar systems).

---

[35] Chris McGrath, 'Setting climate change targets to protect the great barrier reef' *Environmental and Planning Law Journal*, vol. 04, 2007, pp. 182, 192.

[36] For an overview of these initiatives see Rosemary Lyster & Adrian Bradbrook, *Energy law and the environment*, 2006 p. 85–87.

[37] Australian Government, *Securing Australia's Energy Future*, Canberra, *2004;* Australian Government, *Low Emissions Technology Demonstration Fund Policy Framework*, Canberra, 2005.

In aggregate the federal government has set aside a substantial $3.6 billion for addressing climate change. However, it should be noted that only a fraction of this amount has actually been expended. Moreover, there is considerable lack of rigour in terms of objectives and benchmarks,[38] which is one reason for the critical review of Commonwealth greenhouse funding packages by the Australian National Audit Office.[39] In any event, the best measure of their effectiveness is Australia's actual and projected emissions, and the government has freely admitted that there are no signs of any reductions in Australia's carbon footprint in the foreseeable future.

Federal climate change laws

We are left with the conclusion that although national funding of climate programs has increased dramatically under the Howard government, this has not been accompanied by an institutional framework to implement well-defined sustainability objectives.[40] As Christoff has noted, the Commonwealth has been exceptionally reluctant in the area of climate change policy to assert its constitutional capacity to erect a strong legal foundation for national environmental management.[41] Lyster and Bradbrook similarly argue in their recent work on energy law that despite "[possessing] constitutional powers to regulate energy and climate change matters [the government] has done very little to bring these issues within its jurisdiction."[42]

The only federal legislation currently in place which is expressly directed to addressing climate change is the *Renewable Energy (Electricity) Act 2000* (Cwlth) which establishes the Mandatory Renewable Energy Target (MRET). The MRET program seeks to reduce greenhouse gas emissions

---

[38] C Parker, 'The Greenhouse Challenge: Trivial Pursuit?' *Environmental and Planning Law Journal*, vol. 16, 1999, pp. 63, 64.

[39] Lyster and Bradbrook, op cit., pp. 36, 89.

[40] See Peter Christoff, 'Out of chaos, a shining star? Toward a typology of green states' in John Barry & Robyn Eckersley (eds), *The state and the global ecological crisis*, MIT Press, Cambridge 2005, pp. 25–52.

[41] ibid, 36.

[42] Lyster & Bradbrook, op cit., p. 92. Also see Graeme Dennis, 'Climate change: Australian legislative responses', *AMPLA yearbook*, 2002, p. 71.

through the imposition of a mandatory target for electricity retailers to obtain an additional two per cent of their electricity from renewable sources by 2010. The two per cent target was in fact met more than five years ahead of schedule. Although the Howard government initially refused to extend or increase the target to match more ambitious targets adopted in many other countries, in September 2007 the Prime Minister reversed its opposition to an expanded scheme. The new Clean Energy Target (CET) will require around 15 per cent of energy to come from 'clean sources' by 2020, and will effectively roll the renewable energy targets already adopted by several states into a replacement federal scheme.[43]

In addition to the *Renewable Energy (Electricity) Act 2000* (Cwlth) there is a miscellany of legislation having some bearing on climate policy. This includes the *Ozone Protection and Synthetic Greenhouse Gas Management Act 1989* (Cwlth) which was the Commonwealth's legislative response to the Vienna Convention and Montreal Protocol on Substances that Deplete the Ozone Layer. While primarily directed at addressing ozone depletion, it also achieves climate change mitigation objectives as many ozone-depleting substances are also powerful greenhouse gases. There is also the *Energy Efficiency Opportunities Act 2006* (Cwlth) which seeks to improve the identification of opportunities for businesses with large energy demands to improve their energy efficiency.

The Commonwealth's landmark environmental scheme, the *Environment Protection and Biodiversity Act 1999* (Cwlth) (*EPBC Act*), is conspicuously silent on climate change. That Act, which is designed to safeguard Australia's biological diversity and other matters of national environmental significance, prohibits certain activities unless approved by the minister following a specified environmental assessment process. This process is triggered if the activity in question has a significant impact on matters of national environmental significance. However, activities that result or are likely to result in substantial emissions of greenhouse gas emissions (such as land-use changes, or a new coal-fired power plant) are not included – there is no so-called 'greenhouse trigger'. Repeated attempts by opposition parties to

---

[43] http://www.pm.gov.au/media/Release/2007/Media_Release24577.cfm, viewed 19 October 2007.

introduce an amendment to the same effect in the *EPBC Act* have been rebuffed by the government.

National emissions trading scheme

Regardless of the outcome of the 2007 federal election, we can now expect a steady stream of legislation on climate change. Central to this legislative agenda will be a national emissions trading scheme, which both the federal government and opposition are committed to implementing. However, important points of difference in policy between the two major parties remain, and these are likely to be reflected in the detail of their carbon trading schemes when they are released for public scrutiny. In particular the Australian Labor Party is committed to ratifying the Kyoto Protocol, and to crafting a carbon trading scheme consistent with the agreement.

If re-elected, it will be some time before the fine points of the Howard government's legislative program on climate change are released. However, on the basis of policy announcements to date, it is possible to identify what are likely to be its main features. *Australia's Climate Change Policy*, released on 17 July 2007, states that the government will introduce legislation establishing a mandatory energy and greenhouse gas emissions reporting scheme for participants in the national trading scheme, or other entities that intend to provide offsets. Legislation will also be passed to underpin the national emissions trading scheme, and in this regard *Australia's Climate Change Policy* sets out several key design features that will require legislative elaboration:

- 'cap and trade' model of emissions trading
- maximum practical coverage of all sources and sinks, and of all greenhouse gases (with the aim of covering more than 70 per cent of Australia's emissions)
- initial exclusion, but eventual inclusion, of emissions from agriculture and land use from the scheme
- a mixture of free allocation and auctioning of single-year dated emissions permits

- up-front, once-and-for-all, free allocation of permits as compensation to businesses likely to suffer disproportionate loss of value because of introduction of carbon price
- a safety-valve emissions fee designed to limit unanticipated costs to business and the economy, especially in the early years of the scheme
- recognition of a wide range of carbon offsets both domestically and internationally
- capacity to link, over time, to other comparable national and regional schemes
- incentives for firms to undertake abatement in the lead-up to the commencement of the AETS, including through the purchase of offset credits.

State and territory regulation of greenhouse gas emissions

With the Commonwealth a reluctant legislator in relation to climate policy, and with business clamouring for investment certainty, it has been left to the states and territories to adopt a range of legislative responses to climate change over the last decade. There have been a plethora of actual and foreshadowed legislative developments at a state and territory level, the most ambitious being the proposal for a National Greenhouse Gas Emissions Trading Scheme that was scheduled to commence operation by 2010 if the federal government had not committed to a similar scheme.[44]

With the exception of this emissions scheme proposal, the state-level schemes have mostly been developed in a piecemeal way in the absence of federal leadership, and most have been directed to the electricity sector. For instance, in 2003 the New South Wales Government introduced a 'baseline-and-credit' emissions trading scheme through amendments to the *Electricity Supply Act 1995* (NSW). The ACT subsequently introduced a similar scheme through the *Electricity (Greenhouse Gas Emissions) Act 2004* (ACT). Also of note in relation to the electricity sector is the *Victorian Renewable Energy Act 2006* (Vic) which

---

[44] Possible Design for a National Greenhouse Gas Emissions Trading Scheme, 2006.

requires 10 per cent of end use consumption to be sourced from renewable means by 2016. Other relevant laws have included legislation to recognise carbon rights in forest plantations, which is an important element in establishing a carbon trading scheme.[45]

The most ambitious legislative initiative has been that of the South Australian Government through its *Emissions Reduction Act 2007* (SA). The act sets a target to reduce greenhouse gas emissions by 60 per cent from 1990 levels by the end of 2050. It also requires the proportion of renewable energy generated and used in South Australia to rise to 20 per cent. The main objective of the legislation is to provide an overall framework for achieving emissions reductions. But while it enshrines reduction targets in law, it is short on detail as to how these targets are to be achieved; such as by elaborating a system of emissions trading.

Outside the electricity generation sector, most of the states and territories have limited, if any, specific climate change legislation. However, efforts have been made in several cases to consider the greenhouse implications of developments under environmental planning and environmental protection legislation. Although planning legislation makes no reference to climate change, or greenhouse gas emissions, these acts do require broad consideration to be given to environmental impacts and values.[46] Fisher has noted that "even in the absence of such arrangements the current arrangements in Australia are able to address – perhaps obliquely – some of these issues'."[47] This has allowed some courts and tribunals to conclude that, in making planning decisions, authorities need to consider not only the greenhouse gas emissions directly arising from a particular development, but also indirect emissions. Hence, in considering whether approval should be granted to a new coalfield, it is relevant to consider not only the emissions arising

---

[45] See *Carbon Rights Legislation Amendment Act 1998* (NSW); *Forestry and Land Title Amendment Act 2001* (Qld); *Forestry Property Act 2000* (SA); *Forestry Rights Registration Amendment Act 2002* (Tas); *Carbon Rights Act 2003* (WA); *Forestry Rights (Amendment) Act 2001* (Vic).

[46] D F Fisher, 'The statutory relevance of greenhouse gas emissions in environmental regulation', *Environmental and Planning Law Journal*, vol. 24, 2007, pp. 211, 215.

[47] ibid, p. 236.

from the actual extraction of the coal, but also in its combustion to produce energy.

In *Australian Conservation Foundation v Latrobe City Council* [48] the Civil and Administrative Tribunal of Victoria held that an enquiry into the environmental impacts of a new brown coal field to supply the Hazelwood Power Station had to include emissions generated from the use of the coal to generate electricity. Similarly, in *Gray v Minister for Planning* [49] the New South Wales Land and Environment Court found that an environmental impact assessment needed to consider the broad implications of the proposed Anvil Hill coal mine in the Hunter Valley for global warming, including the emissions resulting from burning exported coal in Japan and other likely destinations for the coal, and could not be restricted to the emissions from the mining process itself.

It is important to recognise the limitations of these decisions. They were concerned with the considerations that must be included in the assessment process, and were not reviewing a decision to approve or reject the project. Indeed, following a fresh assessment in conformity with the decision in the *Anvil Hill Case,* the New South Wales Government has given approval to the mine, and there are no apparent grounds for challenging this under New South Wales law.

Conclusions

To date the Australian Government has not assumed legislative authority to restrain Australia's greenhouse gas emissions in any systematic or comprehensive way. Indeed, much federal legislation having a bearing on climate and energy matters has had quite the opposite effect. Taxation arrangements, for instance, have resulted in generous subsidies being provided for the exploration, production and use of fossil fuels rather than renewable alternatives. This suggests that, when embarking on any program of climate law reform, there should also be complete audit of all federal, state and territory laws to assess their impact upon Australia's emissions profile.

---

[48] *Australian Conservation Foundation v Latrobe City Council* (2004) 140 LGERA 100 ('Hazelwood Case').

[49] *Gray v Minister for Planning* (2006) NSWLEC 720 ('Anvil Hill Case').

Existing Australian law that is designed to address climate change is characterised by its disjointed and patchwork character, with effect across different jurisdictions and economic sectors. There is a range of legislative regimes, including environmental planning and protection legislation. This fragmented situation is likely now to change, at least partially, with the federal government and opposition embracing the need for broad legislation to implement a mandatory Australia-wide emissions trading scheme. There are also some hints that a more heavy-handed regulatory approach may be in the offing, particularly in the area of energy efficiency. However, this foreshadowed involvement by the Commonwealth in this critical arena of environmental policy does not mean that the states and territories will no longer have a role to play. Particularly in the areas of development control, they will have the capacity to contribute constructively to Australian climate change law.

Debate over the shape and content of Australia's emerging climate change law cannot take place in isolation from broader discussions concerning the global legal response. Yet the fact that international negotiations are in a state of flux, with many options presented for post-2012 compact,[50] does not relieve Australian governments of their responsibility to legislate to address climate change. As was explained in the Stern Review, "codifying and passing commitments into domestic law can reinforce current and future commitments for action on a global public good [as it] sends a strong signal that a country is sincere in pledging action."[51] To this end, the clear challenge now confronting Australian legislators, after a period of studied intransigence, is to establish a world-leading legal regime that advances shared national and global interests in addressing the climate change crisis.

---

[50] For a survey see Niklas Höhne, Dian Phylipsen & Sara Moltmann, Factors Underpinning Future Action: 2007 Update, DEFRA, 2007; Daniel Bodansky, 'International Climate Efforts Beyond 2012: A Survey of Approaches', 2004.

[51] Stern Review, op cit., p. 462. To this end the United Kingdom's recently released Draft Climate Change Bill 2007 (UK), that makes 60% reductions in emissions by 2050 legally binding, is expressly presented as a unilateral commitment to stimulate international negotiations on the next phase of the Kyoto Protocol. For commentary see Tim Stephens, 'The United Kingdom's Emissions Reduction Legislation' Environmental and Planning Law Journal, vol. 24, 2007, pp. 249–252.

Acknowledgements

Sincere thanks are extended to Gemma Namey for her superb research assistance in the preparation of this chapter.

2

Global warming and discourses of uncertainty: buying time, buying business and engendering risk

Stuart Rosewarne

Abstract

The focus of public discourse on global warming has shifted immeasurably in the last twelve months. With business endorsing this sentiment, the Australian government's longstanding reluctance to accept the science of global warming and the need to implement policies designed to abate greenhouse gas emissions has apparently evaporated. The hitherto economic justifications of uncertainty for not formulating a climate change management framework have given way to the concern to promote a greater degree of investment certainty.

The appointment of the Emissions Trading Task Group in December 2006 appears as a watershed in the government's approach to the challenge of global warming. Yet the group's recommendations, which formed the basis of the recently released government *Climate Change Policy*, remain framed by uncertainty, and this justifies an 'aspirational' approach to policy with the promise of little more than indicative emission targets. While the emissions trading scheme proposal is represented as an additional pillar designed to complement other government initiatives, the Policy seems to be more or less 'business-as-usual'.

The current study questions the logic of the government's reference to uncertainty as a justification for inaction. It argues that resistance to engaging more constructively with global warming is reflective of the commitment to an economic model that is predicated on fossil-fuel based, energy-intensive growth. However, the appeal to uncertainty to justify inaction engenders other uncertainties and risks. Business is responding to these policy failings, but there are other risks that require more robust responses, and these point to the government being caught in a policy cul de sac.

Introduction

The focus of public discourse on global warming has shifted immeasurably in the last twelve months. There is now widespread support for the understanding that unless action is taken soon to mitigate the emission of greenhouse gases, climate change will have adverse consequences for humanity and that these will become magnified with time. With major peak business organisations falling behind this shift in sentiment, the Australian government's longstanding reluctance to accept the science of global warming, or to acknowledge that there is any pressing need to implement policies designed to abate greenhouse gas emissions or ameliorate the potential impacts of climate change, has apparently evaporated. The hitherto economic justifications for not formulating a climate change management framework – based on arguments about the plethora of uncertainties and the potential risks and costs that would arise in adopting what could be considered precipitous initiatives to regulate emissions – have given way to an acceptance of the merits in taking steps to reduce emissions. This sentiment is being echoed by business leaders who are also arguing that in the interests of investment certainty, the details of any emissions regulatory framework should be unveiled sooner rather than later.

The Liberal-National Party coalition, in the ten years that it has held government, has been extremely resistant to adopting any measures to mitigate greenhouse gas emissions, and while it argues, incorrectly, that Australia is on track to meet its Kyoto Protocol emissions target, the government remains resolute in its opposition to ratifying the protocol. However, there seems to have been a sudden change of heart within the coalition government, especially in response to the shifting business sentiment. In late 2006, in a presentation before a Business Council of

Australia, the Prime Minister announced the establishment of an Emissions Trading Task Group to chart a framework to guide policy formulation to meet the challenge of climate change.[1] The task group tabled its report in May 2007, and recommended that Australia introduce an emissions trading system. The recommendations advocated a staggered timetable, proposing an 'aspirational' long-term emissions reduction target be set in 2008, a more modest medium-term target in 2010 to guide investment decisions over 2011 to 2020, and the adoption of a relatively flexible 'cap-and-trade' system that would put a price on carbon emissions from 2111.

Given the government's longstanding opposition to any suggestion for mandating emission reductions or placing a price on carbon, the Prime Minister's endorsement of the task group's key recommendations appears to mark a significant shift in policy focus. This would appear to have been consolidated with the Prime Minister's release of *Australia's Climate Change Policy* in July. The Policy elaborates the shape of a proposed broadly-framed climate change regulatory regime, including a broadly-based system covering most emission sources, a mixture of grandfathering coupled with the auctioning of some emission permits, a penalty system and recognition of early action by business to reduce emissions (Australia, Department of the Prime Minister and Cabinet 2007b; *The Australian Financial Review* 18 July 2007).

However, beyond a broad-brush outline of the direction in which policy appears to be developing, the details of the regulatory framework are suggestive and vague. Most importantly with respect to the key shift in policy direction, *viz.*, an emissions trading system, there is no intention to introduce anything concrete in the immediate future. Clearly-designated emission targets will not be set, and the government has announced that it would propose to set some indicative targets, but that this will not occur until at least 2011. It is proposed to formulate some 'aspirational' goals for the longer term.

---

[1] The Business Council of Australia, which had hitherto been divided on the question of advocating government policy to regulate greenhouse gas emissions, had in 2006 acceded to the merits of an emissions trading system and in November identified what it advocated should be the guiding principles for the trading system.

The qualified nature of the Policy suggests that the measure of the shift in the government's climate change policy could well be overstated. Indeed, recent Prime Ministerial pronouncements, such as the description of the most recent set of climate change management policy initiatives as reflecting a "blend of prudent conservatism and economic liberalism", point to this (*The Sydney Morning Herald* 18 July 2007). There is more reluctance to move forward with policy developments than government pronouncements would indicate.

The present chapter explores the different ways in which 'prudent conservatism and economic liberalism' have been expressed by reflecting on the nature of the arguments proffered in opposition to the formulation of comprehensive strategies to mitigate greenhouse gas emissions, including the refusal to ratify the Kyoto Protocol. The principal focus of attention is on the way in which the government's position has been persistently justified in terms of a conceptual economic rationale framed in terms of risk and uncertainty, on the one hand, and, more concretely on the other, the potentially deleterious effects that emissions mitigation policies would have on the continued growth of energy-intensive and resource sectors and export-revenue earning industries.

This commitment to a fossil-fuel, energy-intensive economic future lies at the heart of the government's opposition to the Kyoto Protocol and the current study reflects on this opposition in examining the strategies the Howard government has sought to progress as an alternative to the emissions-reduction target framework embodied in the Kyoto Protocol. In particular, we consider the establishment of the Asia-Pacific Partnership on Clean Development and Climate as an institutional vehicle for underwriting the continued expansion of the energy-intensive and resource sectors and export-revenue earning industries and the endeavours to progress this through hosting the Asia-Pacific Economic Cooperation forum in September 2007.

This will also necessitate reflecting back on the import of risk and uncertainty in this policy trajectory. The study will conclude by considering the purchase of government policy in the context of a global polity that is demonstrating renewed commitment to the United Nations climate change framework, and pose the question as to whether the government is now caught in a policy cul-de-sac that itself engenders uncertainty and risk.

The challenge of global warming – changes in the wind

There is now overwhelming scientific evidence that human activities are producing greenhouse gas emissions that are resulting in the concentration of gases in the Earth's atmosphere to cause climate change. The most obvious manifestations of this are global warming and extreme weather patterns. It is generally agreed that in all likelihood, unless action is taken, the accelerating pace of industrial development across the globe will result in an exponential growth in concentrations of green house gases (GHG) emissions and the capacity of the global ecology to assimilate emissions will be further compromised. Feedback mechanisms within terrestrial and marine eco-systems responding to climbing temperatures by releasing greenhouse gases will likely exacerbate the severity of climate change.

The release of Al Gore's film *An Undeniable Truth*, the publication of the Stern Review, and the release of the InterGovernmental Panel on Climate Change's most recent reports providing a more definitive scientific defence of the evidence of global warming, followed soon after by the report on the potential impacts of global warming on national weather patterns, have engendered considerable rethinking on the import of global warming. This is evident within the business community. The executives of major corporations acknowledge that global warming will likely impact on their fortunes and are now pressing for some government action to ensure greater certainty for the business environment.[2] Several major corporations have recently joined forces to publicly commit to reducing their emissions and, for some, to become carbon neutral.[3] A number of prominent corporations have signed up to

---

[2] The most recent survey of corporate executives documents a significant shift in corporate thinking on global warming. See: PricewaterhouseCoopers, *Carbon conscious: survey of executive opinion on climate change in Australia*, Sydney, December 2006.
[3] The Australian Business Roundtable on Climate Change was formed by Westpac, Insurance Australia Group, BP Australasia and Origin Energy with the Australian

the Global Disclosure Project, which aims to monitor the efforts of some of the world's largest companies to reduce CO_2 emissions.[4] Companies registered on the Australian Stock Exchange are also coming under pressure from investor groups and fund managers to report on how they are preparing to meet the challenge of climate change (*The Australian Financial Review* 2 June 2006). For some considerable time the Business Council of Australia has been reluctant to declare a policy position on greenhouse gas emissions and climate change because of intense differences among its corporate membership, but has now joined the call for some government action (Business Council of Australia 2006; *The Australian Financial Review* 14 November 2006). The Australian Industry Group has likewise managed to turn its membership around on the need to act (although the Australian Chamber of Commerce and Industry continues its opposition to any interference in the market).[5] The National Farmers Federation now supports a tradeable emissions system because of the potential revenue that would be generated for farming communities through the issue of carbon credits for reducing land clearing and for carbon sequestration in plantations (*The Sydney Morning Herald* 26 October 2006).

Added to this change of temperament in the political climate have been the moves by state Labor governments to establish a national trading emissions scheme (National Emissions Trading Taskforce 2006). In part, responding to public sentiment, state governments have also responded to some sectors of business, and most particularly the finance and

---

Conservation of Australia, in April 2006. IAG had previously joined the WWF, the World Wide Fund for Nature, to establish the Australian Climate Group in 2003, and their reports on the threat of climate change was endorsed by the New South Wales, South Australian and Victorian governments. The Climate Institute, associated with the Australia Institute, launched in October 2005 a $10 million campaign with the support of business to pressure the government to ratify the Kyoto Protocol. There are a growing number of Australian corporations that have signed on to the Global Disclosure Project which aims to monitor the efforts of some of the world's largest companies to reduce CO_2 emissions.

[4] The details and company assessments are available at: http://www.cdproject.net.

[5] PricewaterhouseCooper's survey of business leaders released in December reported that a markedly increasing proportion believed that climate change was strategically significant to their business, and that they would be developing a more proactive stance rather than continue with a compliance-approach.

insurance industries, that have lobbied for greater certainty in governance frameworks as the Kyoto Protocol came into force, as well as for a price on carbon. Their calls for greater policy uniformity no doubt intensified the political pressure upon the Howard government to embrace the need for a more proactive policy framework to meet the challenge of climate change.

The decision to establish the Emissions Trading Task Group, the swift endorsement of the Task Group's recommendations and the issue in July of the government's policy paper *Australia's Climate Change Policy* (2007b) point to a rapid and significant change in the government's position with respect to adopting a comprehensive regulatory framework. It is a change that seems to signal a determination to implement a broadly-based climate change management program. Moreover, when set alongside other key initiatives – most particularly the government's leading role in bringing the United States, Japan and South Korea with China and India to form the Asia-Pacific Partnership on Clean Development and Climate (A-P6),[6] the government's role in the multi-lateral global initiative on forests and climate,[7] and the Howard government ambition to make climate change the principal agenda focus at the Asia-Pacific Economic Co-operation forum that Australia is hosting in September 2007 – it is clear that the government has assumed a quite proactive and dynamic engagement with the climate change challenge in both domestic and international political arenas. The momentum of this engagement has seen the energy and resources

---

[6] In July 2005 the United States, China, India, Japan and Australia announced the establishment of the Asia-Pacific Partnership on Clean Development and Climate partnership (A-P6). This union of developed and developing countries was promoted as a partnership that complemented the ambitions of the Kyoto Protocol by establishing collaborative endeavours to build the institutional capacity and facilitate the development, deployment and transfer of clean technology, as well as more fully involve the private sector. While largely deliberative, the partnership is being developed as an institutional vehicle for engaging the governments of China and India in strategies to meet the challenge of climate change and simultaneously meet increased energy needs. The A-P6 will be discussed in more detail below.

[7] In early 2007, the government announced that Australia had committed $200 million to assist Indonesia and Papua New Guinea to stop illegal logging of forests. In July, the government hosted 70 countries under the umbrella of the global initiative on forests and climate in talks on tackling climate change.

sector, resolute in their opposition to any policies that would impose a charge on carbon emissions, become resigned to the likelihood of their being some form of carbon impost either through a cap-and-trade emissions trading system or a carbon tax adopted in Australia.[8]

The challenge of global warming – the appeal of uncertainty

The time frames proposed for introducing an emissions trading system and setting emission reduction targets outlined in *Australia's Climate Change Policy* and the continuing opposition to ratify the Kyoto Protocol suggest that the government's engagement with a comprehensive climate change policy is a much qualified one. The rationale for this hesitancy has been well articulated. The defining feature of the government's approach to the challenge of climate change has been to resist approaching any initiative that might compromise the economic viability of energy-intensive industries and the fossil-fuel export sector. This preoccupation framed the earlier engagement in the United Nations Framework Convention on Climate Change and the deliberations that led to the Kyoto Protocol. In negotiating emission targets, Australian negotiators won support for special consideration for the unique character of the Australian economy. It was conceded that the fossil-fuel rich country, with its energy-intensive industries and reliance on fossil-fuel exports, would be disproportionately disadvantaged if Australia was set the same greenhouse gas emissions reduction targets as other advanced industrial (or Annex 1) countries. Australia was granted the concession of being permitted to increase the mass of emissions over 1990 levels.

The defence of this commitment to not pursue any policy agenda that would compromise the viability of energy-intensive industries and the fossil-fuel export sector was justified in terms of the conventional economic theory of comparative advantage. Australia's abundant resource endowments defined the character of Australia's incorporation

---

[8] The Australian Coal Association, for instance, predicted that a climate change strategy could see the introduction of an emissions trading scheme as early as 2012 (*The Australian Financial Review* 18 August 2006).

into the global political economy. The robustness of the economy was predicated on these resource endowments and the efficiency with which minerals, through energy-intensive means, could be partially transformed to meet an ever-increasing global demand for iron and steel, aluminium and other metals. The momentum of the economy was also being underpinned by the marked growth in exports of fossil fuels, especially coal and more recently natural gas.

The government's opposition to ratifying the Kyoto Protocol rested on its fear that emission targets would, in the first instance, compromise the future of the resource industry whose success was reliant on the production of high-energy embodied products. A secondary consideration has been that any comprehensive international restriction on carbon emissions could imperil the fossil-fuel, and particularly coal, export industry. The government contended that, given there would be definite economic risks associated with a global regulatory framework that sought to restrict greenhouse gas emissions, more careful consideration had to be focused on arguments about the gravity of global warming predictions, the potential impact of global warming on economic activity and the effectiveness of prospective regulatory frameworks designed to meet the challenge of climate change. Appeal to the economic concept of uncertainty, and the associated economic risks of taking action in the face of uncertainty, became the principal justification for the government's intransigence. This appeal to uncertainty was premised on the unpredictability of, or on the limits to being able to establish with any degree of certainty or probability, several different dimensions of global warming.

A starting point in the preoccupation with uncertainty arose with respect to the science of global warming, which posits an association between the increasing concentrations of carbon dioxide in the atmosphere and global warming. Senior figures within the government referred to the lack of conclusiveness of the science of global warming as providing good reason for exercising caution and holding off imposing restrictions on industry to mitigate emissions. Climatology science was held to be provisional, or worse speculative, and this was reckoned to make for considerable uncertainty in predicting with any accuracy the shape of future climate patterns. There have been several different slants to this scepticism in the science of global warming.

An early argument was founded on the notion that evidence of global warming was in fact inconclusive and the very idea of climate change contestable.[9] There is less and less support for this opinion. A second order argument acknowledged that there is evidence of global warming, but the science sceptics have taken issue with the contention that global warming is the result of anthropogenic emissions, that is, that it is human activity that is the principal source of the greenhouse gas emissions. This contention that there is not a demonstrable association between human activity, emissions and global warming has informed the argument that calls for the urgency to control emissions be treated with extreme caution. The latest assessment by climatologists working under the auspices of the Intergovernmental Panel on Climate Change, which provides overwhelming evidence in support of the anthropogenic origin of global warming, has diminished the appeal of this argument (IPCC 2007a).

Another tack taken by the science sceptics has been to question the predictive capabilities of the science of global warming, notwithstanding the overwhelming thrust of scientific opinion identifying increased concentrations of CO_2 as the principal cause of global warming. Sceptics take issue with the reliability of climate sensitivity assessments which predict the likely temperature changes that will be caused by prospective increases in CO_2 concentrations. While it is conceded that measurements of prospective increases in CO_2 concentrations of climate sensitivity assessments could provide some pointers as to potential impacts, it is argued by the science sceptics that the predictions are at best indicative.[10] A related argument questions the veracity of the IPCC projections of the consequences of global economic growth and the

---

[9] Bjørn Lomberg is among the more celebrated of the sceptics (2001). The Prime Minister has, until recently, displayed a deep-seated scepticism towards the science of climatology and his political opponents continue to deride the Prime Minister as a climate change sceptic.

[10] A. Barrie Pittock's *Climate change: yurning up the heat* (CSIRO, Collingwood and Earthscan) provides a constructive introduction and appraisal of the science of climate change.

likely impact on concentrations of CO_2 (Castles 2006). The projections are held to be exaggerated because they are based on inflated predictions of the pace of economic growth of developing countries with the consequence that the likely growth in greenhouse gas emissions is overstated.

Many of these doubts about the science of global warming have now been cast aside. It is, for example, now widely accepted that global warming is anthropogenic in origin, and the government has publicly jettisoned its long-held scepticism with respect to climate change. The government also acknowledges that China and India, especially as major importers of Australian coal, have become major emitters and this gives cause for concern. In the place of the longstanding scepticism, a new 'realism' defines the government agenda. As the Prime Minister has stated repeatedly since announcing the establishment of the Emissions Trading Task Group, he is a 'climate realist' – the corollary being that he is no longer the climate change sceptic. Nevertheless, the appeal to uncertainty continues to colour the measure of the government's preparedness to legislate to mandate emission reductions. There are several dimensions to this modified take on uncertainty.

It is firmly believed by the government that the pessimism of global warming scientists is unwarranted because it is based on modelling that overstates the likely increase in greenhouse gas emissions that will be generated as the world economy continues to grow. It has been argued that the modelling understates the capacity to enhance efficiency in burning of fossil fuels, the extent to which CO_2 emissions can be sequestrated, such as through better foresting and agricultural practices, and the benefits that will be derived from technological advances. Uncertainty about the character and emissions intensity of production systems in the future, and indeed the positive possibilities of human ingenuity to innovate, is held to justify some caution in the veracity of the modelling of future climate scenarios.

These arguments feed into a related uncertainty associated with the ostensible lack of precision in the global warming models in predicting the pace and magnitude at which greenhouse gas emissions will effect climate change. The debate that followed the release of the most recent

Intergovernmental Panel on Climate Change's assessment of the physical scientific basis of climate change, focused in on climatologists' long-range forecasts which, while estimating increases in global temperatures by the end of this century, ascribed anticipated increases that varied by some four degrees Centigrade (IPCC 2007a). Probability assessments have become more precise, but such assessments must necessarily remain qualified in considering likely climatic impacts through time.

Uncertainty is also held to be manifest with the complexity in modelling the possible impacts across space. The modelling of climate change induced impacts across different locations is not an exact science. Predictions are necessarily subject to a degree of uncertainty given that change is subject to other changes in ecological systems, as well as in human systems. This complicates the efforts to anticipate the impact of climate change on a region or on different economic activities. This has not prevented some very innovative and sophisticated modelling of possible impacts in particular regions, and the IPCC's Group II report on climate change impacts outlines some likely climate impacts across Australia (IPCC 2007b).[11] But the inexactness of climatology science in being able to predict likely impacts and the associated damage costs with much precision has been referenced by government to justify holding off taking any immediate pre-emptive steps to regulate emissions. This has justified the 'let's wait and see' approach. Uncertainty in this instance justifies a preoccupation with adaptation as the need arises.

Another order of uncertainty arises with respect to assessing the costs and benefits of taking action to mitigate greenhouse gas emissions. The costs of taking early action, such as by requiring production systems to adapt, or installing mitigation technologies, appear on the accounting ledger immediately. In contrast, the benefits are generally not immediate;

---

[11] This uncertainty has not, however, prevented some quite critical research that has modelled the potential impacts of climate change in particular regions, including some probable 'hot spots' which would have deleterious consequences for some industries. See, for instance IPCC (2007b). The CSIRO is dedicating considerable resources to impact assessments across different regions and thus industries (Preston and Jones 2006).

they are likely to be more amorphous, and not so readily measurable in accounting, or money, terms.

There is an asymmetry in the timing of the costs and benefits, and this also presents at another level. A government-initiated dedication of capital to a mitigation strategy would have an opportunity cost. The redirection of finite resources entails the diversion of capital from another possible investment program that could have relatively clear and positive and measurable economic outcomes. The incentive to meet immediate calls on public monies, to fund site-specific projects or projects that will meet a set of needs or generate a return within a specific timeframe, are obviously more attractive to governments faced with the choice of dedicating public funds to a climate change mitigation venture whose outcome is uncertain and where the benefit will not be site-specific.

This asymmetry in the costs and benefits of an interventionist program provides a more classic rendition of the concept of economic uncertainty. The uncertainty with respect to the benefits of implementing what can sometimes be very costly initiatives has given government cause for not acting. The appeal in postponing any action to mitigate emissions has been reinforced by the conviction that future technological advances will both make cheaper any required mitigation policies and likely reduce the costs associated with damage rectification.

Underlying this approach to risk is a conviction that the costs of adopting immediate actions to mitigate emissions will not necessarily be offset by prospective future benefits. This conviction is premised on an assessment that discounts the value of costs and benefits into the future *vis-à-vis* the present. Within the conventional economic reckoning the present is valued over the future, and the calculation of the value of benefits and costs through time gives greater weight to the immediate over the future. This logic informs the case for discounting future benefit flows relative to the up-front costs that would occur with the adoption of a mitigation policy. Indeed, the preoccupation with the myriad of uncertainties as giving reason for holding off taking any action tends to feed into an argument that justifies a high rate of discounting future benefits.[12] This has become evident in recent mainstream economists' reflections on the most appropriate rate at which future values should be discounted to ensure the commensurability of future benefits (and any costs) with up-front, present costs.

The release of *The Stern Review* sharpened this debate because *The Review* makes the economic case for implementing policies to stabilise the magnitude of future emissions levels based on a different reflection on future scenarios (Stern 2007). *The Review* argues that early action to address global warming will yield positive benefits at comparatively little long-term cost, whereas postponing any substantial action will fuel the pace and intensity of global warming, exacerbate the damage that climate change will likely cause to future economic activity and thus exaggerate adaptation and rectification costs. The assessment of the economic merits in implementing early action is predicated on the case for setting a low rate of discount because the reference point for the valuing is the state of the global environment and the wellbeing of the global community, and not discrete economic processes for which individual decision makers would likely be able to find a ready substitute. *The Stern Review* locates the logic for both a low rate of discount in terms of the pervasive effect climate change will have on the capacity of the natural environment to sustain humanity, and in terms of the realisation that any meaningful reductions in the level of CO_2 concentrations causing global warming are irreversible in the short- to medium-term and on the pace of global warming into the future. According to this logic, there is a systemically high level of risk associated with global warming; that justifies early action. This reasoning informs the argument for paying greater heed to the real costs that would likely be incurred in redressing the negative consequences of climate change and especially if the wellbeing of future generations is to be secured on terms comparable to those of present-day communities. By contrast, the conventional wisdom within economic discourse holds that a low rate of discount cannot be justified given the level of uncertainty, and that a high rate of discount, or at least a discount rate set by the market, should inform

---

[12] The argument in support of a high rate of discount is bolstered by a confidence in technological development which, it is contended, will enhance the capacity of communities to adapt to and rectify the damage that will be caused by climate change, reducing likely future costs in the process.

decisions regarding allocations of discrete economic resources through time (Productivity Commission 2007).

Finally, the other element in this basket of uncertainty that has occupied the government relates to the global purchase of governance or regulatory frameworks. The government has been forthright in arguing that without a comprehensive international commitment that engages all countries in emission targeting, there is no certainty that any Australian action to mandate greenhouse gas emissions reductions would result in any absolute net reduction in global emissions. The regulatory framework engineered under the Protocol umbrella is held to be of doubtful benefit when it requires only the industrialised Annex I countries to meet emission reduction targets. The potential for free-riding underscores the uncertain benefits of unilateral initiatives.[13]

This notion that Australia would be encumbered by the emission targets set under the Kyoto Protocol, while the developing economies would be free to invite energy-intensive industries to set up without restriction, is held to pose a severe economic risk for Australia should the government ratify the Protocol. The lack of universality of country obligations has instilled this lack of confidence in the capacity of the Kyoto framework to prevent developing countries from inviting energy-intensive enterprises to transfer their operations out of Australia. The belief that this is a real possibility is held to strike at the heart of Australia's international comparative and competitive advantage.[14]

---

[13] The free-rider argument is somewhat specious because the rationale for the differential treatment of Annex I and non-Annex I countries is based on equity grounds and, most importantly, in recognition of the fact that the concentrations of greenhouse gas emissions in the atmosphere, that is, the stock of emissions, reflect the disproportionately large level of greenhouse gases emitted historically by the industrialised economies. The setting of emission targets for Annex I countries also reflects their stronger resource base and capacity to draw on technology to mitigate emissions, as well as adapt to climate change.

[14] The argument has been most forcefully articulated by the Australian Bureau of Agriculture and Resource Economics, but surprisingly there has been next to no empirical research to support the contention. In fact, within environmental economic discourse there is little evidence to support the more general proposition that the weaker environmental regulatory frameworks that tend to exist in developing countries result in polluting industries relocating from

The uncertainty that this perceived deficit in global architecture engenders is held to generate further uncertainty with respect to the status of the infrastructure investment that is so critical to the energy-intensive sectors and fossil-fuel export industries. In most instances the existence of these industries has been contingent on governments giving priority to large-scale investment in public infrastructure which represents significant sunk costs, and generally funding arrangements, as well as borrowing assumptions, are based on the capacity of these investments to be amortised over the life of the venture. Should a change in regulatory arrangements occur, as critics of the Kyoto Protocol contend is the case, this could jeopardise the competitive position of an industry subject to more stringent controls, and this in turn would undermine the fiduciary position of the public agency or government responsible for the infrastructure investment. The uncertainty relating to governance thus has broader reach than the industry or sector directly effected.

Policy making in the age of uncertainty: "a blend of prudent conservatism and economic liberalism"

Uncertainty, it is contended within much conventional economic discourse, should dictate caution in responding to the climate change challenge. Precipitous action to restrict energy use to cut emissions could result in considerable economic costs. The potential economic damage would likely fall first on those industries that are held to be the drivers of the Australian economy, the energy-intensive sector in particular. In the longer term, the more extensive adoption of restrictions on CO_2 emissions would also impact on the coal export industry. It is the embrace of caution that is integral to, and has been held to justify, the orientation of the government's risk-averse strategy with respect to the adoption of policies to meet the challenge of climate change.

A corollary of this line of reasoning contends that the uncertainty with respect to the pace and impact of climate change suggests that priority should be to first focus on dedicating resources to adapting to the changed circumstances. It is argued that, rather than mandating pre-

---

the developed economies where more stringent environmental regulations are in force.

emptive action, adaptation is more economically sensible, and that those feeling the effects of climate change, and not government, are best placed to respond as appropriate. The priority should not be concentrated on placing onerous requirements on business, or on restricting economic growth to contain emissions, but on the formulation of policies that remove impediments to businesses and communities adapting as they deem appropriate to the challenges as these become manifest (McKibbin 2005; *The Australian Financial Review* 20 October 2006; *The Australian* 5 September 2006).[15] The argument that we should be learning to live with climate change has been presented by the Australian Industry Greenhouse Network, a lobby group representing the interests of energy-intensive and resource industries, as the more strategically and economically sensible approach to policy (*The Australian Financial Review* 4 September 2006).

This approach is an essentially conservative one, and in an important respect this resonates with the first component of the Prime Minister's representation of the government's policy approach as a "blend of prudent conservatism and economic liberalism". Even though 'prudent conservatism' has been pivotal in the government's decision not to embrace the emissions trading and target system that lies at the core of the Kyoto Protocol, and which incidentally are formed within an economic liberalist frame, it is important to recognise that there have been other emphases in the government's 'economic liberalism' basket that have been represented as strategic responses to the challenge of climate change. Three particular policy elements formed under the banner of 'economic liberalism' warrant mention. These have emphasised voluntarism, enhancing market efficiency, especially in energy markets, and providing financial incentives to support business initiatives to innovate low-emissions technologies.

A key feature of the government's approach to the challenge of global warming has been its opposition to mandating compliance with emission

---

[15] A variant of this argument is that a comprehensive cap-and-trade emissions system would prove extremely costly and impractical, and force major structural economic transformations. See, for instance, the criticisms of the Stern Review by Brian Fisher, formerly ABARE director, and Henry Ergas (*The Australian Financial Review* 2 November 2006).

reduction objectives. An early initiative, the mandatory renewable energy target, was allowed to lapse. The government has sought to engage business to become more greenhouse savvy, but it has emphasised the merits in voluntarist engagement, rather than mandating this approach. This is consistent with the philosophy that business, rather than government, is best placed to evaluate the risks and responses to uncertainty with respect to climate change. One of the key planks in this policy approach has been the 'Greenhouse Challenge Plus' Program. The program invited companies to voluntarily commit to an emissions reduction plan, in return for which they would be rewarded with a government green seal of approval. The voluntary nature of the scheme was represented as more likely to win the support of business than would be the case with an emissions trading system in which businesses were compelled to participate.[16] The government has been encouraged by corporate involvement in the program, in spite of the government's failure to conduct more than a small number of audits of the companies participating in the 'Greenhouse Challenge Plus' program.[17]

Energy market reform has been another key element in the government's economic liberalism program. The commitment to energy market reform as a vehicle to enhance the efficient utilisation of energy was outlined as a key objective of the 2004 Energy White Paper, *Securing Australia's Energy Future*. An energy reform implementation group was established under the auspices of the Commonwealth and State governments to give effect to National Competition Policy and to generate market conditions that would enhance the efficient production, delivery and utilisation of energy and, in the process, reduce emissions of greenhouse gases. State government control of energy production and distribution has been regarded as the major structural and institutional

---

[16] The Secretary to the Department of Prime Minister and Cabinet, Peter Shergold, who also chaired the Emissions Trading Task Group, maintained that the ambitious reach of the scheme justified the decision to postpone the start of an emissions trading system (*The Australian Financial Review* 15 June 2007).

[17] The government has, however, sought to secure a greater level of commitment to the scheme by passing legislation in 2006, the *Energy Opportunities Act*, to mandate assessment and reporting of energy use by big energy users. The government is proposing to extend this to require more businesses to report on energy and emissions reduction plans.

obstacle to competition and thus energy efficiency. Reform has thus been almost wholly concentrated on effecting the corporatisation and/or privatisation of state-owned generation and retail instrumentalities.

This focus on energy market reforms highlights how pivotal the 'economic liberalism' program has been and continues to be in defining the government's approach to the challenge of climate change. This is evident in domestic policy initiatives. It is also manifest in the government's international diplomatic endeavours, and most obviously through Australia's leadership role in the establishment and focus of the Asia-Pacific Partnership on Clean Development Climate. It was also apparent at the G-20 forum, chaired by the Treasurer and held in Melbourne in November 2006, which resolved to prioritise the objective of 'energy reform', or more particularly energy market liberalisation, in its manifesto (*The Sydney Morning Herald* 13 November 2006).

A third crucial policy component in this 'economic liberalism' program has been based on the principle that, providing the appropriate incentives are in place and there are no institutional obstacles, the free market can be a critically significant catalyst in inducing technological innovation. The initial interest in the possibilities of technological solutions concentrated on the provision of incentives to promote research and development of low-emission and renewable energy technologies, including solar and wind-sourced energy technologies. This was coupled with federal and state governments setting mandatory renewal energy targets with the object of providing clear signals about the future shape of energy markets.

However, the federal government has since abandoned mandatory renewable energy targets. The overwhelming share of government-sourced 'market incentives' are now directed towards underwriting the research and development of technologies that could provide solutions to the major source of greenhouse gas emissions, coal-fired electricity generation and coal-based energy-intensive minerals processing industries. This shift in policy was in large measure a response to the initiatives adopted by energy producers and the resource industry themselves. It followed agreement among companies whose future was tied to coal that they should concentrate resources and coordinate endeavours to research and develop technologies to mitigate CO_2 emissions. With the first of the COAL21 conferences held in 2003, representatives from the electricity generating sector, coal mining companies and aluminium companies, with government support, proposed to commit up to one billion dollars to support research into and development of 'clean coal' technologies and the sequestration of emissions.[18] The government subsequently dedicated up to $500 million, and joined state governments to establish the Low Emissions Technology Fund to underwrite the commitment to the development of 'clean coal' technologies and the continued development of energy-intensive industries and the coal export industry. Through other support schemes, such as establishing cooperative research centres and the provision of tax concessions, the government has sought to accelerate the innovation of 'clean coal' technologies, including more efficient, less polluting methods of burning coal, carbon capture and storage techniques, and most notably geo-sequestration.

The Bush administration's Clean Energy Bill proved an added impetus to this focus. There was some effort directed to tie the COAL21 program into initiatives spawned by the Clean Energy Bill, and this in turn formed a key plank in the Asia-Pacific Partnership on Clean Development and Climate project. 'Low-emission' and 'clean-coal' technologies are held out as affording the means to mitigate CO_2 emissions whilst permitting the continued reliance on coal.

More recently, the government has turned its attention to another technological solution in the form of nuclear power. Nuclear power, the government contends, holds out the promise of delivering 'emissions-free' green power. In the first instance, however, it is evident that the government is primarily interested in facilitating the further expansion of uranium mining to satisfy growing world demand. The establishment of the Switkowski review into 'Uranium Mining, Processing and Nuclear

---

[18] The policy to provide government funding support and taxation incentives for research and development of geo-sequestration was adopted in March 2004. The commitments made by resource and energy companies, with funds to be raised through a voluntary industry-organised levy, were honoured only after the Queensland state government threatened to increase the royalty (*The Australian Financial Review* 18 May 2007).

Energy' in 2006 was a thinly disguised manoeuvre to draw attention to the potential of the growing export market. The inquiry also flagged the potential of nuclear power as providing a source of energy in Australia that is 'green' and which could be added to the suite of technologies adopted to combat global warming.[19] In the immediate future, however, the government is concentrating its resources on removing obstacles to providing infrastructural support for and diplomatic backing for the export of uranium.[20] A commitment has also been made to join with the United States in commissioning further research on the Generation IV nuclear reactor technology.[21]

Energy market reform and the dedication of funds to supporting research and development of 'low emission' and 'clean coal' technology are regarded as the most sensible low-risk responses to meeting the challenge of global warming. When considered alongside the appeal to the myriad of uncertainties that the government has reflected on in considering how to respond to the challenge, and the timidity with which the government has approached the establishment of a planned emissions trading scheme, the actual policy initiatives that have

---

[19] The nomination of Warwick McKibbin to the review would also suggest that the inquiry was repositioning the government on carbon pricing since the recommendation to support the case for nuclear power generation being an economically viable option in Australia is contingent upon an impost on carbon emissions (Switkowski Report, Australia 2006). McKibbin has been a strong advocate for a nationally-determined carbon impost (McKibbin 2005; McKibbin & Wilcoxen 2006).

[20] The Howard government has overridden objections voiced by the Northern Territory administration to the expansion of uranium mining in the Territory, as well as to establishing nuclear waste storage facilities in the Territory. The government has also indicated it will move to draw on its constitutional powers to override state government opposition to uranium mining, which is a source of uncertainty. The government has been quite active in facilitating the negotiation of contracts to enable the export of uranium to Taiwan, China and most recently India, and there are risk management issues associated with these arrangements that the current study will address below.

[21] Paradoxically, given that the Generation IV technology is unproven, as well as the risks associated with nuclear technology and issues relating to the storage of nuclear waste more generally, the Minister for Industry and Resources, Mr Iain McFarlane, has expressed his lack of confidence in future of geo-thermal sources power (*The Australian* 2 August 2007).

been adopted to date are clearly consistent with the "blend of prudent conservatism and economic liberalism" that the Prime Minister has argued is the basis of the government's climate change policy. But it is the conservatism that stands out, and this is reflective of a 'business-as-usual' approach to the challenge of global warming. This conservatism helps explain the government's opposition to ratifying the Kyoto Protocol.

The substance of climate change policy: towards energy security

The one consistent theme in the Howard government's approach to the challenge of climate change has been to avoid committing to any action that would compromise the internationally-competitive position of energy-intensive industries or impede the future of coal exports. The justification for not ratifying the Kyoto Protocol has been made primarily in terms of Australian industry being subject to emissions targets that Australia's main (non-Annex 1) trading partners would not be. The government's plan to establish an emissions trading system proposes a means of addressing this anomaly. The plan is predicated on two principles. The initial steps would be tentative ones, to what has been referred to as a 'soft start' for the business sector as a whole. The government has announced that the start-up date for an emissions trading system would not occur before 2011. Emission reduction targets would be set. Targets would in all likelihood be indicative. The Prime Minister has argued that the primary objective would be to ensure that when the trading system is established it should not impose too great a burden on business. It has been envisaged that the price should not exceed $10 per tonne, and this in effect will determine the setting of the short-term emissions target.[22] A 'safety valve' would provide scope for a 'soft penalty' to cushion possible emission overruns.

The second principle is based on securing the internationally competitive position of energy-intensive industries and energy-intensive exports. The

---

[22] The price at which carbon is currently being traded in voluntary emissions trading markets would suggest that this ceiling will provide little (market-based) incentive for business to pursue emission reduction strategies.

July 2007 *Climate Change Policy* details those sectors of the economy – energy-intensive industries and industries whose operations are reliant upon substantial infrastructure investments – that would be given special treatment when carbon permits are issued. The intention is to 'grandfather' emission entitlements, that is, to issue a quota of carbon permits to businesses which would be comparable to their present emission levels, and to impose a 'soft penalty' on those companies that exceed their allotted emissions quota. In addition, businesses that have recently invested in technologies or adopted strategies to reduce emissions would be rewarded for these initiatives by being issued with an emission quota in excess of the reduced level of emissions, and the quota in excess of the business's needs could be traded in the market.

The *Climate Change Policy* has been well received by companies engaged in energy-intensive activities and the resources sector, and the *Policy* mirrors proposals advocated by the Business Council of Australia in its submission to the Prime Minister's Emissions Trading Task Group. By contrast, there have been some quite formidable criticisms of the failure of the government to pursue more proactive policy initiatives, and in particular steps that would mandate reductions in Australia's carbon footprint, consistent with the Kyoto Protocol. The more strident of the criticisms have argued that the Howard government's climate change policy position has been captive of the international corporations that dominate energy-intensive activities (Hamilton 2007; Pearse 2007).[23]

Considerable evidence has been marshalled in support of this contention that government policy has been largely framed by the dictates of international energy and resource corporations. The evidence seems indisputable. Similar criticisms have been advanced to explain the continuing opposition of the Bush administration to the ratification of the Kyoto Protocol. However, it is important to look beyond this criticism that the definition of government policy has been largely instrumentally determined by particular sections of the business community. The contention fails to explain the apparent lack of influence exercised by other sections of business. It does not explain

---

[23] It is generally acknowledged that American energy corporations have funded much of the research that has questioned the science of global warming (Monbiot 2006).

why the government has proposed introducing an emissions trading system, unless of course this shift in policy can be attributed to a change of heart among the influential captains of industry (and there may be some substance in this). More concretely, it fails to explain the different initiatives implemented and/or proposed by state governments in their endeavours to confront the challenge of climate change, and these have been so significantly different.

In 2005 the state and territory governments in Australia entered into discussions to begin exploring a national emissions trading scheme in recognition that Australia should be more proactive in formulating policies to deal with the challenge of a 'carbon constrained' future. In 2006, the governments established a task force to begin mapping the framework of an emissions trading scheme which they then resolved to establish by 2010 irrespective of whether this had the support of the federal government. The initiative was in part politically motivated, as state Labor governments sought to capture political advantage in the face of the federal Liberal-National Party government's opposition to an emissions trading system. It was also consistent with the interests of some sections of the business community, most notably insurance companies, investment and superannuation funds and financial advisors and traders in the share market, moved by risk management concerns or the opportunity to trade in a new financial instrument.

Yet, notwithstanding this ostensible commitment to the objectives of the Kyoto Protocol, it has to be acknowledged that state governments have done very little to block the continued development of energy-intensive industries and related coal-fired and gas-fired power generation capacity, as well as the further expansion of mining to bolster coal exports.[24] There is an apparent contradiction between the declared policy commitments and actual practices in their support for industrial

---

[24] Reflective of this contradiction, despite continuing to advocate the establishment of the emissions trading scheme, in 2007 the New South Wales government overrode a decision by the NSW Land and Environment Court to block an application to develop a coal mine in the Hunter Valley on a number of grounds that the coal mined would contribute to global warming. The Land and Environment Court decision followed a campaign by local environmentalists against the development proposal.

development. It might also be observed that for all federal Labor's declared commitments to address the challenge of global warming, including immediately ratifying the Kyoto Protocol should it be elected to government, Labor's greenhouse management policies fall short of pursuing any immediate initiatives.

This suggests another explanation for understanding the role of the different levels of government in responding to the climate change challenge that does not reduce policy positions to an instrumentally determined reflection of business demands. It prompts consideration of the structural nature of government policy decisions. Indeed, Australian negotiations within the UN Framework Convention made this structural imperative clear from the outset. The unique character of the Australian economy, the significance of energy-intensive industries, but also the resource, including fossil-fuel based, export industries, justified special treatment in the eyes of Australian diplomatic representatives. It was argued that there were structural reasons why Australia should be granted concessional treatment within the Kyoto framework.

This case for 'special treatment' has been reiterated repeatedly. Australia's Ambassador to the United Nations has made the point most recently as August 2007, in the General Assembly debate on climate change. Mr Hill signalled Australian government endorsement of the need for an effective international framework, then qualified this commitment by advocating a framework "that includes all major emitters, takes account of differing national circumstances and goals for sustainable development and allows countries to adopt a range of policies to reduce their emissions" (Hill 2007). Hill then proceeded to detail the raft of initiatives that the government has pursued in the quest to meet the challenge of climate change. These include setting the agenda at the Asia-Pacific Economic Co-operation forum to be hosted by Australia in September to enable debate on the economic effects of climate change, assuming a lead role in establishing the Asia-Pacific Partnership on Climate Change and Development group, which has brought the US, Japan, South Korea and Australia together with China and India, and supporting the Global Initiative on Forests and Climate Change.

The distinctive feature of each of these initiatives, and more especially so when considered in relation to one another, is that they chart an alternative framework to that constructed under the umbrella of the Kyoto Protocol. Perhaps the most significant in terms of the institutional architecture that has been put in place has been the Asia-Pacific Partnership on Climate Change and Development, or A-P6. Formed in mid-2005, A-P6 was established with the express objective of bringing China and India, as non-Annex I countries and thus not subject to emission target reductions, into dialogue with the US, Australia, Japan and South Korea as signatories to the Kyoto Protocol and, in the case of Japan and South Korea countries that had ratified the Protocol. The ostensible rationale was a more active engagement among the partner countries than was reckoned could occur under the mantle of the Protocol. This would facilitate the diffusion of technology that could facilitate further economic development while simultaneously addressing climate change.

Taking the lead from the Prime Minister's characterisation of Australia's policy approach being a blend of "prudent conservatism and economic liberalism", the interest in establishing the A-P6 can be linked back to the endeavours to construct an institutional framework that secured the structural orientation of the Australian economy. The immediate ambition of the six-country deliberations, the one proffered at the January 2006 meeting of the Asia-Pacific Partnership countries, turned the emphasis of emissions management away from setting emission targets to the development of more efficient ways of producing and utilising fossil-fuel based sources of energy to reduce carbon emissions. The A-P6 forum resolved to garner support for investing in technological solutions to the problem of greenhouse gas emissions, to cooperate in the research and development of low emissions technologies, and to facilitate the diffusion of this technology.[25]

A second platform in the A-P6 program has moved still further away from the Kyoto Protocol's primary ambition to target greenhouse gas emissions to emphasise the importance of energy security. Energy security has emerged as a paramount concern of the United States. The

---

[25] The government's commitment of funds to research and development of 'clean coal technology' has been positioned as an A-P6 initiative.

preoccupation with securing future energy supplies prompted the Bush administration to commission a major study by the National Petroleum Council, an organisation representing American oil and energy corporations (NPC 2007). Indeed, the concern with 'energy security' extends beyond the US and is emblematic of a dramatic reorientation in political discourse internationally. For instance, whereas the G-8 meeting held in Gleneagles in 2005 mapped a 'Plan of Action for Climate Change, Clean Energy and Sustainable Development', the 2006 meeting hosted by Russia declared 'Energy Security' to be the priority. Whereas the 2005 meeting was endeavouring to lay some foundations for the December Montreal meeting of the UNFCCC, the 2006 plan of action was framed by the ambition to open up world energy markets and explore ways to minimise the actual or potentially restrictive practices of state owned or controlled energy reserves. The benefits of economic liberalist policy prescriptions were advocated, including effecting greater transparency in markets, improving the investment climate in the energy sector, enhancing energy efficiency and energy saving, diversifying the energy mix and securing critical energy infrastructure.

A similar reorientation was evident within the European Union. European leaders had already shifted this agenda in formulating the European Union's 'European Energy Charter' the principle objective of which was to liberalise energy markets to promote energy security.

The Australian Government has sought to build on this. The preoccupation with 'energy security' was designated as the priority subject of the November 2006 G-20 forum in Melbourne chaired by the Treasurer Peter Costello – while the subject of climate change was not listed on the agenda (*The Australian Financial Review* 15 November 2006).[26] Costello reported that his ambition was to win agreement at the G-20 forum to promote free trade in energy by combating the

---

[26] The tenor of the G-20 meeting was set by Treasury officials who had already indicated their preoccupation with energy market liberalisation. In the lead up to the forum, Treasury officials had pointed to the deleterious effects of programs to nationalise resources, arguing that such moves discouraged private investment in resource development, engendered uncertainty in energy markets and would contribute to long-term supply shortfalls (*The Sydney Morning Herald* 9 November 2006).

monopolies and the cartels that are frustrating supply and investment. Looking to consolidate support for this appeal to the import of the free market, the chief executives of some of the world's largest energy and resource companies had been invited into the forum (*The Australian* 16 November 2006).[27]

The rationale for this appeal to cooperate on promoting "free trade and open markets" in the interests of enhancing 'energy security' was one that had been laid out before by the Howard government. Helping solve the 'energy security' challenge would be to Australia's obvious advantage, and would help consolidate the nation's standing as the largest exporter of coal, among the largest exporters of natural gas and with the potential to become the largest exporter of uranium. Encapsulating the Howard government's preoccupation with Australia as an exporter of energy not encumbered by the mandating of greenhouse gas emissions, Costello neatly summed up his "vision for achieving global resource security[: establish] an energy and minerals freeway linking suppliers and consumers across the globe" (*The Australian Financial Review* 16 November 2006). A similar position was being promulgated before APEC finance ministers in the lead up to the September APEC forum. The Prime Minister signalled that APEC deliberations would attend to the subjects of climate change and 'energy security', but the real agenda would serve to promote Australia's international fossil fuel export position (*The Australian Financial Review* 13 November 2006). Any progress in advancing agreement on regional climate change policy would necessarily be subordinated to agreement on 'energy security'.

The Australian government's engagement in the A-P6 and the program that the government has devised for the APEC forum have been framed by the concern to secure the internationally competitive position of the energy-intensive resource sector. In so far as the government has sought to engage China and India in the A-P6, winning their endorsement for a regional energy security pact, the government been successful in

---

[27] The irony in the issue of invitations to the chief executives of some of the world's largest energy and resource companies could surely not have gone unnoticed. There has been a substantial consolidation of ownership of companies through mergers and acquisitions of energy and resource companies over the last few years.

elevating the centrality of Australia's comparative advantage as a key supplier of fossil fuels to fire the development of these countries. The enthusiasm with which the government has approached negotiations over the supply of fossil fuel exports to these two countries is further testimony to this preoccupation.

The extent to which this putsch for 'energy security' has been engineered in conjunction with the Bush administration highlights an essential aspect of the rationale for the Howard government's and the Bush administration's refusal to ratify the Kyoto Protocol. Both governments remain wedded to an energy-intensive, fossil-fuel based economy. This is an accumulation model in which the fortunes of the economy are predicated on the continuing reliance upon fossil fuels to fire the engines of the industry and consumption. It is a regime that will be increasingly difficult to readily accommodate within the Kyoto framework.

The Australian opposition to the Kyoto Protocol is captive of two dimensions of this fossil-fuel based economic model. On the one hand, the emission targets advocated within the Kyoto framework will likely impede the continued expansion of energy-intensive industries. On the other, the prospect that the targeting of emissions would be extended to incorporate the rapidly developing economies of China and India could arrest the continued expansion of the coal export industry. Likewise, the confidence that the government places in the potential contribution that Australian exports of uranium could make as a source of 'green' power could be easily undermined, given the energy-intensity of mining and processing the uranium (Barnaby & Kemp 2007; ISA 2006).

This prompts another reflection on the Australian Government's refusal to ratify the Kyoto Protocol. Opposition to the Protocol has entailed more than simply refusing to ratify the Protocol. The opposition is reflected in a raft of initiatives that have gathered pace in the last two years and that are directed at cobbling together an alternative international framework. Australia's UN representative has articulated the different elements of this very neatly before the UN General Assembly (Hill 2007). Hill outlined the several pillars of this alternative that include: focusing the energies of the APEC deliberations to evaluate the economic effects of climate change; the constructive architecture organised in the A-P6, which promises to reduce greenhouse gas emissions by promoting greater energy efficiency fostered through energy market reform and technology innovation and diffusion; and, support to be provided to protect old-growth forests from illegal foresting, with encouragement afforded for reforestation and afforestation through the multilateral Global Initiative on Forests and Climate Change.

Each one of these projects, in one way or another, were they to receive broader endorsement by interested governments, could serve to weaken the Kyoto framework. The original draft agenda for the APEC forum had canvassed the possibility of establishing a regionally-based emissions trading system that would be more flexible in form, and would not be so firmly set within an emissions target objective, as is the case with the Kyoto emissions trading scheme. The proposed system would have been consistent with the ambitions of the A-P6, and it would accommodate the growing demand for energy by the developing economies of China and India. It would, in addition, reward technology innovation and diffusion through the issue of carbon credits. This loosening up of the other side of carbon markets, namely the scope for generating carbon offsets and credits, is a feature of the Global Initiative on Forests. The initiative is proposing to credit reforestation and afforestation programs and thus extend the remit of carbon offsets beyond what has been agreed under the terms of the Kyoto Protocol .[28]

The APEC forum was being promoted as providing the opportunity to build on the foundations of the A-P6. Whereas the A-P6 explored the possibility of a six-country trading scheme, at one stage in the discussions on the APEC agenda the Prime Minister envisaged the multilateral organisation providing the springboard for a regionally-based, namely non-Kyoto based, emissions trading system which, he

---

[28] Pressed by business and leading state economists, the Environment Minister has proselytised the benefits of valuing forests as effective 'greenhouse sinks' and, therefore, worthy of inclusion in a global emissions regulatory regime. And, faced with resistance to the incorporation of the sequestration of carbon because of uncertainties about the real value of forests as carbon sinks, the Minister has entrusted the Australian Greenhouse Office with the task of demonstrating that a carbon accounting system could establish the tools for measuring the value of carbon sequestrated (Hill 2000; Australian Greenhouse Office 2000).

declared, would be of direct benefit to Australian businesses (*The Australian Financial Review* 18 July 2006).

While each of these initiatives may be seen to be chipping away at the foundations of the Kyoto Protocol, to date these manoeuvrings have had only limited purchase.[29] In part this is because the intended objective of effecting a retreat from the ambitions of the UN Framework Convention on Climate Change introduces multiple layers of uncertainty, most especially with respect to the regulatory framework that is likely to be built on the mantle of the Kyoto Protocol as it is renegotiated beyond 2012. The political climate has also shifted considerably. Gore's *An Undeniable Truth*, *The Stern Review* and the recent IPCC reports, as well as a number of influential reports prepared for business, have brought to the fore a greater appreciation of the potential risks in not taking early action to mitigate greenhouse gases (Allen Consulting Group 2006). The consequence has been that support for the fossil-fuel based economic model that has defined the Australian Government's position is fast dissipating.

Revisiting risk and uncertainty in the Kyoto age

It is now more generally accepted that the appeal to uncertainty, to justify not taking early steps to mitigate emissions in the hope of forestalling global warming, places too much emphasis on one side of the economic risk ledger. Business and broader community concerns have turned to reflect more critically on the immediate and longer-term risks and the associated actual and potential costs in postponing moves to establish governance frameworks to regulate greenhouse gas emissions. It is now widely recognised that the failure to act engenders a raft of risks and uncertainties that will likely carry considerable and ever-increasing economic costs.

---

[29] Thus, while there has been considerable publicity celebrating the achievements of A-P6 in Australia, there has been next to no reporting in the media on A-P6 in Japan, South Korea and China, very limited reporting on A-P6 in India, and the US Congress has restricted the magnitude of the Bush administration's A-P6 funding promises.

There is the immediate cost associated with Australia's refusal to ratify the Kyoto Protocol. Australian-registered businesses will not be able to reap the supplementary reward of carbon credits issued under the terms of the Kyoto emissions trading mechanism when investing in emissions reduction projects in developing economies. Australian companies will not be able to benefit from the Kyoto joint implementation schemes or clean development mechanisms and emissions banking system.[30] Similarly, companies cannot earn carbon credit benefits from exporting energy-efficient or renewable energy technologies to developing countries under the terms of the Kyoto Protocol.

The uncertainty relating to commercial transactions that confronts Australian-registered companies under the Kyoto framework extends beyond these obvious Kyoto instruments. It is, for instance, unclear as to whether it would be legitimate for a coal exporter to entice prospective buyers with offers of carbon credits to offset the emissions they would generate when burning coal and thereby assist the buyers to meet their emissions quota obligations. For international corporations, such as BHP-Billiton, the largest publicly-registered company in Australia, this makes for considerable business uncertainty (*The Australian* 29–30 October 2005).

Of comparable and more direct significance has been the impact on business, and especially the fortunes of insurance companies, of the growing number of instances of extreme weather and catastrophic events. *The Stern Review* gave further voice to these concerns by modelling the potential economic risks in not acting in the face of uncertainty. Australian business had previously been acquainted with this quite different reflection on uncertainty through the report prepared by, among others, the Allen Consulting Group (2006). The thrust of these analyses has been that it is no longer appropriate to approach the uncertainties associated with global warming through the conventional economic oeuvre. Global warming will have comprehensive effects, many of which will be economically deleterious and irreversible. Some of these effects will undermine the capacity of communities to sustain

---

[30] The New Zealand government, which is a signatory to the Kyoto Protocol, has been advertising the advantages that Australian companies could reap by transferring their headquarters

themselves. Adapting to the changed environmental circumstances, or resorting to substitutes which a conventional analysis would pose as a solution, may simply not be possible. [31] A very powerful case has been made for acting early to mitigate emissions and thus reduce the magnitude of climate change and the likely measure of economic costs this will likely engender in the future.

In the face of the uncertainties arising from the government's timidity to act decisively in formulating regulations to govern emissions, many businesses have taken the initiative to implement company-based emissions management and carbon monitoring strategies. There is now abundant evidence of businesses which, while not necessarily adapting business practices to be consistent with the Kyoto regime, have established mechanisms internal to the company that provide incentives for more focused monitoring and control of energy use and emissions minimisation. Some have established in-house carbon trading systems as best practice business management. Others have determined that building tradeable emissions platforms in Australia is good business practice in anticipation of the likelihood that the Australian government will eventually be forced to ratify the Protocol.

There is also considerable pressure being brought to bear on companies to adopt emissions management and carbon monitoring strategies. With market capitalisation being influenced by the impact that climate change, and prospective regulatory frameworks, might have on the fortunes of industries and individual enterprises, investment and superannuation funds are factoring into their investment strategies risk assessments appraising the greenhouse gas emissions management credentials of existing and prospective investments. Companies registered on the Australian Stock Exchange are being pressured by investor groups and fund managers to report on how they are preparing to meet the challenge of climate change (*The Australian Financial Review* 2 June 2006). This focus on the green credentials of corporations is not only moved by a concern with the risks attached to the funds management and investment houses' direct investments. It is also motivated by the more

---

[31] The possibility that global warming could undermine the capacity of communities to sustain themselves has spawned a literature on the social and political risks associated with forced migration.

general objective of wanting to minimise the potential global risk that environmental catastrophes present for the stability of stock markets.[32]

Within the financial sector, emissions risk assessments have emerged as integral to the appraisal of companies' long-term exposure to risk. Citigroup has, for instance, provided quite detailed assessments of the carbon profile of the top 100 listed companies in Australia (Citigroup 2006). This translated into an average liability of between one and two per cent of companies' capitalisation. In the case of BlueScope the CO_2 emissions liability amounts to the equivalent of some 3.5 per cent of capitalisation. Such evaluations have brought considerable pressure to bear on companies to begin planning how they will contribute to the mitigation of greenhouse gases.

Indeed, the desire to be registered as a good, and green, corporate citizen has resulted in more formal monitoring and appraisal systems being established in non-government arenas. A number of prominent corporations have signed up to the Global Disclosure Project which monitors the efforts of some of the world's largest companies to reduce CO_2 emissions.[33] The formation of the Australian Climate Group in 2003 has lifted the profile of Australian companies petitioning for action. Several major Australian corporations have recently joined forces to publicly commit to reducing their emissions and, for some, to become carbon neutral.[34]

---

[32] Based on the Carbon Disclosure Project, a coalition of investors, bringing together the National Australia Bank, VicSuper, AMP Capital Investors, BT Financial Group and the Catholic Superannuation Fund, is proposing to request companies that they hold shares in to provide them with details of carbon emissions and energy-emission management policies (*The Age* 5 October 2005).

[33] The details and company assessments are available at: http://www.cdproject.net.

[34] The Australian Business Roundtable on Climate Change was formed by Westpac, Insurance Australia Group, BP Australasia and Origin Energy with the Australian Conservation of Australia, in April 2006. IAG had previously joined the WWF, the World Wide Fund for Nature, to establish the Australian Climate Group in 2003, and their reports on the threat of climate change was endorsed by the New South Wales, South Australian and Victorian governments. The Climate Institute, associated with the Australia Institute, launched in October 2005 a $10 million campaign with the support of business to pressure the government to ratify the Kyoto Protocol. There are a growing number of Australian corporations that have

Attention has also turned to reflecting on the risks posed by climate change to public infrastructure, and the need for government to be taking steps to secure the future integrity of this infrastructure. The government's chief scientific officer has argued the case for measures to be put in place to protect critical public infrastructure from the effects of climate change (*The Financial Review* 17 June 2007). This has prompted calls for moving quickly to begin formulating strategies to facilitate adaptation now.

There is increasing reflection on the risks that could be engendered by the uncertainty in climate change governance given the government's insistence that regulatory frameworks should be nation specific. In a global context, the contention that Australia should be afforded special consideration and that this be built into the climate change institutional framework to "take ... account of differing national circumstances and goals for sustainable development" and which would allow "countries to adopt a range of policies to reduce their needs", is a recipe for governance uncertainty (Hill 2007). Contrary to the position advocated by McKinnon and others, a position that has provided the conceptual justification for Australia's 'special case' argument in the Framework Convention negotiations, international businesses especially are arguing the case for uniformity of approach in an internationally comprehensive regulatory framework. Uniformity provides the most amenable means for aligning costs and management structures and consistency in accounting practices and operations across the global enterprise (Kolk & Pinke 2005). Anything less makes for regulatory uncertainty.

The government's conservative approach to the threat of global warming is engendering uncertainty within the business community, which is demanding action to redress this position. The executives of major corporations acknowledge that global warming will likely impact on their fortunes and are now pressing for some government action to ensure greater certainty in the business investment environment.[35]

---

signed on to the Global Disclosure Project, which aims to monitor the efforts of some of the world's largest companies to reduce CO_2 emissions.

[35] The most recent survey of corporate executives documents a significant shift in corporate thinking on global warming, PricewaterhouseCoopers, 2006.

The government's confidence in the promise of technology has also been called into question. It is, for example, not evident that geo-sequestration will provide a safe and enduring means of storing carbon, let alone one that will be cost effective. The promise of this technology is uncertain, and paradoxically this is not the case with a number of other proven renewable technologies whose development the government has not supported to anywhere near the same extent.

The government's promotion of the economic benefits in expanding uranium exports and possibly establishing nuclear power plants as a solution to global warming speaks volumes about the fixation with maintaining Australia's place in a fossil-fuel intensive global economy.[36] Issues of uncertainty and risk are effectively dismissed as being manageable and this gives cause for considerable alarm.

Yet in its determination to secure the future of Australia as a global supplier of fossil fuels, the government could well be exacerbating the risks and uncertainties in the fossil-fuel intensive economic regime, and there are many. Nuclear power does not provide a short-term means of reducing greenhouse gas emissions. The mining and processing of uranium and construction of nuclear power plants can actually exacerbate the magnitude of CO_2 emissions.

There remains the question of managing and storing nuclear waste, and engaging the uranium-nuclear power industry could well increase the problem, the risks and the costs this presents for Australia. Interests associated with uranium mining and enrichment have been promoting the geological advantages of Australia as a safe site for storing nuclear waste matter. The Switkowski Taskforce concurred with this position, and recommended that storage facilities could be developed as a dimension of a more expansive uranium-nuclear industry in Australia, a position also supported by the International Atomic Energy Agency (The Switkowski Report, Australia 2006; *The Australian* 5–6 August 2006). Discussions between the US President and the Australian Prime Minister on the possibility of Bush administration's proposal to establish

---

[36] The A-P6 forum introduced nuclear power to the energy resource mix as a means of enhancing 'energy security'.

a 'global nuclear energy partnership' appear to be linked to Australia agreeing to establish a nuclear waste storage facility.

The July 2007 recent earthquake that damaged the Kashiwazaki-Kariwa nuclear power plant in Japan, the largest facility in the world, highlights the risks with nuclear power. But there are still greater risks and uncertainties engendered by the pace at which the scale of uranium exports is being expanded because it is occurring in the context of the parlous state of international non-proliferation safeguards. The International Atomic Energy Agency has indicated that its ability to effectively monitor and police access to and use of nuclear material is deficient, and that it does not have the resources to monitor adherence to the Nuclear Non-Proliferation Treaty. The US Department of Homeland Security has reported a doubling of incidents of trafficking and mishandling of nuclear material in the last five years (*The Sydney Morning Herald* 28 December 2006).

Australia has now agreed to export uranium to India, which is not a signatory to the Nuclear Non-Proliferation Treaty. This is occurring under the protective umbrella negotiated by the Bush administration that will provide for IEA inspection of civilian nuclear power plants in return for the US providing nuclear material and technology for civilian purposes. (The arrangement is not dissimilar to the contract to export uranium to Taiwan, which is also not a signatory to the Nuclear Non-Proliferation Treaty,[37] and to the export deal with China, which provides for the uranium to be used only for peaceful purposes, and its use to be monitored by the IAEA.[38] As much as the architects of these

---

[37]. The contract between BHP-Billiton and Taipower to export uranium employed an 'indirect sale arrangement', with uranium being shipped first to the United States for enrichment before being transhipped to Taiwan, and was sanctioned by an Australian-US bilateral agreement (*The Sydney Morning Herald* 18 December 2006). The machinery to bypass obligations under the Nuclear Non-Proliferation Treaty to support an arrangement to export uranium to Taiwan was negotiated in 2001 (http://www.austlii.edu.au/au/other/dfat/nia/2001/28.html).

[38] *The Australian Financial Review* 7 December 2006. Richard Broiwnoski, in his submission to the Switkowski taskforce, raised concerns that the effect of the arrangement would be to further undermine the force of the Nuclear Non-Proliferation Treaty. (http://www.dpmc.gov.au/umpner/submissions/40_sub_umpner.pdf).

arrangements contend that this brings non-signatory nations into an NPT-equivalent fold, the Indian government has sought to console critics that the terms and conditions negotiated with the US will not impede the continuing development of India's nuclear military facilities and nuclear strike capabilities (*The Financial Times* 3 August 2007).

There is good cause to not be too sanguine that these arrangements will contribute to advancing the cause of world peace. The Pakistani government for one has taken issue with the civil nuclear cooperation agreement as possibly triggering an escalation in the arms race on the Indian sub-continent (*The Financial Times* 3 August 2007). The eagerness with which the government has supported major resource companies to strike uranium export contracts has paid little heed to how this has weakened non-proliferation standards and the extent to which this could contribute to unsettling world peace and security. The purchase of the government's commitment to a fossil-fuel export-oriented economy presents real risks to the geo-political order.

The enthusiasm with which the government has promoted Australia's international comparative advantage in fossil-fuels is also likely selling Australia short because, in the eagerness to ensure its position in the 'energy security' agenda, the government has been prepared to negotiate contracts that set prices below international standards.[39] It is this tendency to fall short of meeting international standards and expectations that has framed the Australian Government's approach to meeting the challenge of global warming. This comes at a cost, it feeds uncertainty and exacerbates risk.

---

[39] This was the case with the negotiation of contracts with China for the sale of Liquid Natural Gas, negotiations in which the Prime Minister was directly involved. In fact, when these contracts were being negotiated, not only did the government provide substantial investment assistance, it also provided assurances that it would not support any further developments in a global greenhouse gas emissions regime that would be detrimental to this, the North West Shelf project, as well as other LNG projects.

The Australian government's climate change agenda: a policy cul-de-sac?

The formulation of Australia's climate change management policy initiatives in terms of a "blend of prudent conservatism and economic liberalism" suggests coherence in approach and integrity in policy design. The adherence to 'prudent conservatism' has been motivated by the fixation with acting under conditions of uncertainty. This is by and large in keeping with the orthodox economic convention. The appeal to 'economic liberalism' lends credence to the notion that responses to global warming are best left to decision-making in the free market, and to individuals and businesses to make the decisions in response to the challenge of global warming for they are best placed to make the appropriate decisions in the face of uncertainty.

In many respects, this is quite specious. Firstly, the challenge the world faces from global warming is not one that presents in individual locales or confronts individuals or businesses in isolation. The challenge is one that confronts us all; it is a universal one. Secondly, the nature of uncertainty and the associated risks that have to be addressed are not temporally uniform. They are cumulative, and it is no doubt the case that the damaging impacts of global warming upon the capacity of some communities will be irreversible, and they will become more pronounced. Herein lies the intellectual force of the proposition articulated in *The Stern Review* that uncertainties and certainly the risks that will be engendered by global warming can be mitigated by acting sooner rather than later. And this necessitates governments responding to this logic to formulate and implement policies to mitigate greenhouse gas emissions and to begin developing strategies to facilitate our capacity to adapt to the impacts of climate change.

The Australian Government's conservative approach to the climate change challenge is being overshadowed by events. There has, as observed, been a change in sentiment across the political landscape. The executives of major corporations acknowledge that global warming will likely impact on their fortunes and are now pressing for some government action to ensure greater certainty in the business investment environment.[40] In many instances, business is no longer waiting for the government to take the lead, as across the industrial and financial spectrum, plans are being formulated and practices adopted that place them ahead of the regulatory requirements that government has set.[41]

But the government has not only fallen behind popular opinion in Australia and growing business sentiment on the need for decisive action to be taken. The various initiatives the government has lobbied for within the international, or at least the regional, political arena appear to be falling considerably short of the mark. The A-P6 has not proved to be the defining institution that was envisaged. Nor has the A-P6 proved to be a foundation for refocusing the September Asia-Pacific Economic Cooperation forum. In fact, the ambitions of the government to set the agenda with the object of recovering the momentum of the key concerns Australia sought to project through the A-P6, and then as a springboard for the *Climate Change Policy*, appear to have foundered.

Indeed the Howard government's leadership in debate on the form of an international climate change regulatory framework is looking decidedly like the position of the 'emperor with no clothes'. The government's opposition to the Kyoto Protocol has been maintained in unison with the Bush administration in support of the energy-intensive/fossil-fuel based accumulation model. As we have noted, this partnership was instrumental in the 'clean coal' technology commitment. The A-P6 is, in effect, the embodiment of that partnership. Australia's advocacy of a nuclear energy solution to global warming is the child of the Bush-Howard liaison.

Yet, as much as the energy-intensive/fossil-fuel development agenda is predicated on the American model and the Bush administration's antipathy towards the ratification of the Kyoto Protocol, it is not immediately evident that this position will endure. Bush conceded at the July 2007 Go8 forum to working with and not against others to progress

---

[40] As previously noted, the most recent survey of corporate executives documents a significant shift in corporate thinking on global warming. PricewaterhouseCoopers, 2006.
[41] The same might not be said of some of the peak business and industry councils, which have applauded the government's *Climate Change Policy*.

negotiations on an international regulatory framework in the post-Kyoto UN Framework Convention. The US House of Representatives has passed a series of bills requiring power companies to generate 15 per cent of energy from renewable sources and has imposed taxes on companies which, with tax breaks, will provide further support for renewable energy and conservation.

An even more intriguing development has been the apparent shift in the public position of US oil companies with respect to greenhouse gas emissions regulatory frameworks. In what has been one of the most comprehensive studies of the United States energy market for decades, and one commissioned by the Bush administration to investigate the future security of oil and gas supplies, the National Petroleum Council in *Facing the Hard Truths about Energy* has submitted to the Bush administration what looks like a dramatic rethink on energy and energy security (National Petroleum Council 2007). The report recognises the challenges ahead for the United States, noting the reality of 'peak oil' and, given finite supplies of uranium, the nuclear energy counterpart to 'peak oil'. It also reiterates security concerns, especially with respect to the accumulating risks frustrating the continuity of supplies from traditional sources and the thwarting of endeavours to access non-conventional sources. In a surprising recommendation, the NPC has made a case for responding to the concerns about possible supply shortfalls by arguing that immediate steps should be taken to contain the growing demand for energy. A first step that is advocated is to adopt more concerted efforts to enhance efficiency in energy use. Surprisingly, the report expresses little confidence in the capacity of technological solutions to enable access to hitherto untapped energy sources. While it does not chart an abandonment of the fossil-fuel fired economy, it does stress the need to broaden the range of energy resources drawn upon.

But, in what amounts to an about face for energy company interests, the report chaired by former ExxonMobil chairman, Lee Raymond, advocates efforts to contain the growth in energy consumption and to set a price on CO_2 emissions as a key component in a focused energy demand management strategy. Still more intriguing is the recommendation that this carbon price be introduced in conjunction with "an effective global framework for carbon management incorporating all major emitters of CO_2".[42] The report advocates the United States joining a global framework for managing carbon emissions. This, of course, does not necessarily translate into a Kyoto-based emissions cap-and-trade system, let alone advocating the ratification of the Kyoto Protocol.[43] It does, however, signal an end to the Bush administration's unilateralism in the international political arena. It foreshadows the case for the US becoming more constructively and positively engaged in joining a multilateral framework that has more substance than the A-P6 and which is not predicated on ever-increasing inputs of fossil fuels.

This shift in thinking highlights the potential magnitude of the Australian government's isolation in global warming governance debate. It has become increasingly evident the Australian government's resistance to formulating a well-defined policy to either put a price on carbon or set emission reduction targets or to ratify the Kyoto Protocol has meant that the nation has been placed in a veritable policy cul de sac. The concessions to business that have been signalled – and particularly assurances regarding the grandfathering of emission entitlements and acknowledgement of early initiatives – have not been sufficient to allay concerns that more substance has to be injected into an emissions management policy framework. Key industry sectors have appealed for the government to bring forward a decision to set targets and establish an emissions trading system. Without these and without the government retreating from its opposition to negotiating a more expansive post-Kyoto regulatory framework under the multilateral auspices of the UN Framework Convention on Climate Change, the government will simply be exacerbating the uncertainty that it contends justifies its historical reluctance to engage the challenge of climate change. This can only serve to magnify the risks that are consequent upon inaction, as well as to exaggerate investment uncertainty. The *Climate Change Policy* as it has

---

[42] Interestingly, this coincides with ExxonMobil's public disclaimer that the corporation is no longer funding the conservative think tanks that have been responsible for much of the propaganda questioning the integrity of the science of global warming (*The Australian Financial Review* 10–11 February 2007).

[43]. The US Under-Secretary of State for global affairs, Paula Dobriansky, reiterated that the Bush administration was not entertaining introducing an emissions trading systems, arguing that such systems are unworkable and discourage investment in new technology (*The Sydney Morning Herald* 25 July 2007).

been presented encapsulates the policy cul-de-sac. It is politically, as well as environmentally unsustainable.

Conclusion

The government has over the last decade justified its opposition to the Kyoto Protocol in terms of economic uncertainty. The uncertainties with respect to the pace and intensity that modelling suggests global warming will occur and to the likely economic impacts of climate change, it has been contended, do not justify precipitous initiatives to regulate business activity to reduce GHG emissions. Acting in the face of these uncertainties could present immeasurable economic risks. But there has been more to the government's opposition to the Kyoto Protocol than the possible harm a meaningful climate change could have for the fortunes of Australia's energy-intensive industries. The government has also been concerned to secure the future of another sphere of Australia's international competitive advantage by opposing initiatives that could disadvantage fossil-fuel exports and coal exports in particular. This has driven the government, in partnership with the Bush administration, to lobby regional trading partners to join in moulding an alternative international 'climate change' regulatory framework to the Kyoto Protocol. The success of this endeavour is looking more and more improbable. With the government's *Climate Change Policy*, Australia confronts the challenge of global warming from the vantage point of a policy cul-de-sac.

The government's vision has rested on a myopic appreciation of the analytical purchase of economic uncertainty. This has been made abundantly clear by *The Stern Review* and other investigations of the likely impact of climate change, including CSIRO researchers. These interventions in debate on global warming have turned the government's position on its head. The uncertainties associated with global warming are temporally asymmetrical; the likely damaging, if not devastating, economic impacts will become more pronounced through time. It makes good economic sense to minimise future risks by acting sooner to mitigate GHG emissions and to not postpone this action.

While the government continues to define the thrust of policy in the interests of energy-intensive industries and fossil-fuel exports, the business community more generally has come to the realisation that the real economic risk lies in policy inaction. Certainly some businesses are preoccupied with the commercial opportunities that the production of a new trading instrument, carbon, will present. But a longer term vision has also become entrenched within corporations and investment houses that rest on an appreciation of the fundamental interconnection between the sustainability of the global environment and the future of business. This necessitates a more robust approach to managing uncertainty and risk than the government's conservatism has dictated.

The real challenge in confronting the threat of global warming is how to reorient the focus of economies away from the energy-intensive, fossil-fuel based accumulation model. This necessitates confronting the Australian economy's reliance upon coal-fired resource processing and coal export industries. It requires moving beyond the short-term bias of conventional approaches to economic uncertainty to a longer-term vision that appreciates the comprehensive nature of the challenge that global warming presents, and that it makes no logical human sense to discount the value of the future. It also means giving greater emphasis to the risks that the government is sewing in consolidating its fossil-fuel based accumulation model in removing barriers to uranium exports by agreeing to export uranium to countries that are not signatories to the Nuclear Non-Proliferation Treaty. This is not policy formed on the foundations of a "blend of prudent conservatism and economic liberalism". Nor is it the market at work. Rather, it is a government-initiated recklessness, and it engenders untold risks.

References

Allen Consulting Group, 2006. *Deep cuts in emission economic, social and environmental impacts for Australia*, Melbourne.

Australia, Department of the Prime Minister and Cabinet, 2004. *Securing Australia's energy future*, Canberra.

Australia, Department of the Prime Minister and Cabinet 2006. *Uranium mining, processing and nuclear energy – opportunities for Australia*, Canberra (the Switkowski report).

Australia, Department of the Prime Minister and Cabinet, Prime Ministerial Taskforce Group on Emissions Trading, 2007a. *Report of the task force on emissions trading*, Canberra.

Australia, Department of the Prime Minister and Cabinet, 2007b. *Australia's climate change policy: our economy, our environment, our future*, Canberra.

Australian Greenhouse Office, 1998. *The national greenhouse strategy: strategic framework for advancing Australia's greenhouse response*, Canberra.

Australian Business Roundtable on Climate Change, 2006. *The business case for early action*.

Barnaby F & Kemp J (eds), 2007. *Secure energy: civil nuclear power, security and global warming*, Oxford research group: briefing paper.

Buckingham D, 2000. *Strategic greenhouse issues for Australia*, http://www.bca.com.au/Content.aspx?ContentID=87529, 5 May.

Castles I, 2006. 'Ian Castles on unsatisfactory explanations & climate modelling', April 30, available at: *Jennifer Marohasy, a weblog of politics & the environment*, http://www.jennifermarohasy.com/blog/archives/001250.html.

The CNA Corporation, 2007. *National security and the threat of climate change*, Washington, D.C.

CSIRO, 2006. *Climate change impacts on Australia and the benefits of early action to reduce global greenhouse gas emissions,*

Hamilton C, 2007. *Scorcher: the dirty politics of climate change*, Black

Hill Senator R, 2000. 'Opening Address', High level forum on greenhouse sinks, 18 April.

Hill Senator R, Ambassador and permanent representative of Australia to the United Nations, 1 August. UN General Assembly, thematic debate: 'Climate change as a global challenge'.

Hoffman A J, 2005. Climate change strategy: the business logic behind voluntary greenhouse gas reductions, *California Management Review* vol. 47, no 3, Spring, pp. 21–45.

Integrated Sustainability Analysis (ISA), the University of Sydney, 2006. *Life-cycle energy and greenhouse gas emissions of nuclear energy in Australia*, Centre for Integrated Analysis at the University of Sydney.

Intergovernmental Panel on Climate Change (IPCC), 2007. *Climate change 2007: the physical scientific basis – summary for policymakers*, a Citigroup assessment of risks and opportunities, February 2007. Contribution of working group I to the fourth assessment Report of the Intergovernmental Panel on Climate Change, Geneva.

Intergovernmental Panel on Climate Change (IPCC), 2007. *Climate change 2007: climate change impacts, adaptation and vulnerability – summary for policymakers*, contribution of working group II to the fourth assessment report of the Intergovernmental Panel on Climate Change, Geneva.

Intergovernmental Panel on Climate Change (IPCC), 2007) *Climate change 2007: mitigation of climate change – summary for policymakers*, contribution of working group III to the fourth assessment report of the Intergovernmental Panel on Climate Change, Geneva.

Kolk A & Pinke J, 2005. 'Business responses to climate change: identifying emergent strategies', *California Management Review*, vol. 47, no. 3, Spring, pp. 6–20.

Lomberg B, 2001. *The sceptical environmentalist: measuring the real state of the world*, Cambridge University Press.

McKibbin W, 2005. 'Sensible climate policy', *Issues brief*, Lowy Institute for International Policy, Sydney, February.

McKibbin W & Wilcoxen P, 2006. 'A credible foundation for long-term international vo-operation on climate change', www.brookings.edu/views/papers/mckibbin/200606bdpie171.htm.

Monbiot G, 2006. *Heat: How to stop the planet burning*, Allen & Unwin, London.

National Petroleum Council, 2007. *Facing the hard truths about energy: a comprehensive view to 2030 of global oil and natural gas.*

National Emissions Trading. *Possible design for a national emissions trading scheme: a discussion paper prepared by the National Emissions Trading Taskforce*, (an initiative of state and territory governments).

Pearse G, 2007. *High and dry*, Penguin, Ringwood, Victoria.

Pittock A, 2005. *Climate change: turning up the heat*, CSIRO Publishing, Collingwood, Victoria.

Pindyck R S, 2006. 'Uncertainty in environmental economics', *NBER Working Paper 12752*, National Bureau of Economic Research, Cambridge, Massachusetts.

Preston B L & Jones R N, 2006. *Climate change impacts on Australia and the benefits of early action to reduce global greenhouse gas emissions*, CSIRO, Aspendale, Victoria.

PricewaterhouseCooper, 2006. *Carbon Conscious*, Sydney.

Productivity Commission, 2007. *Productivity commission submission to the Prime Ministerial Task Group on Emissions Trading*, Canberra.

Rolph B & Pryor E, 2007. *Climate change and the ASX100*.

Stern N, 2007. *The economics of climate change: the Stern Review*, Cabinet Office – HM Treasury, Cambridge University Press, UK.

The World Bank, 2006. *Carbon Market Report*, October.

3

State of the environment reporting by local government: Australian evidence on compliance and content

Rosina Mladenovic and Sandra van der Laan

Abstract

This chapter explores State of the Environment (SoE) reporting by local governments. SoE reporting is an integral part of local government strategic planning and management processes and, in the state of New South Wales (NSW) in Australia, SoE reporting is mandatory. A study was conducted to analyse the content of 2003 supplementary SoE reports and their compliance with reporting guidelines. A sample of 136 SoE reports was analysed using the NSW Department of Local Government State of the Environment (SoE) Reporting Guidelines as a framework for content analysis. The results revealed significant variability in the SoE reporting practices. This variability was encountered, not only in volume of information reported, but also in the nature of the issues addressed, the indicators employed and in compliance with the guidelines. Further, while SoE reports are intended to provide data integral to the development of strategic management plans and processes, on average across all environmental sectors, only half of the councils surveyed provided information in sufficient specificity to address the environmental issues identified in SoE reports. In conclusion, we argue that councils are experiencing difficulties in implementing the requirements of the Local Government Act in relation to SoE reporting.

Introduction

Local and regional communities rely on local government to provide a number of essential services and to manage and protect the natural environment in which they live (DLG, 2000). In line with the increasing global focus on environmental management, the provisions of the New South Wales *Local Government Act* 1993 (hereinafter referred to as the Act) have sought to integrate environmental issues into the strategic planning and performance of principal activities of NSW councils. The Act introduced pioneering requirements for local governments in NSW to prepare a number of reports to be included with annual reports (part 4, s. 428). These legislative requirements include comparative information on actual and projected performance of principal activities during that year, a State of the Environment (SoE) report, a report on the condition of infrastructure over which the council has responsibility and a report on access and equity activities of the council.[1] The intent of these requirements is to provide key information as inputs into strategic planning processes and as a mechanism for the subsequent evaluation of council performance. The reforms introduced by the Act are consistent with the 'New Public Management' trend in the public sector world-wide to achieve greater efficiency, quantification of achievements and accountability (Lapsley 1999).

Councils have a critical role at the micro-level in activities as diverse as social development through to environmental management. Examples of local government functions and services include: construction and maintenance of roads, waste collection and management, recreation, protection and conservation of heritage (both Indigenous and non-Indigenous), health, community services, building, planning and development approval (e. g. land development and use which has consequences for water resources, soil degradation, biodiversity and

---

[1] Infrastructure reports provide information, both financial and non-financial, on the physical condition and costs to repair council infrastructure (e.g. roads and buildings). Access and equity reports provide information, both financial and non-financial, on programs and plans that are aimed at improving services and access for particular groups (e.g. people with disabilities and the aged).

climate change), administration, and in some cases water and sewerage (DTRS 2003).

Examining and understanding the planning, management, accountability and reporting processes of local councils is essential. Unlike the corporation, where there is a financial and physical separation between the majority of key stakeholders and the operations of the organisation, a much more immediate financial and geographical relationship exists between the activities of local government and its major stakeholders. This increases the need for transparent planning and management, as well as an extension of traditional notions of accountability, particularly in relation to the natural environment.

This chapter seeks to provide insights into the extent of reporting and the information content of SoE reports prepared by NSW local government through an examination of the compliance of local government authorities with the applicable legislation.

State of the Environment Reporting

In 1999, the NSW Department of Local Government (DLG) issued NSW State of the Environment (SoE) Reporting Guidelines, to assist local governments to satisfy their reporting requirements. These guidelines assert that the local SoE report is primarily a management tool of council and has the potential to influence virtually all of the functions of council, given most of those functions have environmental implications (DLG 1999). Indeed, SoE reports are considered so integral to local government planning and management that they are included as part of the annual report[2] and SoE reports must be submitted to the NSW Department of Local Government (DLG).

Furthermore, the Act mandates that councils undertake strategic planning. A council's management plan is the strategic mechanism within which planning, policy making and management may take place. "Councils play a major role in creating the environment within which

---

[2] SoE reports must be included in the annual report. However, "the SoE report is often submitted as a separate document due to its size or because it has been prepared as a regional SoE report with other councils" (DLG 2004a, p. 117).

the local and regional community pursue their objectives" (DLG 2000, p. 5), and the SoE report provides critical information for the development and evaluation of strategic planning and council activities.

Despite the prescriptive approach taken by the NSW DLG in issuing comprehensive SoE reporting guidelines and the legislative mandate to report, the current study finds that SoE reporting by NSW local councils is extremely variable. Further, in many cases, SoE reports do not provide information in sufficient specificity to be useful for developing management plans. These results suggest that issues in relation to usefulness, consistency and comparability of SoE reports are important areas requiring further investigation.

This chapter is structured as follows. The next two sections provide background information on the preparation and use of SoE reports, including a review of the extant literature, and outline the significance of the research undertaken in the present study. This is followed by a discussion of the research methods employed to gather and analyse the data. The final two sections present the results of the research, a discussion of the findings, preliminary conclusions and some suggestions for future research.

Economic significance of local government environmental activities

SoE reporting is important both as an accountability mechanism and an input into strategic planning by councils. Local government is a major player in protecting Australia's environment and in managing its natural resources (ABS 2002). Environmental activities are those that prevent, reduce or eliminate pressures on the environment arising from social and economic activities. They also encompass environmental repair and restoration activities. Australia wide, significant amounts of economic resources are managed and controlled by local government for environmental activities.

In 2002–03 local government in Australia received over $2.6 billion for environment protection activities[3] through state and Commonwealth government contributions, as well as rate revenue which amounted to 13 per cent of total revenue for councils. In 2002–03 current expenditure by local councils on natural resource management activities (including the management, allocation and efficient use of natural resources and recreational management of parks, beaches and reserves) totaled $1.5 billion with natural resource management capital expenditure of $422 million. This amounted to 8 per cent and 9 per cent, respectively of councils' total current and capital expenditure. State governments contributed $105 million ($29m Commonwealth) to local government for environmental protection activities and $46 million ($11m Commonwealth) for resource management activities. The majority of funding was for waste-water management activities ($70m or 53% of government contributed environment protection funding) and water supply activities ($33m or 58% of natural resource management funding) (ABS 2004).

These figures highlight the economic significance of environmental expenditure at the local government level and the importance of conducting research in this area. Given the magnitude of local government expenditure on the environment, the importance of the SoE report as an accountability mechanism and its central role in local government strategic planning and management, this research investigates compliance of NSW local government SoE reports with the DLG guidelines (described below) and provides insights into the nature, scope and content of such reports based on the analysis of 2003 SoE reports.

---

[3] 2002–03 data is reported as it is relevant to the time period of the SoE reports analysed in this chapter. Further, all dollar figures reported are in Australian dollars.

Literature

New Public Management

The ideas behind New Public Management (NPM)[4] focus on removing or minimising differences between the public and private sector and shifting the emphasis to results-driven accountability rather than process accountability (Guthrie, Olsen & Humphrey 1999, Hood 1991). The NPM trend has been characterised by, amongst other things, "the displacement of old-style public administration with a new management focus in public services ... [and] quantification as a means of demonstrating achievements (efficiency gains, new levels of performance) and of holding responsible persons accountable" (Lapsley 1999, p. 201).

> The emphasis in the use of public sector resources [has] changed from a concern with legalistic conceptions of stewardship to the need to ensure that services [are] provided in the most efficient and effective manner. At the heart of these reforms has been a move away from an obsessive concern with accountability for inputs to a keener focus on outputs and outcomes (Funnell & Cooper 1998, p. 81).

SoE reporting in NSW local government can be seen as embedding these NPM style concepts in mandatory legislative requirements. While no market-based jurisdiction has yet imposed extensive mandatory environmental reporting requirements in annual reporting in the private sector, reporting is required in other forms[5] for organisations with significant environmental impacts and accountabilities. In this respect, the inclusion of environmental information as part of the annual reporting regime could be regarded as 'revolutionary'. In terms of accountability, the guidelines under which the SoE reports are

---

[4] The term 'New Public Management' encompasses the idea of 'New Public Financial Management' which focuses on reforms to financial management and systems and therefore, inevitably, the role of accounting and accountants (Guthrie, Olsen & Humphrey 1999).

[5] For example, in Australia, reporting to the relevant Environmental Protection Authority or producing return data for the National Greenhouse Inventory.

produced reinforce the primacy of accountability in terms of results. The framework for reporting, the 'Pressure-State-Response' model, as well as recommending the incorporation of comparative information as best practice, support the notion of 'results driven' accountabilities for local government.

State of the environment reporting

There is an extensive literature on the preparation of SoE reports, from both international and domestic sources, however, there is little academic research on SoE reporting and little is known about the content and usefulness of these reports for their intended aims. This research aims to address this lacuna.

Much of the existing literature focuses on report preparation and emanates from government agencies, non-government organisations (NGOs) and professional bodies (see for e.g. Boshier 2002; CSIRO 1998; EEA 1999; NETCAB 2000). The focus on report preparation implies that SoE reports are a potentially powerful tool for communicating environmental information to policy-makers and stakeholders. Hence, this literature focuses on the identification, selection and implementation of appropriate reporting indicators and providing guidelines for reporting.

The extant academic literature on SoE reporting is predominantly descriptive. A Canadian study by Campbell and Maclaren (1995) examining municipal SoE reporting in that jurisdiction criticised the lack of common indicators, organising frameworks and data accessibility. It suggested that these factors impede the utility of SoE reporting. These findings were echoed in an Australian study (Lloyd 1996) on early efforts at state and national SoE reporting which called for the strengthening of quantitative measures and the employment of an agreed set of environmental indicators. Another Australian study (Anderson 1997), reviewed the Australian national State of the Environment report. This study outlined both the positive aspects and shortcomings of the report, and provided comprehensive suggestions for improving future reports.

Gibson and Guthrie (1995) conducted a survey examining the quantity of environmental disclosures in annual reports in Australia of both public and private sector entities, and concluded that "we are still a long way from any useful common meaningful and systematic reporting practice by organisations" (p. 123). In an attempt to provide meaningful information, the introduction of SoE reporting and associated reporting guidelines for NSW local government could be regarded as a systematic framework to address this issue.

Burritt and Welch (1997) analysed a sample of Commonwealth public sector entities over a ten-year period in an attempt to address the lack of research on environmental disclosures in the public sector. Their exploratory study concluded that disclosure levels increased over the period examined. However, concerns were raised regarding the lack of comparability of information and the "dampening effect of a commercial orientation on environmental disclosures" (p. 15).

Another recent study in the Australian context, Frost and Seamer (2002), analysed NSW public sector entities' adoption of environmental reporting practices in their annual reporting, finding an association between disclosures and the level of environmental 'sensitivity' of the entity's operations. This paper also called for more research to be conducted on the information content of environmental disclosures and whether such disclosures are used to educate and inform or change/manipulate the reader's perspective of the environmental performance of the entity.

The studies summarised above focus on the extent and nature of environmental disclosures in the public sector. A number of recent studies (e.g. see Ball 2002, 2004; Marcuccio & Steccolini 2003) have a different focus, namely the exploration of the theoretical motivations for local government (social and) environmental reporting or the lack of it.

From the above review of the literature it is evident that significant gaps exist in contemporary environmental reporting research in the public sector, in particular in relation to the nature of and usefulness of environmental reporting. The present research aims to add to our understanding of environmental reporting in an Australian context. This is particularly relevant as prior research has not examined scope, content and compliance in a mandatory reporting environment.

Research Method

Nature and size of sample

SoE reports were collected from the population of NSW local councils. "Councils must produce a comprehensive SoE report every four years, and at least a supplementary report every other year" (DLG 1999, p. 10). Data were collected in 2004 and as such, this study examines 2003 supplementary SoE reports, as the next comprehensive reports were not due to be submitted to the DLG until 30 November 2004 (DLG 2004b).

Table 3.1 Local councils and SoE reports: population and sample information

Population:	Number
2003 NSW local councils	174

	Number	% of population
Sample of 2003 SoE reports:		
Report accessed and analysed	136	78
Council did not prepare a SoE report	6	4
Council does not prepare a SoE report – council data are included as part of a regional report	11	6
Council sent an incorrect report	6	4
No SoE report received despite repeated requests	13	8
TOTAL	174	100

SoE reports are submitted and are accessible from the NSW DLG. However, given that stakeholders are likely to approach the specific council for environmental information, we chose to obtain the reports from each of the local councils to explore the accessibility of these data. Many SoE reports were easily accessed on council websites, however, where reports could not be found on websites, councils were contacted by email and/or telephone. The population of local councils in NSW was determined from the Report on the Operation of the Local Government (NOLG 2003). In 2003, there were 174 councils in NSW, however, this number has since declined to 152 following a series of mergers. Of the 174 councils, 157 councils produced a SoE report and we obtained 136 reports (86% of the 157 available reports) as listed in Table 3.1 Reports were collected over the period June to December 2004. Table 3.1 summarises the sample data obtained and provides explanations for the missing information.

Methodology

The SoE reports were analysed employing content analysis. Content analysis involves the systematic analysis of documents through the development and use of coding systems to identify and quantify information in documents (Cozby 1997). This is an appropriate research technique for the current study as it can be used to "objectively and systematically make inferences about intentions, attitudes and values of individuals by identifying specified characteristics in textual message. The unobtrusive nature of content analysis makes it well suited for strategic management research" (Morris 1994 p. 903). The documents were human-coded. Morris (1994) compares human-coded content analysis to computerised coding of the same text communications and her results suggest that the two methods may be equally effective.

To investigate local council compliance with legislative requirements and reporting guidelines, a coding system was developed based on the NSW State of the Environment (SoE) Reporting Guidelines (DLG 1999). SoE reports are expected to address the eight environmental sectors of land, air, water, biodiversity, waste, noise, Aboriginal heritage and non-Aboriginal heritage. Councils are encouraged to provide regional data as necessary and prepare their reports using the Pressure-State-Response (PSR) model (OECD 2003), that is:

- Pressure – identification of issues
- State – reporting on the current status (including the provision of comparative data and community involvement in the collection of data to monitor the environment)

- Response – description of the council's strategic management plan to respond to the issues identified (DLG 1999).

The sample of NSW SoE reports was analysed by two coders. The researchers developed the classification scheme and trained two coders to complete the data analysis. Training involved the development of a template and detailed explanations for the coding of each of the items in the template. The coders independently classified the data based on the classification scheme. A comparison of the results of their initial analysis revealed some differences and these were resolved by the two researchers by re-examining all of the cases with discrepancies between the coders. It is important to note that a textual analysis employing a classification scheme requires some level of subjective judgement. In some cases, classification discrepancies between the coders were not easily resolved and the researchers worked together to make a final decision in each of these cases.

Research findings

The findings are reported in two broad categories consistent with the research objectives of investigating the compliance and content of SoE reports. The first category explores councils' compliance with the legislation implemented and their consistency with the DLG guidelines for preparing SoE reports. The second category provides insights into the scope and content of the SoE reports and general observations about reporting practices adopted by local councils.

Compliance issues

To assist local councils in the application of the legislative requirements and to provide guidance on the preparation and presentation of SoE reports, the NSW DLG produced an extensive document entitled 'Environmental Guidelines – State of the Environment Reporting by Local Government – Promoting Ecologically Sustainable Development' (DLG 1999). "The guidelines outline the various steps in preparing an SoE report: assessing the scope and content, identifying the issues, identifying environmental indicators, collecting and managing data, presenting results, submitting the report" (DLG, 1999, p. 3). The guidelines, therefore, provided the framework within which the reports were examined. The reports were scrutinised in relation to the preferred model, including the adoption of the Pressure-State-Response (PSR) model, reporting on a regional basis and community involvement in data collection and monitoring. The results are presented in Table 3.2.

Table 3.2 Compliance with SoE reporting guidelines

Compliance with guidelines	PSR model	Community	Community, government agencies	Regional data
Yes	90 (66%)	37 (27%)	79 (58%)	85 (63%)
No	46 (34%)	99 (73%)	57 (42%)	51 (37%)
Total	136 (100%)	136 (100%)	136 (100%)	136 (100%)

PSR model

Reporting guidelines recommend that councils adopt the PSR model for their SoE reporting: "For comprehensive SoE reports councils must identify and apply appropriate environmental indicators for each environmental sector, considering and applying the Pressure-State-Response (PSR) model" (DLG 1999, p. 13). SoE reports were examined for their adoption of the model. Of the sample of 136 reports examined, 66 per cent employed the PSR model.

Further, the prescribed PSR model was frequently inconsistently applied, for example: by omitting one of the three PSR elements; by posing elements as questions – for example, 'what are the issues?', 'what is being done?'; and by substituting terms such as 'indicators' or 'assessment' for the PSR descriptors. In some cases the PSR model was presented in a table to summarise the main issues for each of the eight environmental sectors. These tables were used to report on the current state of the environmental sector and to highlight the key issues. However, in some cases the main PSR elements were only mentioned in these tables, as opposed to within the main body of the report.

Community

The Act mandates that "[f]or all SoE reports, councils must: involve the community (including environmental groups) in monitoring changes to the environment over time" (DLG 1999, p. 16). The key purpose of involving the local community is to assist the local government authority in the collection of data for the SoE report. For the purposes of our analysis the term 'community' was defined in two ways. First, community was defined as traditional community groups, such as landcare groups and non-government organisations e.g. Greenpeace. Second, it was defined more broadly to include both the traditional groups, as well as government agencies (e.g. Environment Protection Authority and National Parks and Wildlife Service).

Employing a traditional definition of community groups, the results reveal a low proportion of councils (27%) provide evidence of community involvement in data collection and monitoring in SoE reports in at least one of the eight environmental sectors. It appears that for the majority of councils, this directive is not followed. However, taking a broader definition of community to include other government agencies, the results show a higher level of compliance (58%) as evidenced in Table 3.2.

Regional

The guidelines state that "[r]eporting for local SoE reports on a regional rather than an individual council basis is encouraged" (DLG 1999, p. 11) and the sample of SoE reports were analysed for presence of regional data, such as catchment areas, as relevant. Table 3.2 shows that 63 per cent of councils provide regional data. The advantages of reporting on a regional basis include: many issues are regional in nature; cooperation among councils can reduce time and resources in the preparation of reports; and environmental information is often collected on a regional, rather than a council basis by external authorities (DLG 1999).

Scope and content of SoE reports

As well as the reporting guidelines outlining a model for councils to adopt for reporting, the Act also outlines appropriate indicators which councils should report against, essentially defining the environmental sectors for which local governments have some responsibility and concomitant accountability.

The Act requires:
> [t]he first SoE report of a council for the financial year ending after each election of the councilors must be a comprehensive SoE, which:

> Addresses the eight environmental sectors of land, air, water, biodiversity, waste, noise, Aboriginal heritage and non-Aboriginal heritage ...

A supplementary SoE report must ...
> Update the trends in environmental indicators that are important to each environmental sector (DLG 1999, p. 10).

The guidelines also encourage the production of comparative data.
> The quality and value of environmental indicator data presented in local SoE reports can be enhanced by:
> - Analysing trends ...
> - Placing current levels in context ...
> - Comparing measured values of the indicator to agreed standards or goals (DLG 1999, p. 19).

Further, the SoE report is part of the council's management planning and annual reporting.

> For it to be effective, the management planning and the SoE reporting processes should be linked together in a manner that ensures that the relevant information and proposed directions fed from one into the other ... The SoE report should report on the environmental issues identified in the management plan, as well as identifying other issues affecting the area, and may suggest tangible and achievable responses to those issues" (DLG 2000, p. 53).

Table 3.3 reports the results of the analysis of the content of the SoE reports based on the guidelines outlined above. Each SoE report was analysed to ascertain whether: councils reported on all eight environmental sectors; comparative data were provided; and councils provided a 'response' (future actions, aims or objectives) to address the identified environmental issues for that sector.

Table 3.3 Scope and content of SoE reports for the eight environmental sectors. Number of SoE reports

Environmental sector	Reporting (number)		Comparative		Response		
	Yes	No	Yes	No	General	Specific	None
Land	130	6	69	67	34	86	16
Air	113	23	71	65	42	69	25
Water	125	11	77	59	27	97	12
Biodiversity	129	7	54	82	47	82	7
Waste	131	5	86	50	35	86	15
Noise	100	36	61	75	49	39	48
Aboriginal heritage	94	42	20	116	37	40	59
Non-Aboriginal heritage	117	19	27	109	47	61	28
Average across 8 sectors (%)	**86**	**14**	**43**	**57**	**29**	**52**	**19**

Reporting

In the analysis (coding) employed for this research, reporting was defined as the provision of financial or other information on the current state of the environmental sector. The following statement was considered an example of reporting in the environmental sector 'land':

> Table 4 summarises the number of DAs received and determined and the number of construction licenses issued

by Council during 2002/03. (Wollongong City Council 2003, p. 20.

In contrast, the following statement was not considered an example of reporting as it is too general and does not provide data on the current state of the environmental sector:

> Noise related complaints normally relate to vehicle noise in urban areas, domestic dogs barking in village areas and noise associated with industry. Noise issues have not been a problem in the shire community over the reporting period. (Severn Shire Council 2003, p. iv)

Discussion of Results

Table 3.3 reveals that on average, across the eight environmental sectors, 86 per cent of SoE reports contain information on the current state of the environment. It is important to note that sectors such as land and waste have many fewer examples of non-reporting than sectors such as noise and Aboriginal heritage. In some cases councils noted that they did not have sufficient resources or the appropriate equipment to monitor the environment or reported data gaps. Illustrative extracts in relation to the environmental sectors 'air' and 'noise' are provided below:

> There is no routine monitoring outside of Canberra ... Without a monitoring station in place it is not possible to know if local effects are causing pollutant accumulation. (Mulwaree Shire Council 2003 p. 1).

> Transport noise would be the main type of noise pollution ... No scientific studies have been undertaken on this issue ... (Lockhart Shire Council 2003, p. 24).

The analysis of SoE reports provided clear evidence that councils experience difficulty in determining both what information, and how to measure that information, in discharging their SoE reporting responsibilities. For example, in relation to noise, reporting for most councils consisted of listing the number of noise complaints reported to council, as opposed to recording the output from a measurement device, such as a sound level metre. Measurement issues in relation to 'air' are echoed by Tumut Council (2003, p. 2) noting it is not clear 'what' the measurement unit is.

> Air quality can be assessed on broad or fine scales: an entire region, an urban air shed, an individual valley or a room within a building ... The careful siting and rigorous operation of measuring devices is essential to monitor air quality. However, this task is complex and needs regular updating. (Tumut Council 2003, p. 2)

In most cases, where councils reported on air quality, limited data was provided (e.g. number of Environmental Protection Authority Pollution Licenses issued) and was not comprehensive.

Comparative data

The SoE guidelines state that the quality and value of environmental indicator data presented in local SoE reports can be enhanced by the provision of comparative data. Comparative data can provide clear evidence of the impact of council activities and programs on the environment, both over time and across councils. For example, in the 2002–2003 SoE update, Hurstville City Council (p. 18) provides comparative figures on domestic waste for the period 1995–2002. The data provides evidence of the effectiveness of the council's waste management initiatives to reduce waste going to landfill (21,413 tonnes in 1995 down to 16,052 tonnes in 2002). However, on average, across the eight environmental sectors, 43 per cent of councils provided comparative data in their reporting as evidenced in Table 3.3. One council stated: "comparisons to noise complaints from previous years are inconclusive because of recent updating of council's records management system from manual to electronic records management" (Auburn Council 2002/2003, p. 56). Of the councils which provided comparative data, most provided 'intra council' data on the required eight sectors and there were fewer councils that provided comparisons to other councils, benchmarks or best practice figures. Consistent with NPM style reforms, benchmarking against best practice and accountability in terms of results is encouraged by the guidelines.

Response

A final area explored was whether councils provided suggested 'responses' (or aims or objectives) to environmental issues identified. This was considered relevant, given council management plans draw upon the information presented in the SoE and, under the PSR SoE reporting model, councils are required to provide a suggested response(s) to address issues identified. Responses were classified as: general, specific or none (no response).

A response was classified as 'specific', if a response to the issue/area/indicator to be addressed was clearly outlined or a specific action was articulated. Statements in SoE reports illustrating 'specific' responses include the following:

> Undertake audit of herbicide use to identify if more environmentally friendly alternatives are available as part of the development of an organisation wide procurement policy. (Coffs Harbour City Council 2003, p. 39)

> The strategy identifies four key areas where we must achieve outcomes: avoiding and preventing waste; increased use of renewable and recovered materials; reducing toxicity in products and materials; and reducing litter and illegal dumping. The strategy identifies broad targets for each outcome area ..." (Cessnock City Council 2003, p. 25)

And, to addressing woodsmoke pollution:

> When the new LEP (Local Environment Plan) is adopted council will require dwellings to have at least a 3.5 star rating under the House Energy Rating Scheme (NatHERS). (Bingarra Shire Council 2003, p. 13).

On the other hand, where a council's response consisted of broad (motherhood-type) statements, these were classified as 'general'. An example of a general statement is provided below:

> Council and the community must continue to strive towards a reduction in waste to ensure more sustainable levels are reached. (Camden Council 2003, p. 50).

Table 3.3 reveals that, on average, across all of the environmental sectors, 19 per cent of councils did not provide any response, 29 per cent provided a general 'motherhood statement' style responses and 52 per cent provided a specific response which could be integrated into the councils' management plan. Once again, there is observed variability across the eight environmental sectors with councils providing more specific responses in the sectors of land, air, water, biodiversity and waste and significantly less suggested responses in the sectors of noise, Indigenous heritage and non-Indigenous heritage.

Further observations

NSW council supplementary SoE reports vary significantly. This result is consistent with findings of prior research reviewed earlier in this chapter (see, e.g. Campbell & Maclaren 1995; Lloyd 1996). Whilst the DLG acknowledges the necessity for autonomy of councils in identifying the issues relevant to their area (DLG 1999), the lack of data availability in some cases and overall consistency and comparability between reports needs to be considered. Extremes in length, detail and coverage were apparent, despite the prescriptive guidelines issued by the DLG.

Length

SoE reports varied in length from four pages (e.g. Coolah Shire Council) to several hundred pages (e.g. Great Lakes Shire Council's report is 228 pages). The 2003 reports are supplementary SoE reports. A supplementary SoE report is only required to update trends in environmental indicators that are important to each environmental sector. However, in the vast majority of cases, the supplementary report could be considered as a 'comprehensive' report, given there was no reference to previous comprehensive reports.

Detail

Many SoE reports focused on plans to be prepared or plans already developed, but which are reported elsewhere, rather than identifying specific strategic actions to address problems. Stand-alone plans (such as environmental management plans), as sources of information about council plans or strategy in relation to environmental issues, were frequently referred to, but the detail of information relevant to the SoE report was not included.

Many SoE reports also contained significant background information on the local population and the local area including, in many cases, specific sections entitled 'social' or 'cultural' information. Interestingly, the Act requires a separate social and community plan.

Conclusions and suggestions for future research

The articulated purpose of SoE reporting in local government is two-fold. Generation of these reports for internal users is to support planning and decision making processes. For external users these reports are meant to serve as an accountability mechanism to a broad range of stakeholders through the provision of reliable, relevant and comparable environmental information, as well as providing stakeholders with an indication of the environmental policy of council through articulated 'responses' to environmental pressures. In NSW, the DLG asserts that the SoE report is a primary management tool and has the potential to influence virtually all of the functions of council (DLG 1999), however our study provides little empirical evidence to support this contention.

This research examined local council compliance with SoE reporting guidelines and related legislation as well as providing insights into the scope and content of 2003 supplementary SoE reports. Considerable variability in local council reporting practices was found by analysing an extensive sample of 136 NSW SoE reports.

In terms of compliance, the results revealed that 66 per cent of councils employed the required Pressure-State-Response (PSR) reporting model; a low proportion of councils (27%) provided evidence of community involvement in data collection and monitoring in SoE reports; and 63 per cent of councils provided regional data. With respect to the scope and content, the analysis revealed that, of the required eight environmental sectors, most of the sectors were treated comprehensively with the exceptions of 'noise', 'non-Aboriginal heritage' and, in particular, 'Aboriginal heritage'. Additional research is required to investigate the possible reasons for the lack of reporting in these areas.

The most significant finding of this study is that, while SoE reports are intended to provide critical data internally for the development of management plans, on average across all environmental sectors, half the councils (52%) provided tangible and achievable responses to address the issues identified in the SoE report. Further, 43 per cent of councils provided comparative data, which are valuable for identifying trends in the impact of councils' activities on the environment over time. Given the magnitude of economic resources expended by local government on the local environment, the role of the SoE report as an accountability mechanism and its central role in local government strategic planning and management, further research is needed to better understand how SoE reporting could be improved and effectively integrated into council management planning processes.

Statutory requirements for the preparation of a SoE reports as a preliminary to the compilation of formal management plans, impose significant costs on the local government sector. An interesting question to be investigated is: whether these requirements are merely viewed as another reporting imposition from the state and prepared only as evidence of compliance, or whether they are relevant in strategic planning and management and the evaluation and management of local and regional environment issues. Further research to assess the extent to which these requirements are effective in achieving their intended objectives is critical.

The revolutionary requirements of the NSW Local Government Act for every council to produce extensive environmental information could be regarded as a manifestation of new public management. The guidelines directing the reporting process focus on results driven accountabilities and on the efficient effective provision of public services. However, consistent with prior research, NSW local councils experience difficulties in determining both what to report and how. More work is required for councils to be able to determine appropriate tools and metrics with which to report their environmental responsibilities and activities in ways that enable consistency, comparability and accountability.

Acknowledgements

The authors gratefully acknowledge the financial support provided by the University of Sydney, Faculty of Economics and Business Special Research Grant scheme, as well as the NSW Department of Local Government for their assistance with data collection. The authors would also like to thank James Guthrie, Bob Walker and the participants at the University of Sydney, Discipline of Accounting Seminar Series for their helpful comments on earlier versions of this work.

References

Auburn Council, 2002/2003. *Supplementary state of the environment report*, Auburn Council.

Australian Bureau of Statistics (ABS), 2002. *Environment expenditure, local government, Australia*, 4611.0, ABS, Canberra.

Australian Bureau of Statistics (ABS), 2004, *Environment expenditure, local government, Australia*, 4611.0, ABS, Canberra.

Anderson E, (ed.), 1997. 'State of the environment 1996', *Australian Journal of Environmental Management*, vol. 4, pp. 157–184.

Ball A, 2002. *Sustainability accounting in UK local government: an agenda for research*, ACCA Research Report, no. 78, London.

Ball A, 2004. 'A sustainability project for the UK local government sector? Testing the social theory mapping process and locating a frame of reference', *Critical Perspectives on Accounting*, vol. 15, pp. 1009–35.

Bingarra Shire Council, Australia, 2003. *State of the Environment Report*, Bingarra Shire Council.

Boshier J, 2002. 'Preparing the 2001 state of the environment report', *Australian Journal of Environmental Management*, vol. 9, pp. 141–2.

Burritt R L & Welch S, 1997. 'Australian commonwealth entities: an analysis of their environmental disclosures', *Abacus*, vol. 33, no. 1, pp. 1–15.

Camden Council, Australia, 2003. *State of the environment supplementary report 2002–2003*, Camden Council.

Campbell M E & Maclaren V W, 1995. 'An overview of municipal state of the environment reporting in Canada', *Canadian Journal of Public Health*, vol. 86, no. 6, pp. 408–413.

Cessnock City Council, Australia, 2003. *State of the environment report 2002–2003*, Cessnock City Council.

Coffs Harbour City Council (2003), *Coffs Harbour State of the Environment Supplementary Report 2003*.

Coolah Shire Council, Australia, 2003. *Annual Report 2002/2003*, Coolah Shire Council.

Cozby P, 1997. *Methods in behavioural research*, 6th ed., Mayfield.

CSIRO, 1998. *A guidebook to environmental indicators*, CSIRO, Australia.

Department of Local Government (DLG), 1999. *Environmental guidelines – state of the environment reporting by local government – promoting ecologically sustainable development*, DLG, Canberra.

Department of Local Government (DLG), 2000. *Management planning for NSW local government – guidelines*, DLG, Canberra.

Department of Local Government (DLG), 2004a. *Strategic tasks 2004–2005*, DLG, Canberra.

Department of Local Government (DLG), 2004b. *Comparative information on NSW local government councils 2002–2003*, DLG, Canberra.

Department of Transport and Regional Services (DTRS), 2003. *Local government national report 2002–03 – Report on the operation of local government*, DTRS, Canberra.

European Environment Agency (EEA), 1999. *State of the environment reporting: institutional and legal arrangements in Europe*, European Environment Agency, Copenhagen.

Frost G R & Seamer M, 2002. 'Adoption of environmental reporting and management practices: an analysis of New South Wales public sector entities', *Financial Accountability & Management*, vol. 18, no. 2, pp. 103–127.

Funnell W & Cooper K, 1998. *Public sector accounting and accountability*, UNSW Press Ltd, Sydney.

Great Lakes Council, Australia, 2003. *Supplementary state of the environment report 02/03*, Great Lakes Council.

Gibson R & Guthrie J, 1995. 'Recent environmental disclosures in annual reports of Australian public and private sector organisations', *Accounting Forum*, vol. 19, no. 2/3, pp. 111–127.

Guthrie J, Olsen O & Humphrey C, 1999. 'Debating developments in new financial management: the limits of global theorising and some new ways forward', *Financial Accountability & Management*, vol. 15, no. 3 & 4, pp. 209–228.

Hood C, 1991. 'A public management for all seasons?', *Public Administration*, vol. 69, pp. 3–19.

Hurstville City Council, Australia (2002-2003) *State of the Environment Update*.

Lockhart Shire Council, Australia, 2003. *State of the environment report*, Lockhart Shire Council.

Lapsley I, 1999. 'Accounting and the new public management: instruments of substantive efficiency or a rationalising modernity?',

Financial Accountability & Management, vol. 15, no. 3 & 4, pp. 201–07.

Lloyd B, 1996. 'State of the environment reporting in Australia: a review', *Australian Journal of Environmental Management*, vol. 3, pp. 151–162.

Marcuccio M & Steccolini I, 2003, 'Social and environmental reporting in local government; a new Italian fashion?' *SDA Bocconi, Working Paper N. 105/03.*

Morris R, 1994. 'Computerised content analysis in management research: a demonstration of advantages and limitations', *Journal of Management*, vol. 4, pp. 903–31.

Mulwaree Shire Council, Australia, 2003. *State of the environment report*, Mulwaree Shire Council.

National Office of Local Government (NOLG), 2003. *2002–2003 Report on the operation of the Local Government (Financial Assistance) Act 1995*, NOLG, www.nolg.gov.au/publications.

Networking and Capacity Building Programme (NETCAB), 2000. *SoE Info*, no.4.

NSW Local Government Act (NSW) 1993

Organisation for Economic Co-operation and Development (OECD), 2003. *OECD environmental indicators – development, measurement and use*, reference paper, OECD.

Severn Shire Council, Australia, 2003. *Supplementary state of the environment report*, Severn Shire Council.

Tumut Council, Australia, 2003. *State of the environment report*, Tumut Council.

Wollongong City Council, Australia, 2003. *State of the environment report*, Wollongong City Council.

4

Framing responsibility: global firms' environmental motivations

John Mikler

Abstract

A recurring theme in international political economy is that responsibility for regulation is moving from the public to the private sphere, particularly from states to globally integrated markets. One of the clearest cases of this is multinational corporations (MNCs) increasingly adopting codes of conduct for the impact of their activities, including environmental impacts. MNCs also produce reports in which they present their environmental credentials. However, by analysing the reports of the most global MNCs, this chapter finds that the institutional basis of capitalist relations in firms' home states is a key determiner of their environmental motivations. This reflects, and supports, the insights of the Varieties of Capitalism Approach. It suggests that, rather than conceiving of firms' environmental motivations as global, even the most global firms view their environmental responsibilities through national lenses that reflect, and support, certain national institutional preferences over others.

Introduction

Multinational corporations (MNCs) are perhaps the most important economic actors shaping the contemporary global economy. Their dominance of world production, trade and investment is such that 50 per cent of the world's largest economic units are MNCs (measured by sales revenues), and the other 50 per cent are nation states (measured by gross national product) (Dicken 2003 p. 274). As MNCs rival states in their command of material resources, there is no shortage of commentary asserting that globally integrated markets, in which MNCs are the main players, are increasingly more powerful than nation states. Nobody has made the case more clearly, or colourfully, since Strange declared that markets are now "the masters over the governments of states" (Strange 1996, p. 4), with states themselves increasingly "merely the handmaidens of firms" (Strange 1997, p. 184). This point was so obvious to her that she said everyone knew it to be the case except academics, declaring that "the common sense of common people is a better guide to understanding than most of the academic theories being taught in universities" (Strange 1996, p. 3). As the rhetoric of globalisation began to take hold in the 1990s, commentators analysing the implications began to see it as unavoidable that business, as the "most powerful institution on the planet" and therefore the "dominant institution in society" must "take responsibility" for its actions (Korten quoted in Lawrence, Weber & Post 2005, p. 47).

Against this backdrop, the OECD (2001b) has noted a growing profusion of corporate codes of conduct since the 1990s, with MNCs the primary source. This phenomenon is characterised by many authors as a rise in the importance of private authority, because it is MNCs themselves that are establishing the rules by which they face their public obligations, rather than nation states or international organisations regulating to impose these obligations on them (e.g. see the contributions in Cutler, Haufler & Porter 1999). This raises the question: just what is it that is motivating firms in the commitments they are making? The claim made in this chapter is that rather than global convergence, significant motivational differences for codes of conduct exist between firms. That different firms should be driven by different imperatives is not surprising. However, the analysis presented in this chapter demonstrates two important points. First, the differences between firms are based on the location of their home state, not the markets they dominate, nor where they make most of their sales, and not even necessarily where most of their assets and employees are located. Secondly, even highly global firms demonstrate this trend. This points to the enduring importance of national interests in MNCs' codes of conduct, or more accurately, the enduring importance of firms' nationality even when their operations and material interests are global.

To focus the analysis, this chapter examines firms' statements with respect to environmental responsibility. However, the intention is not to analyse the environmental initiatives of MNCs. This is done, most accessibly on a sector-by-sector basis, by others (e.g. with respect to the auto industry see Austin et al 2003; OECD 2004; UNEP & ACEA 2000). The question of whether such initiatives represent real commitments or merely 'greenwashing' is not a debate entered into either. It too is considered elsewhere, such as in Mikler (2005)[1]. Instead, the purpose here is to focus on what MNCs themselves say is driving them to take environmental initiatives, and therefore how they themselves perceive the environmental impact of their products and their role in ameliorating this impact. The contention is that the home states of MNCs are, from an institutional perspective, particularly central to how they approach the question of addressing the environmental impacts of their activities.

The analysis proceeds as follows. First, the case is made for focusing specifically on firm's motivations with respect to the environment. Corporate responsibility is too large a 'playing field' on which to consider the questions, so environmental responsibility is the focus of empirical analysis. The increasing relevance of environmental responsibility to public, as well as private actors is highlighted. Secondly, the case is made for why an institutional approach to the question of environmental responsibility is warranted, as opposed to the mainstream rationalist liberal economic approach. Thirdly, the enduring institutional importance of firms' home states is outlined, as suggested by the Varieties of Capitalism (VOC) approach (e.g. see Hall & Soskice 2001). Finally, the results of a content analysis of the top five global German, US and Japanese MNCs' environmental/sustainability or corporate citizenship reports is presented. These firms are the most global in the sense they have the highest transnationality indexes (TNIs) – i.e. they have high proportions of their total assets, sales and employment located outside their home state.

---

[1] In this article, the issue of climate change and the performance of the European, US and Japanese auto industries vis-à-vis carbon dioxide emission regulations is considered.

The analysis highlights the enduring importance of national institutional variations in capitalist relations for firms' motivations. This is despite the firms chosen being the most global in their operations and interests. The US firms remain most focused on the material drivers of market forces. However, other modes of coordinating activity are of greater importance for the German and Japanese firms. The German firms display a predisposition for a partnership approach with the state which incorporates a desire to proactively promote regulations and regulatory targets. The Japanese firms are driven by a concern for a broader range of stakeholders and a deep sense of their responsibility to society. They are greatly concerned about their social standing, or their place in society, that goes well beyond instrumental material goals. The German firms share this predisposition, albeit to a lesser extent.

While there may be ongoing debate about ensuring that the commitments of firms are real, the debate about nationally appropriate and conducive paths to environmental commitments must therefore also be a key consideration. Even as business becomes more global, national institutions affect the manner in which firms of different nationalities perceive their interests in addressing environmental problems. Rather than a universal, global solution to the environmental impact of business, or visions of global codes of conduct, a variety of approaches depending on firms' nationalities is appropriate: market forces and market mechanisms for US firms; close state–business cooperation and coordination for German firms, with society as a key stakeholder in the process; and strategies through which business and society drive the process for Japanese firms reflecting firms' deep awareness of their social obligations.

Environmental responsibility

Firms' claims concerning their responsibilities extend across a broad landscape, encompassing a diverse range of areas. This makes understanding firms' motivations for their codes of conduct problematic. Inevitably, one confronts the notion of corporate social responsibility (CSR), which exacerbates the problem because of a lack of definitional clarity. 'CSR' is often used interchangeably with other terms, such as 'corporate sustainability', 'corporate responsibility' or 'corporate citizenship'. Although the United Nations Environment Programme (UNEP) has stated that environmental sustainability and CSR are separate fields (UNEP 2002), they are regarded as inseparable in much of the literature and by firms themselves (e.g. see Florini 2003a, 2003b; OECD 2001a). In particular, the OECD says environmental sustainability is a sub-category of CSR along with labour standards, human rights, disclosure of information, corporate governance, public safety, privacy protection and consumer protection (OECD, 2001a).[2] The business case for CSR is put by the World Business Council for Sustainable Development (WBCSD) which agrees with a broader definition that encompasses human rights, employee rights, supplier relations, community involvement and environmental protection (Holliday, Schmidheiny & Watts 2002; WBCSD 1998, 2000).

Why focus on the environmental aspects of CSR – i.e. a small sub-set of the whole? Apart from tractability for the sake of analysis, the first reason is the growing international significance of environmental issues. International organisations have significantly raised the profile of environmental concerns since the early 1990s. For example, the UNEP views the 1992 Rio Earth Summit[3] as a watershed in the discussion of environmental sustainability from which sustainable development initiatives have sprung, such as the high profile Kyoto Protocol signed in 1997 and subsequently ratified by nearly all its signatories.[4] Even the World Trade Organization (WTO) recognises that "environment, gender and labour concerns are on the agenda in ways that would have been deemed illegitimate in the 1970s" (O'Brien et al, 2000, p. 231). The WTO therefore established its Committee on Trade and Environment in 1995 at its inception. At the same time, throughout the 1990s a series of international agreements with business also emerged. One of these is the Global Compact, announced in 1999, which brings companies together with UN agencies, labour and civil society to support nine principles in

---

[2] Another OECD publication lists the "eight broad issue areas" of CSR as accountability, business conduct, community involvement, corporate governance, environment, human rights, consumer protection and labor relations (OECD 2001b, p. 61–63).
[3] This is the colloquial name for the United Nations Conference on Environment and Development held in Rio de Janeiro on 3–14 June 1992 (UN, n. d. a).
[4] Australia, Kazakhstan, Croatia, Monaco and the United States are the only non-ratifiers (see UNFCCC, n. d. a, n. d. b, n. d. c).

the areas of human rights, labour and the environment. Another agreement is the Global Reporting Initiative (GRI), started in 1997 by the Coalition of Environmentally Responsible Economies (CERES) and now an official collaborating centre of the UNEP that works in cooperation with the UN's Global Compact (GRI 2002; UN, n. d. b).

Secondly, commentators such as Florini (2003a, 2003b) identify CSR as having come to the fore as an *ideological shift* that started in the 1990s. Indeed, there is a growing body of research that shows environmental sustainability, along with other socially responsible behaviour on the part of MNCs, to be driven by *voluntary* initiatives. Such initiatives are further identified as being a *global* phenomenon. In the area of environmental responsibility, the WBCSD was established at the same time as the 1992 Rio Earth Summit and has been working ever since to be at the forefront of the business response to sustainable development. It is a coalition of 165 companies drawn from 30 countries and 20 industry sectors. It also links a network of 43 national and regional business councils and partner organisations in 39 countries. Thus, it may be said to be a manifestation of a broader acceptance by corporations of the importance of environmental issues as a key component of CSR that commenced in the 1990s (Florini 2003a, 2003b; Holliday, Schmidheiny & Watts 2002; Karliner 1997; OECD 2001a, 2001b).[5]

Thirdly, outspoken critics of international capitalism, regarding the environment, suggest that we are actually witnessing a fundamental change in how firms do business worldwide as they incorporate environmental sustainability concerns in their operations. For example, before the mid-1990s any action to address environmental concerns was a response to social activism or government regulations, rather than the industry taking action proactively (Hawken, Lovins & Lovins 1999 p. 24). Indeed, in 1993 David Suzuki, a strident critic of capitalism, globalisation and the environmental degradation in which it results worldwide, declared:

---

[5] Karliner points out that over this timeframe the environment began to be taken seriously by business, and with this came the emergence of corporate environmental departments and policies, and senior executives coming to be in charge of environmental issues (Karliner 1997 p. 30).

Environmentally responsible corporations may seem like an oxymoron. But as pressure by ecologically aware consumers and activists increases, more and more businesses are cloaking themselves in green rhetoric. How genuine is it or can it be ? (Suzuki 1993, p. 135)

His answer in 1993 was that it was not genuine, and that "the ground rules of profit make it hard to be a friend to the environment" so that "amid...the suicidal demand for steady growth, happy stories are few" (Suzuki 1993, p. 135). But by 2002 he notes a philosophical shift within corporate hierarchies manifested in attitudinal changes, such as General Motors supporting a 50 per cent tax on petrol for environmental reasons (Suzuki & Dressel 2002, p. 289–290). He similarly applauds the attitudinal change within Ford, quoting its Chairman who said in his speech to a Greenpeace business conference on 5 October 2000:

We're at a crucial point in the world's history. Our oceans and forests are suffering; species are disappearing; the climate is changing...Enlightened corporations are beginning to...realise that they can no longer separate themselves from what is going on around them. That, ultimately, they can only be as successful as the communities and the world that they exist in ... I personally believe that sustainability is the most important issue facing the automotive industry in general in the 21st century (Suzuki & Dressel 2002, p. 290–291)

Within the space of one decade, Suzuki's attitude changed from pessimism to a decidedly more optimistic view of the possibilities for business environmental responsibility.[6]

Finally, environmental reporting by firms in many cases preceded reporting on CSR more generally.[7] Starting in the late 1980s to early 1990s, an increasing number of large corporations, mostly MNCs, began producing such reports. These reports represent a desire by firms to represent themselves as environmentally concerned (whether in image or

---

[6] A similar viewpoint is evident in Hawken, Lovins & Lovins (1999).

[7] This is an observation based on perusing the reporting of firms since the early 1990s. Many started with environmental reports, or environmental statements and guidelines that have subsequently been incorporated into broader corporate citizenship or social responsibility reports.

fact) suggesting an increase in the strategic importance of environmental considerations during this time period.

Given the increasing global visibility of environmental concerns, and the importance of environmental responsibility as a key sub-category within CSR more broadly, the question of how to conceptualise firms' motivations to address their environmental impacts arises. The case for an institutional approach to answering this question is made in the following section.

Material 'calculus' versus institutional 'culture'

The key assumption in mainstream liberal economic approaches is rationality, defined in terms of a priori assumed self-interest (Crane & Amawi 1997; Green & Shapiro 1994; Helleiner 2003; Ordeshook, 1993).[8] They are seen as primarily employing "instrumental logics of calculation (calculus logics)" to achieve their material ends (Hay 2006a; see also Hay 2006b; March & Olsen 1989, 1998). The mainstream view is therefore fundamentally based on a materialist perspective in which firms act instrumentally to make profits in markets. They may also act to increase their power, but it is their *material* power in terms of market outcomes. This is the basis on which rationality is assumed: rational choice defined in terms of materialist profit and power maximising outcomes.

Environmental problems are usually characterised as cases of market failure due to externalities (the classic papers are Coase 1960; Hardin 1968).[9] Environmental externalities cause market failure because the environment is often ignored by markets. Therefore, the price of goods and services does not reflect the environmental impacts of their production and consumption. This is because economic actors lack property rights over the environment, meaning they can ignore the

---

[8] Ordeshook (1993) presents a useful overview, Crane and Amawi (1997) present a description of classical liberalism, while Helleiner (2003) discusses economic liberalism from a critical perspective. Green and Shapiro (1994) analyse and criticise rationalism as a way of conceiving the actions of actors more generally.

[9] Of course, a basic explanation of the concept may now be found in almost any mainstream economics or politics textbook.

negative environmental effects of their actions. The cost of environmental externalities is often borne by others who were not responsible for them. This is highly likely because the environment is often a public good in the sense that it may be jointly consumed by several agents at the same time. When the public good attribute of the environment is a global or transborder phenomenon, as is often the case, then the environment is said to be in the realm of the 'global commons'. Far from market failure being the exception, "environmental externalities are pervasive" (Ekins et al 1994, p. 7). What then might motivate firms to address their environmental impacts? The standard answer to this question follows the logic of the firm conceived as a rational agent that employs an instrumental logic of material calculus in order to maximise returns.[10] Therefore, the material factors of market forces and effective state regulation are to the fore.

The materialist perspective has proved to be a parsimonious way of explaining economic actors' behaviour, including the behaviour of individuals, firms, states and international relations between states. However, it is challenged by analyses that are grounded more in institutional perspectives. Institutional perspectives have been promoted by scholars such as North (1990), March and Olsen (1989, 1998), and even Goldstein and Keohane (1993). The materialist, rational choice based approach has been modified (e.g. Denzau & North 1994) or attacked in the process (see Blyth 1997, 2003; Hay 2002, 2004; Green & Shapiro 1994). The body of literature on institutional theoretical approaches has now grown to the point where there are a variety of theoretical approaches embracing institutionalism, from those that emphasise the contextual or historically constructed nature of rationality, to those that virtually discard rationality altogether to focus on cultural and identity aspects – that is agency (Hay 2006b; Lowndes 2002).[11] What they have in common is that, at the very least, they do not define actors' rationality in terms of a priori assumptions ascribing actors' motivations.

---

[10] The term is used loosely here to encompass profits, shareholder value, market share etc.

[11] For example, Hay (2006b) identifies four versions of institutionalism. Those where rationality features most are rational choice institutionalism and historical institutionalism. Those which tend to discard rationality are normative/sociological institutionalism and constructivist institutionalism.

Instead, their starting point is that actors are motivated by certain norms that prescribe and proscribe appropriate action. When such norms become institutionalised, they have a taken-for-'grantedness' about them so that behaving in a manner commensurate with them may be taken for 'rational' behaviour, but not necessarily rational behaviour in the liberal economic sense. In short, they apply "norm-driven logics of appropriateness (cultural logics)" (Hay 2006a; see also Hay 2006b; March & Olsen 1989, 1998).

Liberal economic versus institutional perspectives are therefore delineated by the manner in which rational choice is applied in the former, versus the role of norms of behaviour in the latter. Followers of the mainstream liberal economic perspective understand the world in terms of material interests, with actors acting as if applying a material calculus based on a logic of consequentialism (the outcomes of taking certain courses of action), whereas institutionalists accentuate the role of ideas and social behaviour (i.e. norms) based on a logic of appropriateness (i.e. that there is an appropriate way to act not necessarily contingent on the outcome of such behaviour) (March & Olsen 1989, 1998; Hasenclever Mayer & Rittberg 1997). The following section outlines how an institutional perspective may be applied to MNCs, and makes the case for why this should be done at a national rather than global level as argued by the VOC approach.

National perceptions of interests: the institutional importance of firms' home states and the varieties of capitalism approach

Before discussing the implications of institutional perspectives, a simple and clear definition of the terms is required. North defines 'norms' as "shared common beliefs" that give rise to 'institutions' defined as "the rules of the game in a society or, more formally ... the humanly devised constraints that shape interaction" (North 1990, p. 3 and p. 14). A more specific definition of the institutions to which norms give rise is provided by Hall and Soskice who say institutions are "a set of rules, formal or informal, that actors generally follow, whether for normative, cognitive, or material reasons" (Hall & Soskice 2001, p. 9). Institutional perspectives thus challenge the rational choice mechanism in the liberal economic model by seeing the role of ideas, beliefs and the resulting norms of behaviour – i.e. socially appropriate ways of behaving – as providing richer explanations of how decisions are made and institutions constructed.

In institutional, as well material terms, MNCs are not 'placeless' entities. As Dicken notes, they are "produced through an intricate process of embedding in which the cognitive, cultural, social, political and economic characteristics of the national home base play a dominant part" (Dicken 1998, p. 196). Although it would be an over-simplification to say that all MNCs from one home state are the same, firms from the same home state share certain national characteristics. In this light, the VOC approach is an institutional approach which observes that different capitalist states have different histories, cultures and structures that inform the nature of their capitalist relations, and that far from convergence on a single (liberal) global model, the persistence of different national institutional potentials gives rise to the persistence of different national capitalisms (Berger 1996; Boyer 1996; Coates 2005; Dore 2000; Dore, Lazonik & O'Sullivan 1999; Hall and Soskice, 2001).

Given their different institutional potentials, the VOC approach sees capitalist states as lying on a continuum between liberal market economies (LMEs) and coordinated market economies (CMEs). The United States is seen as the archetypal LME, while Germany and Japan are CMEs. While these are all capitalist countries, their institutions establish different 'rules of the game'. This has implications for how environmental problems are addressed, and indeed the success or otherwise of strategies for addressing them, because of the underlying idea that "in any national economy, firms will gravitate towards the mode of coordination for which there is institutional support" (Hall & Soskice, 2001, p. 8–9).

Broadly speaking, firms in LMEs coordinate their activities via hierarchically organised firms competing in markets. In preferring market coordination of economic activity, they make their decisions based on market signals that define shorter-term profit levels. In regulatory terms, they therefore prefer deregulation over heavier state guidance and intervention. When they are subject to regulation, firms in LMEs will react more efficiently to clearly specified regulations, especially those aimed at altering market price signals.

Firms in CMEs are characterised by more non-market cooperative relationships to coordinate economic activity. It is not primarily the market and its price signals that determine their behaviour, but relationships based on cooperative networks. Firms in CMEs tend more towards consensus decision-making between a greater range of stakeholders internal and external to the firm based on long-established networks. They will react more efficiently to regulations based on negotiated and agreed rules and standards (Hall & Soskice 2001).

Obviously, the division between firms favouring deregulated market competition in LMEs versus cooperative coordination in CMEs is a very broad one. Underlying this divide are a myriad of aspects, the nuances of which are discussed by Hall and Soskice (2001) and others (e.g. Dore 2000; Doremus et al 1999; Hampden-Turner & Trompenaars, 1993; Pauly & Reich 1997; Vitols 2001;).[12] The ones most applicable to the analysis here relate to state–business relations and the role of markets. The major divide between LMEs and CMEs with respect to state–business relations is the extent to which the state and business cooperate to achieve mutual objectives. Firms in LMEs tend to pressure their governments for deregulation. They believe in free markets operating on laissez faire principles unless there is a clear case for state intervention due to market failure (the similarities with the liberal economic model are therefore obvious). By contrast, firms in CMEs expect the state to be an activist one, a partner in the market with them. As a result, in addition to being strategically coordinated by markets, firms in CMEs are to a large extent also state-coordinated.

The nature of state-business relations is related to the divide between LMEs and CMEs on the role of markets. A belief in minimal government intervention and laissez faire principles in LMEs leads to a preference for markets as organisers of economic activity. This is true in both the product (i.e. goods and services) and financial spheres. In CMEs, state-business cooperation and coordination to achieve mutual

---

[12] The following brief summary draws on all of these.

objectives is reflected in a view that markets are one among a variety of mechanisms for organising economic activity on a more relational, cooperative basis. This means that while firms in LMEs act on market signals to make profits in the short term and pay dividends to shareholders, firms in CMEs act to enhance their reputation through closer relational ties with external stakeholders (e.g. social groups and society more generally) and internal stakeholders (e.g. employees and other related firms) and thereby also become economically successful.

The key overall point is that, as the WBCSD notes, these institutional differences determine how environmental issues are addressed in different states, the extent to which corporations take the lead in encouraging change and the type of action they take (WBCSD 2004). Institutional differences suggest that, in addition to the material factors of market forces and state regulation, normative questions of social concerns and internal company beliefs should also be the subject of enquiry. The latter should be particularly relevant for CME-based firms.

Analysis of firms' reports

Germany, the United States and Japan are the world's largest economies. This is true in terms of gross national product, as well as manufacturing production, exports and imports. They are also the top three states for services imports and are ranked in the top five for services exports (Dicken, 2003). Furthermore, there is a significant established body of literature demonstrating the institutional importance of firms' home states with respect to these three economically dominant states (e. g. see Doremus et. al. 1999; Pauly & Reich, 1997). With this in mind, five MNCs each from Germany, the United States and Japan were chosen and the contents of their latest reports as at November 2006 analysed.[13]

The aim of analysing firms' environmental reports is to comparatively judge German, US and Japanese firms' rationales for their environmental initiatives. Of course, firms' environmental reports are not an objective representation of firms' attitudes. By definition, objective measures of attitude are unachievable precisely because attitudes are always subjective

---

[13] Therefore, the reports in question relate to 2005–2006.

phenomena. What these reports represent is the culmination of the efforts of teams of people qualified in, and responsible for, presenting information that casts their firm in the best possible light. There are therefore two important reasons for examining them. First, what is of interest here is what firms from different states, and indeed the same state, perceive as constituting 'the best possible light'. These reports present firms' understanding of how their environmental strategies should be 'best' presented. Secondly, because considerable effort goes into publishing a written report, it presents what each company believes to be its key messages. While it is true that all the firms examined have websites containing environmental information, these are updated regularly and change over time. However, a written report endures and presents, in one comprehensive document, the activities a firm believes are most important to communicate for the period it covers.

The firms chosen were selected on the basis of their TNIs. The TNI is used by the United Nations Conference on Trade and Environment (UNCTAD) as a measure of the extent to which firms are global in their operations. It is a simple composite average of foreign assets, sales and employment to total assets, sales and employment. The rationale for choosing firms with the highest TNIs was that the firms selected should be the least likely case to test the hypothesis that firms' home states matter – i.e., that national institutional contexts predominate over global interests.[14]

The firms chosen produce a variety of reports. Some are more focused on environmental sustainability, while others include environmental initiatives within their broader corporate social responsibility/citizenship reporting. For the latter, sections outlining environmental responsibility were the focus. Three sections of the reports were analysed. First, executive statements presenting the view of the CEO and other board members that appear at the front of reports were examined because these 'set the scene' of the report by presenting the view of its contents by the highest office holder/s. Secondly, environmental 'vision statements' were examined. These relate to a section/s presenting the firm's vision with respect to environmental performance. Thirdly, actual

---

[14] This is a standard methodological device explained in Eckstein (1975 pp. 113–123) and King Keohane & Verba (1994 pp. 208–212).

policy guidelines were examined, if included in the reports, or a web link provided for the reader. These sections implement the company's vision by setting in concise form for its employees clear rules for action on environmental issues. Although these three sections account for a small proportion of the reports – and there was considerable variation in the level of detail firms presented – the aim of focusing on these sections was that they permit a comparative analysis on an as-near-as-equal basis between what are otherwise often stylistically dissimilar reports. While the variations are acknowledged, these sections are where rationales for action are found, rather than descriptions of the action undertaken. They present *why* the firm is taking environmental action, and what environmental responsibility means to it, as opposed to just a report of actions taken.

Statements in these sections were coded for the material factors of market forces and state regulation, and for the normative factors of social concerns and internal company beliefs. Sub-categories within these were also identified and coded. Detailed definitions of the categories and sub-categories, as well as the actual process of coding statements in these sections, are provided in the 'Methodological Appendix'. The percentage of codes on material versus normative factors is considered first, followed by a quantitative and qualitative analysis of coding for the sub-categories below these. The analysis aims to highlight the actual proportional differences in codes between firms (i.e. relative emphasis), as well as the qualitative nature of the statements codes represent (i.e. motivations ascribed).

A complete list of the firms chosen is shown in Table 4.1, along with the proportion of sales, assets and employment outside their home state.[15] What is immediately apparent is something that has been noted by other commentators: even for the most global of firms their TNI is, on average, not very high (see Dicken 1998, 2003; Rugman 2005; and, for a general overview of the arguments, Hay 2006c). The TNI of the top five firms from each state is no higher than around 70 per cent, with the majority in the range of 46–60 per cent. There are other factors that

---

[15] AES Corporation, a US electricity, gas and water company, had the highest TNI of all US MNCs but was omitted as no environmental, sustainability or social responsibility reporting was discernable.

undermine the assertion that firms such as these are increasingly transnational in their operations, such as the extent to which firms are bi-national rather than transnational, or regional rather than global. These issues are not investigated here. It suffices to say that even a cursory glance at the data demonstrates that the most global MNCs are not as global as one might think.

Table 4.1 The Transnationality of the selected MNCs, 2004

	TNI (%)	Foreign assets as a proportion of total assets (%)	Foreign sales as a proportion of total sales (%)	Foreign employment as a proportion of total employment (%)
Germany				
1. BMW	67	61	73	67
2. Bertelsmann	63	56	70	64
3. Siemens	62	61	63	62
4. Volkswagen	56	49	72	48
5. BASF	54	60	59	43
Japan				
1. Honda Motor	69	73	77	56
2. Nissan Motor	61	52	70	61
3. Sony Corp.	57	41	70	60
4. Toyota Motor	49	53	60	36
5. Mitsui and Co.	46	49	43	46
US				
1. Coca Cola	71	61	69	81
2. McDonald's	66	74	66	57
3. ExxonMobil	63	69	70	50
4. Hewlett–Packard	62	60	63	62
5. Procter & Gamble	57	59	55	57

Source: UNCTAD 2006, *World Investment Report 2006*, United Nations, New York & Geneva.

What is also noticeable is that for twelve of the firms, the proportion of foreign sales in total sales is the same or higher than their TNI. By contrast, the proportion of foreign assets in total assets is the same or lower for eight of them, and the proportion of foreign employment in total employment is the same or lower for twelve of them. Therefore, it is mostly sales, rather than the location of their assets or employment, that is the driver of their transnationality. Although adherents to the liberal economic view will say that sales are surely the most predominant of material interests for firms and that this will be their primary motivator, we shall see this is not the case.

Material versus normative factors

Table 4.2 summarises the results of coding the environmental reports. In proportional terms there is considerable variation in the coding results, although on average it is notable that more normative rationales for action were coded regardless of firms' nationality.[16] However, for the Japanese firms there is the clearest bias towards normative factors. On average, 77 per cent of Japanese firms' codes are for normative factors, and Honda scores highest of all firms with 96 per cent of codes on normative factors.

The reason normative factors are important for the Japanese firms is mostly fairly evenly split between social concerns and internal company beliefs, but social concerns are more important to them than the German or US firms. Although there is considerable variation in the results for German and US firms, on average 45 per cent of codes applied to the Japanese firms' reports relate to social concerns, versus just 21 per cent of codes for the German firms and 34 per cent for the US firms.

---

[16] The averages for each state are calculated as a weighted average of the codes for individual firms – e.g. if one firm had 100 codes in total and 40 of these are for market forces, and another had 150 codes in total also with 40 on market forces, the average is calculated as (40+40)/(100+150)x100=32 per cent.

Table 4.2 Coding of Material versus Normative Factors

	Market Forces (%)	State Regulation (%)	Total Material (%)	Social Concerns (%)	Internal Company Beliefs (%)	Total Normative (%)	All Material And Normative Codes (%)	All Material And Normative Codes (No.)
Germany								
BMW	45	16	61	29	11	39	100	38
Bertelsmann	10	3	13	36	51	87	100	39
Siemens	5	27	32	20	49	68	100	41
Volkswagen	23	32	55	8	37	45	100	62
BASF	35	24	59	22	18	41	100	49
German Average	**24**	**22**	**45**	**21**	**33**	**55**	**100**	**Total 229**
Japan								
Honda Motor	4	0	4	52	43	96	100	23
Nissan Motor	30	2	31	48	21	69	100	61
Sony Corp	17	24	40	29	31	60	100	42
Toyota Motor	9	7	16	44	40	84	100	43
Mitsui & Co.	11	5	16	51	33	84	100	57
Japan Average	**16**	**8**	**23**	**45**	**32**	**77**	**100**	**Total 226**
US								
Coca Cola	27	9	36	41	23	64	100	22
McDonald's	23	4	28	49	23	72	100	47
ExxonMobil	26	19	44	15	41	56	100	27
Hewlett–Packard	42	11	53	35	13	47	100	55
Procter & Gamble	31	10	41	24	34	59	100	29
US Average	**31**	**10**	**41**	**34**	**24**	**59**	**100**	**Total: 180**

Source: Company Reports

In terms of material factors, the US firms have proportionally the most codes for market forces. On average, 31 per cent of codes applied to their reports relate to these, by comparison with 24 and 16 per cent for the German and Japanese firms respectively. Although there is considerable variation in the results for German and Japanese firms (from less than 10% to 45%), US firms are most consistent in having codes applied on market forces (23% to 42%). The German firms have a higher proportion of codes for state regulation than do the US and Japanese firms. On average, 22 per cent of the codes applied to German firms' reports relate to state regulation, as opposed to 8 and 10 per cent for the Japanese and US firms, respectively.

There are firms that are exceptions. When they are excluded the national trends are more pronounced. For example, the coding on BMW's report makes it look more like a US firm. Forty-five per cent of its codes are for market forces and only 16 per cent for state regulation. If it is excluded from the German average, German firms appear even more focused on state regulations than do Japanese or US firms. Similarly, Bertelsmann has far fewer codes on material factors than its German counterparts and Sony has noticeably more codes for state regulation than do the other Japanese firms. Exceptions such as these, and the sub-national variations in the results generally, are worth bearing in mind. They probably reflect the small sample size.

Despite the variations in the results, one can say that, although normative factors are not unimportant for US firms, it is nevertheless clear that US firms are the most concerned with the material factor of market forces. This relates to LME firms' preference for market coordination of economic activity. The German firms are most concerned with state regulation. The Japanese firms are most concerned with normative factors overall, plus they have the highest proportion of codes for social concerns. This reflects a CME preference for a more coordinated state–business approach to firm strategies in the case of Germany, and a broader perspective of firms' interests beyond short-term material returns based on market forces in the case of Japan.

Unpacking these overall proportional averages is the purpose of Tables 4.3 to 4.6 which present the results of coding in the sub-categories within market forces, state regulation, social concerns and internal company beliefs.

Material factors – market forces in detail

Turning first to market forces (Table 4.3), there are few clear national patterns in evidence. Individual firms' preferences predominate on whether market forces are important in terms of responding to competitive pressures, safeguarding financial returns or proactively embracing opportunities. It is perhaps interesting to note that, excepting Siemens and Toyota, when firms make statements about market forces they are not overwhelmingly driven by competitive pressures from consumers and other firms, as standard liberal economic renderings of firms' motivations assert. Beyond this, it is not possible to add to the overall observation that the US firms make proportionally more statements relating to market forces than do the German and Japanese firms.

There are also few discernable qualitative differences between the statements made by firms regarding competition and safeguarding or enhancing their business position. Regardless of their nationality, firms mention factors such as satisfying consumers, remaining competitive, ensuring they continue to grow, and that this will either drive or constrain their efforts with respect to environmental responsibility. But distinct national qualitative differences are discernable for proactive action. German and US firms are clearly more materialist, with statements about seizing opportunities to ensure they remain competitive, often couched in terms of market leadership, and an over-arching belief that there is a link between environmental responsibility and economic success. For example, Coca Cola says that benefiting the environment is worthwhile because "it makes good business sense", as does Hewlett-Packard when it says "good citizenship is good business". Similarly, BMW undertakes environmental initiatives because "sustainable actions provide the basis for viable development". However, the language used by two of the Japanese firms, Mitsui and Nissan, is less materialist. Mitsui talks of improving the firm's corporate value via "engaging in conscientious activities giving full consideration to the social significance of [its] presence and a strong awareness of [its] ties with the environment". Nissan declares: "we have to create sustainable value by enriching people's lives". Indeed, Nissan says that its social and environmental responsibilities are "very deeply tied to [its] business itself". Therefore, the imperatives of market forces are seen in more normative than material terms for the Japanese companies.

Overall, regardless of the sub-category, market forces are most important for the US firms: their environmental initiatives are driven or constrained by market forces. This is consistent with the importance of market forces in the US LME variety of capitalism, as opposed to one factor among many, and more an underlying than primary concern in CMEs. However, it is interesting to note that German firms' statements are similar. By contrast, two of the Japanese firms express their aspirations and identification of business opportunities in language that implies something more than market success and winning a competitive battle. In CME-style, broader strategic goals are the aim in which they identify environmental responsibility as being at the heart of their conceptualisation of what their business and its success are all about. They exhibit a more relational, societal basis to achieving their material goals.

Material factors – state regulation in detail

Turning to state regulation (Table 4.4), a range of national and international agreements and regulations are mentioned by all the firms. The US and German firms (with the exception of Bertelsmann) have a greater proportion of their codes on voluntary agreements than do the Japanese firms (with the exception of Nissan). But there is considerable sub-national variation in the proportional coding for binding regulations. For example, one could say that when they do make statements about binding regulations, Japanese firms do so more often than firms of other nationalities. But it could equally be said that two of the Japanese firms make no statements regarding binding regulations at all.

Table 4.3 Material factors – market forces in detail

	Competition (%)	Safeguarding Business Position (%)	Proactive Action (%)	Total Market Forces (%)	Total Market Forces (no.)
GERMANY					
BMW	18	35	47	100	17
Bertelsmann	25	25	50	100	4
Siemens	50	50	0	100	2
Volkswagen	36	21	43	100	14
BASF	12	65	24	100	17
GERMAN AVERAGE	**22**	**41**	**37**	**100**	**Total: 54**
JAPAN					
Honda Motor	0	100	0	100	1
Nissan Motor	39	28	33	100	18
Sony Corporation	43	29	29	100	7
Toyota Motor	50	50	0	100	4
Mitsui and Co Ltd.	0	67	33	100	6
JAPAN AVERAGE	**33**	**39**	**28**	**100**	**Total: 36**
US					
Coca Cola	0	83	14	100	7
McDonald's	36	9	55	100	11
ExxonMobil	14	71	14	100	7
Hewlett–Packard	26	35	39	100	23
Proctor & Gamble	0	44	56	100	9
US AVERAGE	**19**	**42**	**39**	**100**	**Total: 57**

Source: Company reports.

Table 4.4 Material factors – state regulation in detail

	Voluntary Agreements (%)	Binding Regulations (%)	Input to the Policy Process (%)	Total State Regulation (%)	Total State Regulation (No.)
GERMANY					
BMW	33	33	33	100	6
Bertelsmann	0	100	0	100	1
Siemens	55	45	0	100	11
Volkswagen	35	30	35	100	20
BASF	50	33	17	100	12
GERMAN AVERAGE	**42**	**36**	**22**	**100**	**Total: 50**
JAPAN					
Honda Motor	0	0	0	100	0
Nissan Motor	100	0	0	100	1
Sony Corporation	30	60	10	100	10
Toyota Motor	0	100	0	100	3
Mitsui and Co Ltd.	33	67	0	100	3
JAPAN AVERAGE	**29**	**65**	**6**	**100**	**Total: 17**
US					
Coca Cola		0	50	100	2
McDonald's	50	50	0	100	2
ExxonMobil	40	20	40	100	5
Hewlett–Packard	33	33	33	100	6
Proctor & Gamble	67	33	0	100	3
US AVERAGE	**44**	**28**	**28**	**100**	**Total: 18**

Source: Company reports.

The clearest national differences are evident in the qualitative nature of the statements made. There is a clear difference between the US and Japanese firms versus the German ones. The US and Japanese firms primarily highlight compliance with regulations, although Procter and

Gamble refers to the "letter and spirit of the law", and Toyota to the "language and spirit of the law". Thus, these two firms to some extent go beyond statements about simple compliance. However, *all* the German firms do this. BASF and BMW state that they support the goals, as well as the targets of the Kyoto Protocol, Bertelsmann talks of the "spirit and letter of the law", Siemens repeatedly refers to going "above and beyond statutory requirements", and Volkswagen states that it *respects* the law and exceeds what is legally prescribed. Therefore, while all the firms say they comply with regulations, the German firms appear to have the most affinity for regulations and aim to exceed regulatory requirements.

The US and German firms are most likely to make statements on input to the policy process. Of the Japanese firms, only Sony mentions providing such input, and makes one reference to so doing. Clearly, this is not a priority for the Japanese firms, as they do not choose to highlight it in their reports. However, there is a qualitative difference in how the US and German firms discuss policy input. The US firms stress their cooperation with government and related organisations to find solutions, performing an "active and constructive role" (ExxonMobil), or "helping to shape a broad array of policies" (Hewlett–Packard). Coca Cola stresses that it cooperates in order to "address global environmental challenges". The German firms make similar statements, but they additionally highlight their role in proactively suggesting policy solutions. For example, BASF says it "actively contributed to alternative proposals" on regulations. Volkswagen sees itself as entering the "public debate", and working "hand-in-hand … to shape a socially and ecologically sustainable development process" because it is "both legitimate and necessary to present [its] expert knowledge to politicians and authorities and contribute [its] experience to help shape socially responsible background conditions". Therefore, while both the German and US highlight a constructive and cooperative approach, the German firms more clearly highlight the manner in which they proactively suggest regulatory solutions to environmental issues.

Overall, the following findings are evident on state regulation. As well as coding proportionally more for state regulation than the US and Japanese firms, the German firms share a preference with the US firms for a more voluntaristic approach to state regulation. In addition to preferring a voluntaristic approach, the German firms also stress exceeding regulatory requirements and providing input to government on regulations to drive the policy development process. In a qualitative sense, they do so more strongly than do the US firms. These observations fit with a more CME-style of regulation setting and implementation: a voluntaristic approach based on extensive state–firm discussion and consensus building, in the context of a belief that private firms have public responsibilities to fulfil above and beyond regulatory requirements.

By contrast, the LME-based US firms are supportive, but less 'enamoured' of regulations. Although the US firms seek to provide input to the policy process, this is less out of a desire to proactively shape regulations, than a matter of ensuring they have a say in the outcome of them. The distinction is subtle, but their statements suggest that the purpose of their involvement is to ensure that their material interests are not infringed, rather than reflect a commitment to developing regulations that successfully address environmental issues. Indeed, ExxonMobil's desire for involvement is that it wants to help shape "our energy future" – that is, the material interests of the company. Viewed in this light, the US firms' preference for voluntary agreements is related to an LME desire for minimal formal regulation. The Japanese firms stress compliance with regulations more than anything else, but sub-national variations in their coding proportions make clear conclusions problematic. However, they do make the weakest statements with respect to regulations. As with the coding of statements made by German firms for market forces, this is somewhat at odds with what the VOC approach suggests.

Normative Factors – Social Concerns in Detail

For social concerns (Table 4.5), it is interesting to note that none of the firms, regardless of their nationality, strongly cite responding to general social concern/ raised awareness of environmental issues. On average, less than 10 per cent of codes are on this aspect of social concern. Even so, despite there being a small number of statements, there are national qualitative differences in the statements made. The two US firms that make statements regarding social concerns relate these to material factors, i.e. they view social concern through a materialist 'lens'. McDonald's expresses a hope that firms' socially responsible endeavours "will come to have more influence on consumers' purchasing habits", while ExxonMobil sees social concern for the environment in terms of causing "the public greater concern about the supply and cost of energy". The German and Japanese firms do not draw such a clear materialist link in their rendering of social concerns. The two German firms that make statements in this regard note that there are always social concerns that must be faced, and not just for their impact on material outcomes. However, two of the Japanese firms, Nissan and Honda, go further to see increased social awareness of environmental problems as requiring a response in and of itself.[17] For example, Nissan notes the emergence of a "passionate critique of modern consumer society" to the extent that social concern for the environment is so heightened that "not since the race to put a man on the moon in the 1960s has a community of engineers faced such a stark challenge".

The material versus normative perspectives delineating the US firms from the German and Japanese firms is further borne out in the proportions of codes applied for statements regarding responsibility to society versus business stakeholders. German and Japanese express more a belief that they owe a responsibility to society in general (59% and 54% respectively on average), while for US firms the responsibility they highlight is skewed towards stakeholders more directly related to their business (37% for stakeholders, versus 32% for society). These national differences are commensurate with the LME-nature of US firms, in the sense that those associated with the material interests of the business, even indirectly, are referred to more than is the case for CME-based German and Japanese firms that have a more holistic view of their responsibility to society. Thus, even if the German firms share a materialist predilection for market forces with the US firms, they do not do so for social concerns. For the US firms, greater business relevance for the responsibility they owe to those affected by their actions appears required than is the case for the German and Japanese firms.

---

[17] In other words, responsible action doesn't require a payoff.

Table 4.5 Normative Factors – Social Concerns in Detail

	General Social Concern/ Raised Awareness (%)	Firm Image (%)	Responsibility to Society (%)	Responsibility to Stakeholders (%)	Total Social Concerns (%)	Total Social Concerns (no.)
GERMANY						
BMW	9	36	36	18	100	11
Bertelsmann	0	0	79	21	100	14
Siemens	0	0	88	13	100	8
Volkswagen	20	0	60	20	100	5
BASF	0	9	36	55	100	11
GERMAN AVERAGE	**4**	**10**	**59**	**27**	**100**	**Total: 49**
JAPAN						
Honda Motor	8	33	50	8	100	12
Nissan Motor	14	21	45	21	100	29
Sony Corp	0	8	58	33	100	12
Toyota Motor	16	5	53	26	100	19
Mitsui and Co	3	28	66	3	100	29
JAPAN AVERAGE	**9**	**20**	**54**	**17**	**100**	**Total: 101**
US						
Coca Cola	0	0	33	67	100	9
McDonald's	13	39	22	26	100	23
ExxonMobil	25	0	25	50	100	4
Hewlett–Packard	0	32	37	32	100	19
Proctor & Gamble	0	0	57	43	100	7
US AVERAGE	**6**	**24**	**32**	**37**	**100**	**Total: 62**

Source: Company reports.

The material versus normative divide is also evident in qualitative terms. While all firms, regardless of nationality, discuss their responsibility to stakeholders, the US firms do so more in terms that this is important to their business interests: creating value for customers, meeting stakeholder expectations, addressing stakeholder concerns that are related to business operations or affect these, etc. For example, McDonalds states that its business depends on serving "the interest of [its] diverse stakeholders", and Procter and Gamble states that "consumers reward [it] with leadership sales, profit and value creation" when it does the right thing. However, some of the German and Japanese firms go beyond such statements to exhibit a far deeper vision of their stakeholder relationships. They see acting responsibility to stakeholders as valuable in and of itself. For example, Bertelsmann states that "in the view of our shareholders, the possession of property creates an obligation to the community". The difference is most pronounced for the Japanese firms. Nissan sees its relationship with stakeholders not just in terms of interests, but the creation of "trust". Sony sees its responsibility to stakeholders as part of its "mission and passion". Toyota says that stakeholder expectations are not just important for the material interests of the company, but that they go to the question of "the type of company that Toyota is". As such, Toyota discusses stakeholder responsibility in terms of "harmony" and "respecting societal norms".

The division between the US versus German and Japanese firms is similarly evident for statements on responsibility to society more generally. This is evident in two respects. First, while all the firms refer to their responsibility to society, three of the German firms and one Japanese firm see themselves as *part* of society and enmeshed in it, as opposed to the US firms which see themselves as outside society with responsibility *to* it. Of the US firms, Coca Cola comes close in saying it wishes to be "a responsible global citizen who makes a difference", and McDonald's describes itself as "a responsible corporate citizen", but BASF declares "we are part of society", Bertelsmann says it is "a social player" and Volkswagen says it is "an active member of civil society". Honda similarly defines itself as "a responsible member of society". Therefore, their location with respect to society is different: the German and Japanese firms are more part of it, whereas the US firms are responsible to it, and their 'citizenship' is more explicitly corporate in nature.

Secondly, while the US firms accept that they bear responsibility to society for their actions, the German and Japanese firms have a more profound conception of their role. Bertelsmann states that "in a market economy a corporation derives its legitimacy by making a valuable contribution to society" and desires to "actively contribute to progress and the continuous evolution of social systems". Similarly, Siemens hopes to "create a better world". Such a social 'mission' is not highlighted as explicitly by the US firms. The Japanese firms go furthest, making statements that can only be described as *messianic*. They characterise themselves as on a 'mission' to do nothing less than save the world. Mitsui declares it "will contribute to the creation of a future where the dreams of the inhabitants of our irreplaceable Earth can be fulfilled". Perhaps most tellingly, rather than seeking a balance between business material versus social objectives, Mitsui sees that "profits will *naturally* follow as long as we do good work – work that is valued by society",[18] and says that it aims "to save the world, to save people". Mitsui is in good company with the other Japanese firms. Honda wishes to "create a sustainable society", Sony sees itself as on a "societal mission" where "preserving the natural environment ... helps humanity to attain the dream of a healthy and happy life", and Toyota asserts its "passion" to "contribute to society" and "lead the times" through effort that will "contribute to the realisation of a sustainable society".

This leaves us with comments regarding firm image. The proportional coding of statements for firm image suggests no clear national differences. There is a wide range of sub-national coding percentages in all cases. However, as one would expect of a concept such as 'image', qualitative differences reveal clearer national trends. What is noticeable, yet again, is that image is about material success in markets for the US firms, rather than a more normative vision in the case of the German and Japanese firms. The two US firms that mention aspects of firm image take the attitude that building trust and brand image is part of doing business, and strengthening the firm's brand. Thus, Hewlett–Packard makes statements that it sees its efforts as promoting value for

---

[18] Emphasis added.

customers, and therefore its efforts are part of its imperative to "pursue customer loyalty, profit, market leadership and growth". Similarly, McDonald's sees its initiatives as important because they "could make a difference in a customer's choice of whether to visit [its] restaurants or not". The two German firms that had codes applied for firm image also make statements that show they are aware of the potential material benefits of more environmentally enlightened behaviour, but such statements are weaker. For example, BASF sees a good reputation as potentially contributing to "long term success", and BMW notes that "trust is the basis for (its) success". However, a good reputation appears to be worthy in and of itself for BMW as well. For example, the firm states that "in terms of sustainability, a company is particularly credible and effective when it takes responsibility for its products throughout their entire life cycle". Japanese firms, once again, make the most emotive statements. They desire to be seen as social leaders commanding respect and standing in the community for what they do. The sense that they are part *of* society, already identified above, is once again to the fore. Mitsui makes the following pronouncement: "making it a principle to be fair and humble, we, with sincerity and in good faith, will strive to be worthy of the trust society places in us". In a similar vein, Honda says it "will work to provide joy and excitement to people so that they will value Honda as a company" because the firm's mission "is to become a company that people throughout the world will want to exist". Similarly, Toyota seeks to be seen as a company which "emphasises fairness and good faith, acts with courage and determination, and displays abundant vitality and dignity". It is fair to say that none of the US or German firms approach the same strongly normative basis with respect to their standing in society that is inherent in the statements made by the Japanese firms.

Coding within the sub-categories of social concerns therefore demonstrates one of the clearest material versus normative divisions in rationales for action between the US firms and the German and Japanese firms. The US firms have an LME focus on the material impact on their business, or those most closely related to it, rather than on society generally. They are also more materially focused in qualitative terms. There should be no mistake that US firms' statements on their responsibility to society are strong. Their actions have an acknowledged effect on it, and this is where their rationale for action lies. There is nothing 'weak' about such sentiments. But the German and Japanese firms draw as strong, if not stronger links, and in some cases also bridge the gap between themselves and society. In addition to being environmentally responsible, German firms wish to make the world a better place, while Japanese firms wish to at least transform and preferably save it! Therefore, in addition to coding more strongly in proportional terms for responsibility to society, the German and Japanese firms make stronger qualitative statements than do their US counterparts. They are most likely to see changing social concerns as a cause for action, and they have a more holistic vision of social and stakeholder responsibility beyond their material interests. They are rather more proactive on social attitudes than reactive. This supports the idea that as CME-based firms they can substantially alter their behaviour on the basis of social concerns, not just on the basis of market forces, and may do so regardless of a direct demand from society for such behaviour.

Normative factors - internal company beliefs in detail

Finally, for internal company beliefs (Table 4.6), it is clear that all the firms, regardless of their nationality, cite corporate policies or guidelines. However, the US firms (with the exception of ExxonMobil) make proportionally more statements regarding path dependence (with the exception of Bertelsmann). Therefore, US firms' internal motivations are more associated with a history of acting in a responsible manner than is the case for German and Japanese firms. Two alternative explanations are possible for this. One is that the German and Japanese firms are more inner-directed on environmental responsibility, because they cite firm-wide guidelines, corporate beliefs and strategies that are not contingent on the 'stickiness' of historical trends. Alternatively, it could indicate that corporate policy in respect of the environment is more entrenched in the US firms because of longer-standing commitments. No clear finding is possible. However, it is interesting to note that in all cases leaders' visions are not so important in setting internal company beliefs. This further supports the thesis of the VOC approach, as the implication is that firms' motivations are structural rather than a matter of agency, i.e. underlying institutions have greater explanatory weight than the role of individuals in senior positions.

Table 4.6 Normative Factors – Internal Company Beliefs in Detail

	Corporate Policy (%)	History/Path Dependence (%)	Leader's Vision (%)	Total Internal Company Beliefs (%)	Total Internal Company Beliefs (no.)
GERMANY					
BMW	75	25	0	100	4
Bertelsmann	55	45	0	100	20
Siemens	80	20	0	100	20
Volkswagen	83	13	4	100	23
BASF	89	11	0	100	9
GERMAN AVERAGE	**75**	**24**	**1**	**100**	**Total: 76**
JAPAN					
Honda Motor	70	20	10	100	10
Nissan Motor	85	8	8	100	13
Sony Corporation	77	8	15	100	13
Toyota Motor	88	12	0	100	17
Mitsui and Co Ltd.	63	11	26	100	19
JAPAN AVERAGE	**76**	**11**	**13**	**100**	**Total: 72**
US					
Coca Cola	60	40	0	100	5
McDonald's	36	45	18	100	11
ExxonMobil	91	0	9	100	11
Hewlett–Packard	57	43	0	100	7
Proctor & Gamble	60	30	10	100	10
US AVERAGE	**61**	**30**	**9**	**100**	**Total: 44**

Source: Company Reports.

Qualitatively, it appears that statements on corporate policy fall into three categories: we do it because it is a good thing to do, or it is the "right thing" (i.e. no explicit reasons offered); we do it because it is good for us (i.e. instrumental material reasons); and we do it because of a higher vision or a matter of identity (i.e. a strong statement of belief that goes above and beyond material concerns). Regardless of nationality, when firms make statements indicating they have a corporate policy that underlies their drive for environmental responsibility, they fall into each of these categories. The variations seem to be more firm-specific than a matter of nationality. For example, of the US firms, ExxonMobil simply states that "we firmly believe that the way we achieve results is as important as the results themselves". This is a statement falling in the first category. Coca Cola links its internal belief in sustainability to its desire for "growth". This statement falls in the second category. McDonald's makes statements that fall into the third category when it says that its commitments are a matter of identity: "this is about who we are".

Therefore, the main observation remains that in quantitative terms, German and Japanese firms have proportionally more statements on average coded for internal company beliefs than do US firms. The more internally-driven nature of firm strategies under Japanese and German CME capitalism, as opposed to US LME capitalism, is exhibited. In all cases, leaders' visions are less important, further supporting the VOC thesis in the sense that what is being observed are structural forces with an institutional basis rather than the agency of individuals. National qualitative differences are harder to discern. As a result, it could be concluded that national differences are not as strong as in other areas. But this author would contend that another conclusion is possible. This is because statements given with respect to market forces, state regulation and social concerns should be more the focus for identifying rationales, and national differences in them. Citing internal company beliefs indicates something else: the extent to which such rationales have been internalised by the companies. Therefore, for example, if one combines the national quantitative variations in coding for internal company beliefs with those for social concerns, the findings in regard to material versus normative rationales for action are further |strengthened. That is, German and Japanese firms are not only more normatively/holistically driven with respect to their conception of their social responsibilities; they have internalised this drive to a greater extent as a matter of corporate policy, and are doing so regardless of historical factors.

Conclusion

Two caveats are warranted before drawing conclusions. First, in many respects, this chapter represents a pilot study. The statistical significance of the results is open to question as only a handful of firms is considered. There is a need to extend the study, not just in terms of coverage, but also to see how firms' motivations evolve over time. Secondly, in addition to the small number of observations, there are also considerable sub-national variations in the results that made it difficult to draw clear conclusions at times (e.g. with respect to the Japanese firms' statements on state regulation). So, to some extent national similarities and points of difference have been emphasised over these sub-national variations. However, this is necessary in any comparative analysis. One wishes to tease out the similarities and differences within and between groups/categories, whether in terms of absolutes or degree, and the resulting implications.[19] Despite these caveats, there are clear findings that reflect and support the insights of the VOC approach.

For anyone accustomed to applying an LME 'lens', the US firms' rationales for action seem most 'rational' and 'believable'. The rationales they present for environmental responsibility are couched more in material terms, particularly what the market dictates. The preference for market modes of economic coordination in LMEs is thus clearly evident in the statements they make. In adhering to regulations, they prefer voluntary to imposed regulation. They meet rather than exceed government regulations, and the purpose of being involved in the policy process is not so much to proactively address environmental issues, as to simply be involved per se. This reflects a preference for arms-length government involvement in markets in LMEs. Normative factors, such as social concerns, are also dealt with significantly for how they impact on, or relate to, material interests. Although social concerns are important to the US firms, these are seen more in terms of how they affect material outcomes, and the interests of stakeholders predominate

---

[19] The methodological issues are discussed in detail in Adcock and Collier (2001), Collier and Adcock (1999), Collier and Mahon (1993), and Sartori (1970).

(i.e. those with an interest in, and who are directly affected by, firms' material interests). Again, the LME model, based as it is on market modes of economic coordination (including a concern for concepts such as shareholder value and profits in the shorter term) supports such a perspective. In LME fashion, internal company beliefs appear less important than for the CME-based firms.

In true CME fashion, non-market modes of coordinating economic activity prevail for the Japanese firms. They emphasise normative factors over material considerations. They stress the importance of social concerns/attitudes as strategic motivators. Even on material factors, normative considerations come into play. Responsibility to society generally predominates as their rationale for action. Material interests flow from these (i.e. they are dependent on them), rather than material interests dominating strategic thinking. The German firms share their Japanese counterparts' focus on society and social responsibility, and this balances their material motivations with respect to market forces. They *like* regulation, not just complying with regulatory requirements, but exceeding them. They work in partnership with government to proactively develop regulations that address environmental concerns. Like the Japanese firms, a CME predisposition is indicated for non-market modes of coordinating economic activity. This is true in terms of social attitudes, but even more so in terms of a desire for a partnership approach with regulators.

Not only does the analysis support the insights of the VOC approach, but given that the MNCs whose reports were analysed have the highest TNIs, it is clear that national institutional variations permeate the reporting of these most global firms, and therefore the motivations they cite for action with respect to environmental responsibility. They remain institutionally embedded in the home states where they have their headquarters and strategic decisions are made. Indeed, this is regardless of how they see themselves. For example, Nissan sees itself as a "global corporation" and Procter and Gamble states it is a "global company". By contrast Volkswagen describes itself as "a global player with German roots" and Mitsui declares that "with companies like Mitsui that are engaged in business around the world, the emphasis of CSR differs depending on the region". Whichever way they perceive themselves, the unavoidable conclusion is that in many ways they remain, at their core, national companies with global interests. Therefore, although ensuring firms make credible environmental commitments is an important consideration, and that these commitments effectively address environmental problems, the question of nationally conducive paths to so doing is no less important.

The findings undermine the mainstream liberal economic perspective on economic actors' motivations that any concern for the environment must be the result of materially-driven instrumental 'calculus'.[20] As such, if firms are to take environmental concerns into account, it must be because it is in their interest to do so, with this interest defined in instrumental materialist terms. Although such a clear causal path is intuitively appealing and logically plausible, it has clear limitations. Constructing economic actors in this manner is overly simplistic because it suffers from what Katzenstein terms "vulgar rationalism" as it "infers the motives of actors from behaviourally revealed preferences" (Katzenstein 1996, p. 27). Instead, a deeper understanding of firms' motivations is to be found in highlighting the importance of the institutional lenses through which firms perceive their material interests. Of course, it is not that material interests are irrelevant. It is simply that they may not be the issue. What is instead at issue is whether MNCs perceive their interests in more material or normative terms. Of course, in either case their interests are 'material' in the sense that they matter to firms, or are perceived by them as being important in how they convey their motivations. This is confusing and takes us potentially down another path covered by authors such as Hay (2006a, 2006b). It raises many questions of ontology and epistemology, covered rather well, again by Hay (2006d). In this chapter, the focus of the empirical analysis was instead simplified (hopefully not overly) to whether MNCs ascribe their motivations more to material versus normative factors.

It is also important to stress that there are no absolutes. Environmental issues are complex, firms are complex organisations, and the intersection

---

[20] Or, at the very least, they undermine the idea that firms' perceptions of how their environmental strategies should be 'best' presented in reporting is universal – i.e. that as they go global in their operations they see their audience as expecting some universal basis for their environmental conduct.

of various factors and the forces they exert on firm strategies are not straightforward. Therefore, the conclusions reached need to be qualified by acknowledging that US firms are obviously concerned about their social responsibility, as are German and Japanese firms about making profits. The results of the analysis demonstrate this too (e.g. even if proportionally fewer of the codes applied to the Japanese firms' reports relate to market forces than is the case for the US firms, there are still statements about market forces in their reports). There is also a complex mixture of national and specific firm traits bound up in these conclusions. Even so, there are clear points of national difference in emphasis between the firms considered. The US firms have a materialist predilection for reacting to market forces. Social attitudes are therefore unlikely to strongly influence their strategic thinking unless these translate into market outcomes. This is reflected in their viewing their responsibility to society primarily in business stakeholder terms. By contrast, German and, especially Japanese firms are more normatively driven via a belief that they bear a responsibility to society more generally. German firms regard regulations as not being imposed on them, so much as an important factor in their business strategies that they are proactively involved in setting to address their environmental responsibilities.

Implications for strategies to address environmental impacts emerge on the basis that these should reflect national institutional preferences. Markets and state regulations drive and constrain US firms. It would therefore probably be best if social groups focus their attentions on changing consumer preferences or lobbying government. However, close stakeholder consultation and cooperation for German firms in partnership with government is most appropriate. In the case of Japan, social concerns exert a strong influence, and a strategy that challenges firms to address the environmental impact of their actions via internally-driven corporate policies on the basis of these will work best. Thus, a one-size-fits-all approach to regulation on the basis that business is 'global' misses the point that, even for the most global MNCs, the institutional importance of their home states' VOC remains predominant in how they perceive their interests and what motivates them to make environmentally responsible commitments.

This finding therefore suggests that 'global' codes of conduct are problematic. Where they are proposed, they potentially represent an attempt to homogenise rules for markets in a manner that reflects, and supports, certain national institutional perspectives over others. Advocacy of global codes begs the question: whose codes? Based on which version of capitalism? It should be seen for what it represents: a political act that seeks to promote and internationally project one institutional version of capitalism rather than another, rather than a response to the inevitable economic imperatives of global markets. Alternatively, even if the codes themselves do not do this, the mechanisms through which they are put into effect and enforced should vary according to VOC variations. There is certainly an LME/CME divide for the firms examined here, and there are sub-divisions within this divide (e.g. German firms' coordination via state–business cooperation on regulation versus Japanese firms' concern for their place in society). These variations impact on the motivations of firms themselves.

Methodological Appendix

Coding was applied for statements made by firms of rationales for action relating to material and normative factors. First, coding was applied to statements pertaining to the two material factors of market forces and state regulation. Coding for market forces was undertaken for statements identifying forces that affect the firm's financial bottom line and its economic performance as a result of the products it sells. These included:

- Competition
  - consumer demand – the need to take account of consumer preferences or demand (e.g. tying efforts on the environment to demand for these, or stating that market forces temper what can be done)
  - competitive pressure from other firms – in markets or within the industry as a whole

- Safeguarding business position

    - profits and sales – references to maintaining or increasing these generally
    - shareholder value – providing value to shareholders, or stock performance generally
    - risk management – identification of the environmental as a business risk factor that must be addressed

- Proactive action

    - market share/leadership – having products on the market, or leading in their development, as a business strategy that drives environmental product development initiatives
    - grasping business opportunities – environmental responsibility and producing products that reflect this represents a business opportunity

State regulation relates to references to national and international voluntary agreements, as well as binding regulations, plus input to the policy process in the development of regulations. Therefore, coding was applied to statements in the following sub-categories:

- Voluntary agreements

    - national voluntary agreements made and supported jointly between the industry and regulatory authorities
    - international voluntary agreements (e.g. CERES and the GRI)

- Binding regulations

    - national regulations required by law
    - international agreements ratified by states (e.g. the Montreal and Kyoto Protocols)

- Input to the policy process

    - input to/the provision of advice on national regulations and regulatory settings

- attendance at/input to meetings convened by international organisations such as the UNEP, or participation in international forums where environmental performance is addressed including meetings held by industry groups such as the WBCSD

Secondly, coding was applied for the normative factors of social concerns and internal company beliefs. Codes in both these categories relate to normative motivators beyond material factors alone. Social concerns relate to statements highlighting non-market forces to do with social perceptions of environmental concerns. These included:

- General social concern

  - a recognition of increased social concern/raised awareness with respect to the environment and the need to respond to this

- Firm image

  - brand value – the value of the name of the company and what it represents, especially in terms of loyalty and price premiums that it can extract for its products
  - building trust – references to trust, respect and generally high standing in a more general sense than brand value

- Responsibility to society

  - a responsibility to society generally, nationally or globally

- Responsibility to stakeholders

  - a responsibility to those directly affected by the company's operations, including customers, suppliers, employees and the government

Internal company beliefs relate to statements that demonstrate endogenous factors leading firms to take the environment seriously. These included:

- Corporate Policy

- a statement that environmental responsibility is a matter of corporate belief, including references to guiding principles, guidelines for operation, and policies that codify or implement company environmental strategies

- History/path dependence

  - the firm characterises itself as one that has always taken the environmental impacts of its activities seriously, and thus continues to be one where concern for the environment is part of how it does business – i.e. the continuation of a long-held commitment and strategy

- Leader's vision

  - the leader her/himself identifies, or is identified as having, a commitment to the environment and action that is aimed at reducing the environmental impacts of the firm's products

The rules for coding statements were that:

- All coding was based on *rationales* for action, not on action itself. All coded statements answer the question of *why* action is being taken, rather than the fact that action is being taken
- Passages could be coded more than once. For example, a statement that it is necessary to respond to social concerns and that in so doing market share will be increased relates to codes for both market forces and social concerns
- Paragraphs were the maximum unit for coding. No coding was applied across paragraphs for the reason that each represents a new idea, or a new idea on the same subject
- Sometimes the same code was applied more than once within a paragraph if separated by a sentence/sentences that represented another idea. However, contiguous sentences expressing a rationale for action based on the same idea were not coded separately

Coding of statements made by firms in their reports was performed using QSR NVIVO version 7.0. In order to ensure inter-coder reliability, the process of coding involved three iterations. Separate coding of firms' reports was undertaken by two different coders, one of whom was the author, over the course of November to December 2006. This was followed by a final joint-coding review with both coders present in January 2007.

Acknowledgements

Much thanks are due to my Research Assistant, Ms Katharina Kahsche, for her enthusiasm, initiative and hard work.

References

Adcock R & Collier D, 2001. 'Measurement validity: a shared standard for qualitative and quantitative research', *American Political Science Review*, vol. 95, no.3, pp. 529–546.

Austin D, Rosinki N, Sauer A & le Duc C, 2003. *Changing drivers: the impact of climate change on competitiveness and value creation in the automotive industry*, Sustainable Asset Management and World Resources Institute, http://pdf.wri.org/changing_drivers_full_report.pdf, accessed 10 January 2004.

Berger S, 1996. 'Introduction', in Berger S & Dore R, (eds.), *National diversity and global capitalism*, Cornell University Press, Ithaca.

Blyth, 2003. 'Structures do not come with instruction sheets: interests, ideas and progress in political science', *Perspectives on Politics*, vol. 1, no. 4, pp. 695–706.

Blyth M, 1997. 'Any more bright ideas? The ideational turn of comparative political economy', *Comparative Politics*, vol. 29, no. 1, pp. 229–50.

Boyer R, 1996. 'The convergence hypothesis revisited: globalization but still the century of nations?', in Berger S & Dore R (eds.), *National diversity and global capitalism*, Cornell University Press, Ithaca.

Coase R, 1960. 'The problem of social cost', *The Journal of Law and Economics*, vol. 3, October 1960, pp. 1–44.

Coates D, 2005. 'Paradigms of explanation', in Coates D (ed.), *Varieties of capitalism, varieties of approaches*, Palgrave Macmillan, Hampshire.

Collier D & Adcock R, 1999. 'Democracy and dichotomies: a pragmatic approach to choices about concepts', *Annual Review of Political Science*, vol. 2, pp. 537–65.

Collier D & Mahon J, 1993. 'Conceptual stretching revisited: adapting categories in comparative analysis', *American Political Science Review*, vol. 87, no. 4, pp. 845–55.

Crane G T & Amawi A, 1997. 'Classical liberalism', in Crane, G T, and Amawi A (eds.), The theoretical evolution of international political economy, Oxford University Press, Oxford.

Cutler A, Haufler V & Porter T (eds.), 1999. *Private authority and international affairs*, State University of New York Press, Albany.

Denzau A & North D, 1994. 'Shared mental models: ideologies and institutions', *Kyklos*, vol. 47, no. 1, pp. 3–31.

Dicken P, 1998. *Global Shift: Transforming the World Economy*, 3rd ed., London: Paul Chapman Publishing.

Dicken P, 2003. *Global shift: transforming the world economy*, 4th ed., Sage Publications, London.

Dore R, 2000. *Stock market capitalism: welfare capitalism: japan and germany versus the Anglo Saxons*, Oxford University Press, Oxford and New York.

Dore R, Lazonick W, & O'Sullivan M, 1999. 'Varieties of capitalism in the twentieth century', *Oxford Review of Economic Policy*, vol. 15, no. 4, pp. 102–120.

Doremus P N, Keller W W, Pauly L W & Reich S, 1999. *The myth of the global corporation*, Princeton University Press, Princeton.

Eckstein H, 1975. 'Case study and theory in political science', in Greenstein F I, and Polsby N W (eds.), *Strategies of Enquiry*, Addison-Wesley Publishing Company, Reading, Massachusetts.

Ekins P, Folke C, & Costanza R, 1994. 'Trade, environment and development: the issues in perspective', *Ecological Economics*, vol. 9, no. 1, pp. 1–12.

Florini A, 2003a 'Business and global governance: the growing role of corporate codes of conduct', *Brookings Review*, Spring 2003, pp. 4–8.

Florini A, 2003b. *The coming democracy: new rules for running a new world*, Island Press, Washington.

Goldstein J & Keohane R, 1993. 'Ideas and foreign policy: an analytical framework', in Goldstein J & Keohane R (eds.), *Ideas and foreign policy: beliefs, institutions and political change*, Cornell University Press, Ithaca.

Green D P & Shapiro I, 1994. *Pathologies of rational choice theory: a critique of applications in political science,*: Yale University Press, New Haven and London.

GRI, 2002. *Sustainability reporting guidelines, 2002*, http://www.global reporting.org/guidelines/2002/GRI_guidelines_print.pdf, accessed 10 December.

Hall P A & Soskice D, 2001. 'An Introduction to varieties of capitalism', in Hall P A & Soskice D (eds.), *Varieties of capitalism: the institutional foundations of comparative advantage*, Oxford University Press, Oxford.

Hampden-Turner C & Trompenaars A, 1993. *The seven cultures of capitalism: value systems for creating wealth in the United States, Japan, Germany, France, Britain, Sweden and the Netherlands*, Currency Doubleday, New York.

Hardin G, 1968. 'The tragedy of the commons', *Science*, vol. 162, pp. 1243–1248.

Hasenclever A, Mayer P & Rittberg V, 1997. *Theories of International Regimes*, Cambridge University Press, Cambridge.

Hawken P, Lovins A & Lovins H, 1999. *Natural capitalism: creating the next industrial revolution*, Little Brown and Co, New York.

Hay C, 2002. *Political Analysis*, Palgrave, Basingstoke.

Hay C, 2004. 'Ideas, interests and institutions in the political economy of great transformations', *Review or International Political Economy*, vol. 11, no. 1, pp. 204–226.

Hay C, 2006a. 'Constructivist institutionalism…or, why ideas into interests don't go', paper presented at the American Political Science Association Conference, Philadelphia, 31 August to 3 September 2006.

Hay C, 2006b. 'Constructivist institutionalism', in Rhodes R, Binder S & Rockman B (eds.), *The Oxford handbook of political institutions*, Oxford University Press, Oxford.

Hay C, 2006c. 'Globalisation and public policy', in Rhodes R, Binder S & Rockman B (eds.), *The Oxford handbook of political institutions*, Oxford University Press, Oxford.

Hay C, 2006d. 'Political ontology', in Rhodes R, Binder S & Rockman B (eds.), *The Oxford handbook of political institutions*, Oxford University Press, Oxford.

Helleiner E, 2003. 'Economic liberalism and its critics: the past as prologue', *Review of International Political Economy*, vol. 10, no. 4, pp. 685–696.

Holliday Jr, C O, Schmidheiny S & Watts P, 2002. *Walking the talk*, Greenleaf, Sheffield.

Karliner J, 1997. *The corporate planet*, Sierra Club Books, San Francisco.

Katzenstein P J, 1996. *Cultural norms and national security: police and military in postwar Japan*, Cornell University Press, Ithaca.

King G, Keohane R & Verba S, 1994. *Designing social inquiry: scientific inference in social research*, Princeton University Press, Princeton.

Lawrence A, Weber J & Post J, 2005. *Business and society: corporate strategy, public policy, ethics*, 11th ed., McGraw Hill, Boston.

Lowndes V, 2002. 'Institutionalism', in Marsh D & Stoker G (eds.), *Theory and methods in political science*, 2nd ed., Palgrave Macmillan, Houndmills, Basingstoke, Hampshire.

March J G & Olsen J P, 1989. *Rediscovering institutions: the organizational basis of politics*, The Free Press, New York.

March J G & Olsen J P, 1998. 'The institutional dynamics of international political orders', *International Organization*, vol. 52, no. 4, pp. 943–969.

Mikler J, 2005. 'Institutional reasons for the effect of environmental regulations: passenger car CO_2 emissions in the EU, US and Japan', *Global Society*, vol. 19, no. 4, pp. 409–444.

North D C, 1990. *Institutions, institutional change and economic performance*, Cambridge University Press, Cambridge.

O'Brien R, Goetz A, Scholte J & Williams M, 2000. *Contesting global governance: multilateral economic institutions and global social movements*, Cambridge University Press, Cambridge.

OECD, 2001a. *Corporate responsibility: private initiatives and public goals*, OECD, Paris.

OECD, 2001b. *OECD guidelines for multinational enterprises, global instruments for corporate responsibility*, Annual Report 2001, Paris, OECD.

OECD, 2004. Can cars come clean? Strategies for low-emission vehicles, OECD, Paris.

Ordeshook P C, 1993. 'The development of contemporary political theory', in Barnett W A, Hinich M J & Schofield N J (eds.), *Political economy: institutions, competition and representation*, Cambridge University Press, Cambridge.

Pauly L W & Reich S, 1997. 'National structures and multinational corporate behaviour: enduring differences in the age of globalization', *International Organization*, vol. 51, no. 1, pp. 1–30.

Rugman A M, 2005. *The regional multinationals: MNEs and 'global' strategic management*, Cambridge University Press, Cambridge.

Sartori G, 1970. 'Concept misformation in comparative politics', *American Political Science Review*, vol. 6, no. 4, pp. 1033–1053.

Strange S, 1996. *The retreat of the state: the diffusion of power in the world economy*. Cambridge University Press, Cambridge.

Strange S, 1997. 'The future of global capitalism; or will divergence persist forever?'. In Crouch C & Streeck W (eds.), *Political economy of modern capitalism: mapping convergence and diversity*, Sage Publications, London.

Suzuki D, 1993. *Time to Change*, Allen and Unwin, St Leonards.

Suzuki D & Dressel H, 2002. *Good news for a change: hope for a troubled planet*, Allen and Unwin, Toronto.

UN, no date a. *Earth summit: UN conference on environment and development*, http://www.un.org/geninfo/bp/enviro.html, accessed 8 February 2006.

UN, no date b. *The global compact*, http://www.unglobalcompact. org/Portal/, accessed 25 August 2003.

UNCTAD, 2006. *World Investment Report 2006*, United Nations, New York and Geneva.

UNEP, 2002. Industry as a partner for sustainable development: 10 years after Rio: the UNEP assessment, http://www.uneptie. org/Outreach/wssd/contributions/publications/pub_global.htm, accessed 13 June 2003.

UNEP & ACEA, 2002. *Industry as a partner for sustainable development: automotive*,http://www.uneptie.org/outreach/wssd/docs/sectors/ final/automotive.pdf, accessed 14 May 2003.

UNFCCC, no date a. *Kyoto Protocol*, http://unfccc.int/essential_ background/kyoto_protocol/items/2613.php, accessed 12 February 2005.

UNFCCC, no date b. *Status of ratification*, http://unfccc.int/ essential_background/kyoto_protocol/status_of_ratification/items /2613.php, accessed 12 February 2006.

UNFCCC, no date c. *Kyoto Protocol: status of ratification*, http://unfccc.int/files/essential_background/kyoto_protocol/appl ication/pdf/kpstats.pdf, accessed 12 February 2006.

Vitols S, 2001. 'Varieties of corporate governance: comparing Germany and the UK', in Hall P A & Soskice D (eds.), *Varieties of capitalism: the institutional foundations of comparative advantage*, Oxford University Press, Oxford.

WBCSD, 1998. *Corporate social responsibility: meeting changing expectations*, http://www.wbcsd.org, accessed 17 August 2003.

WBCSD, 2000. *Corporate social responsibility: making good business sense*, http://www.wbcsd.org, accessed 17 August 2003.

WBCSD (2004), Mobility 2030: Meeting the Challenges of Sustainability, Geneva: WBCSD.

5

Economising water: the changing status of water in the political economy

Danielle Spruyt

Abstract

The status of water in the political economy is changing. Economic and population expansion confront boundaries to water supply, redefining fresh water as a limited and vulnerable resource. The signalled potential for absolute limits to water use, and the need to determine allocation among competing users, initiates a critical re-examination of water management from environmental and economic perspectives. National water management policy is increasingly framed in terms of the principles that underpin environmental economic theory, with water management defined as an economic management challenge. Tradeable water titles and market exchange are adopted as the means by which to resolve questions of distribution among extractive users, to initiate the efficient use of increasingly scarce water resources and to effect environmental outcomes.

The incorporation of water into economic discourse, and more crucially the attempt to determine water values either through market process or through hypothetical valuations, is a pivotal stage in water management. This study highlights the location of contests over water use on the terrain of economic method, and maps the social and environmental developments that follow from the commodification of water. Rights to use water are increasingly linked to the imperative to use water for productive gain, an approach that does not provide a final resolution to contest between commercial and environmental interests in water use.

This shift in policy emphasis challenges the environment to earn its right to water.

Introduction: economising water

Water is a crucial component of ecological systems, "part of the natural environment that performs important and irreplaceable functions" (Ekins, Folke & Groot 2003, p. 2). Water provides essential support services to human life: "a person can only survive five days without water. Besides the air we breathe, water is the most important resource for sustaining human life" (Hall-Wallace, et al 2003, p. 3). Water provides also for sanitation, recreation and leisure, and is used extensively in the production processes pursued by humans. Water endows both "use and exchange values to the objects that we build and the purchases we make" (Stroshane 2003, p. 34). In tandem, water supports the vast range of aquatic and terrestrial plant and animal life upon which humans depend.

The spectre of water shortage has become one of the pressing environmental parameters faced by the civilisations of the 21st century. Contemporary industrial and developing societies have flagged limits to both the availability of fresh water and the capacity of hydrological systems to accommodate the waste products of production processes. The existence of actual and absolute limits to water supply continues to be debated. Yet water limits have manifested in real and explicit ways, presenting examples of regional limits to further exploitation, and framing emerging conflicts in resource utilisation. Environmental boundaries, both physically and politically defined, have presented as tangible challenges to the sustainability of contemporary systems of production and trajectories of economic development.

As such, water provides new governance challenges to State bodies that have historically claimed responsibility both for developing water supplies and for establishing access to and framing the allocation of resources. In tandem, economic theory, as a study of the allocation of scarce resources between competing uses, lends itself neatly to questions of water management in the current era of emphasised water shortage.

The development of economic theory to incorporate concerns of environmental scarcity provides solutions tailored to the infrastructure of contemporary economies. Australian water management is increasingly positioned as an economic management challenge, and water management policy increasingly references economic theory and economic instruments. Tradeable water titles and market exchange are adopted as the means by which to resolve questions of distribution among extractive users, to initiate the efficient use of increasingly scarce water resources and to effect environmental outcomes.

The incorporation of water into economic discourse, and more crucially the attempt to determine water values either through market process or through hypothetical valuations, is a pivotal stage in water management. The increasing references to the use of economic instruments in water management both redefine the economic status of water, and redefine the role of government institutions in water management. Water, conventionally perceived as an unlimited and free contribution to production (subject to technological constraints and to the costs of delivery), has been both recognised and formalised as an economic good. Some water is vested in private ownership arrangements, holding the ability to draw a market price. In association, unlimited rights to use water for productive purposes are being replaced by the need to realise gains from water use to maintain competitiveness as an economic user. As part of this reconceptualisation of water use, environmental claims on water are being challenged to prove value from use.

The identified change in water management will be explored in four synchronous processes or events in this chapter. The first is the anticipated arrival at environmental limits, or (with reference to H C Coombs 1990) a return to the challenges of scarcity. The second is the interrogation of water management and the contests over water resources that emerge from both anticipated and physically realised water limits and thresholds. The third process is the incorporation of water into economic discourse and the eclectic and broad support that this reinterpretation of the water problematic achieves. The fourth process is the subsequent traction of proposed market responses in informing water management discussion and directing the commodification of water. Within this progression of change in water management, both emerging environmental sustainability considerations and emerging business interests can be tracked as informing response to expanding water use and scarcity.

The present study then highlights the location of contests over water use on the terrain of economic method, and maps the social and environmental developments that follow from the commodification of water. Rights to use water are increasingly linked to the imperative to use water for productive gain, an approach that does not provide a final resolution to contest between commercial and environmental interests in water use. This shift in policy emphasis challenges the environment to earn its right to water.

The realisation of scarcity

Australia is conventionally described as an arid continent with regions of water wealth. Natural limits to water supply have been a periodic and localised concern for the expansion of Australian settlement (Pigram 2006; Powell 2000; Smith 1998). A 're-arrival' at scarcity has forced reassessment of water management. The traditional expectations on the state to harness and facilitate water access are becoming increasingly subject to an emerging criteria of evaluation that incorporates economic and environmental sustainability considerations.

The states of Australia historically assumed responsibility for the provision of water for production and for consumption. Following the failure of early private and cooperative water supply schemes in the colonies, the governments of Australia assumed the role of water supply in terms of the public good (Paterson 1987; Quiggin 2001; Smith 1998). Sponsorship of the transformation of hydrological systems and the large-scale development of water infrastructures was defined and legitimated in terms of the provision of water for the development of irrigated agricultural activity and urban infrastructure. Systems of water access, distribution and use were moulded within the institutional and ideological framework of a development-focused society that sought both to settle and to productively utilise the interior of a recently claimed land mass. The establishment of closer settlement schemes and soldier-settlement schemes were progressed in the development of irrigation communities (Smith 1998). The development of urban infrastructures addressed sanitation (Powell 1997). Infrastructure-development projects were not expected to directly return government investments, but rather to provide impetus and opportunity for the expansion of economic growth (Smith 1998).

The technocratic- and development-focused approach to water management was both widely accepted, and initially successful in its ambitions. An extensive irrigated agricultural sector has developed, accounting for an estimated 25 per cent of the total gross value of Australian agricultural output at around $7 billion per year (Cape 1997 in Quiggin 2001). The Murray-Darling Basin of the south-east of Australia, accounts for 70 per cent of total irrigated land (Quiggin 2001). Increased capacity enabled and encouraged the expansion and spread of productive uses and of population settlement, leading to further demands for water supply. The technocratic approach did not represent a 'just add water' recipe for economic growth. The Ord and the Burdekin irrigation projects are cited as examples of the failure of economic growth to respond to the development of water infrastructures (Smith 1998). The technocratic approach did allow a development trajectory that was unconstrained by water limits and that paid limited attention to the potential for physical limits to water supply. In contemporary assessment, water infrastructures have developed as both generous and physically inefficient in their husbandry of water resources. High levels of water have been lost in storage and conveyancing through high evaporation from dams and irrigation channels, open bores, poorly maintained (leaking) infrastructures, and stormwater and sewerage disposal. Systems of water re-use remain largely undeveloped. Contemporary levels of water demand are a measure of access, availability, and contemporary technology, and are therefore socially rather than physically defined.

Available water resources are fully committed in many of the areas in which settlement and economic activity are focused. Available and accessible water supplies are unable to meet the established needs or projected further growth of most cities and many towns. The major cities have been subject to water restrictions. In Victoria for example, Melbourne and more than 270 towns have had water restrictions applied

(Edwards 2003). The inter-annual variations of Australian rainfall patterns manifest as water shortage and financial losses in catchments that are utilised at capacity. The Murray-Darling Basin, the largest and most extensively utilised catchment, is regularly unable to supply irrigation demand (Connell 2007). Currently established water demands are seen as unsustainable (Cullen 2006b; Connell 2007). The degradation of water sources further threatens current and potential supplies.[1] The potential of human engendered environmental changes, such as global warming and land clearing to contribute to changes in weather patterns and thus compound freshwater supply concerns, is increasingly emphasised (e.g. Hennessy, et al 2006). Further, modifications to waterways have increased the vulnerability to environmental events, such as pollution, flood, salinity infiltration, and algal blooms, that may push a freshwater system beyond a critical threshold, making entire systems unusable (Galaz no date). Environmental parameters have presented boundaries to the scale of activity within a region. For some commentators, water presents as a potential constraint on development (Cullen 2006b). For others, the situation is perceived as a water crisis that threatens Australia's economic sustainability (Masters 2001, cited in Isaac 2003).

Freshwater is increasingly recognised as a finite resource, both nationally and globally. Water shortage, as with water use, is socially constructed (Johnston 2003). Pressure on water resources has come from growing populations, economic expansion, enhanced technological capacity and changing use patterns. Water use rates exceed replenishment rates in important river systems and aquifers (Gleick 1993, Pearce 2006, WWF 2007a). In turn, water is increasingly recognised as a fragile resource (Gleick 1993).[2] The scale and style of water use creates impositions upon ecological systems that threaten biodiversity, regeneration, and the ongoing viability of water supplies (Pimentel et al 2004). The

---

[1] 'The chemical contamination of the Botany sands in Sydney has reduced options for Sydney's water supply' (Cullen 2006a, p. 4).

[2] *Water in crisis* presents a comprehensive and comparative range of data on the quality and quantity of global water resources, and is a significant and much cited contribution to subsequent research on water resources. Gleick signals the rising costs of water harvesting. It may become too expensive (power and technology costs) to access more remote water supplies. The economic and hydrological resources are not necessarily available for new water projects (Gleick 1993).

experience of water shortage suggests the expansion of expressed human requirements beyond the capacity of the environment to provide and accommodate.

The potential for absolute limits to water supply and consequent limits to the expansion of human use both continues to be debated, on a terrain reminiscent of the classical economists predictions, of arrival at a stationary state, with Ricardian signalling of limits, Malthusian emphasis on increasing impact, and reference to the role of technology and human ingenuity in offsetting arrival at a stationary state.[3] Redress is sought through technologically induced efficiencies in water use and proposed avenues of further supply. In the meantime, the realisation of limits to water supply manifests in the contests over water resources that arise from the inability of water supplies to satisfy all interests and demands in water use. Rather than absolute limits to water supply and economic activity, water scarcity becomes apparent in relative scarcities between competing interests in water use. Ward and Michelsen identify competition "among kinds of uses, between geographic location of use, between current and future uses, between endangered species saved from extinction and food production displaced from saving the species, and between water resources developed or used and other resources displaced by that water development and use" (2002, p. 424).

---

[3] The concept of a limit to economic growth due to the parameters of environment was identified early in analysis of developing industrial capitalism. The classical economists (Smith, Ricardo) signalled the ability of natural resource limits to restrict economic growth. The stationary state was understood as the eventual conclusion to economic growth. The economy would continue to expand while natural resources, in relation to population, remained abundant. However, the fixed supply of land and natural resources, and the propensity of the population to increase, determined progression towards a stationary state (Deane 1978). J S Mill identified the role of technology in offsetting the diminishing returns of agriculture, while recognising an eventual stationary state (Pearce & Kerry 1990). The foreseen restrictions to economic growth did not eventuate. From 1850 to 1970, economic growth is understood to have appeared sustainable indefinitely (Pearce & Kerry 1990). The classical economists are, in retrospect, seen within to have underestimated the role of human ingenuity and technology in manipulating the physical environment.

Water contest and the challenges of governance

Limits to available water, and the exclusivity of some water use processes, presage that not all water demands within a catchment can be satisfied. Emerging water scarcities from physical and predicted water limits and thresholds engender contest over available resources and conflict between competing needs (Stewart & Jones 2003). The range of conflicts is diverse, reflecting the spectrum of interests in water use. Two predominant conflicts can be identified in the contest over water resources: one conflict is between extractive uses and environmental needs; the second conflict is between competing appropriations for both production and for direct consumption.

The protection of river system health and associated aquatic life competes with the productive potential of water resources. From an environmental perspective, the movement of the economy towards full capacity utilisation of available water resources undermines the ecosystem services provided by hydrological function, such as biodiversity. Water extractions compete also with the human utilisation of water systems for non-extractive purposes, including general amenity, recreational fishing, and water activities. Environmentally-framed concerns draw attention to the role of increasing economic impositions in undermining the shared uses of waterways, and of the perceived threats initiated by the search for supplementary resources. The political activism of individuals and groups has sought to protect targeted resources and regions from appropriation or degradation, for example the promotion of environmental values over hydropower in the Franklin River Dispute (Hutton & Connors 1999), and competition between agriculture and identified environmental needs and allocations for wetlands in the Macquarie Marshes (Stewart & Jones 2003). Further, environmental lobbying has put environmental concerns on policy agendas, with the incorporation of environmental considerations into legislative and approval processes (Connell 2007; Hutton & Connors 1999). In this way, environmental interests provide politically defined parameters and constraints to the exploration/development of further water resources, and tangible challenges to appropriative uses of water.

Environmental considerations more broadly defined present a theoretical challenge to the conventional preoccupation with the delivery of water to sustain production. The expression of environmental interests challenges the disengagement of water from complex ecological systems implicit in the utilisation of water as a resource for production. The impact of systems of production and consumption upon hydrological systems identifies economic activity as a concern for water management. Tensions involving water use and management can usefully be understood as having been driven by the opportunities and demands of economic development as a commodity-defined process. In response to the focus of policy and practice in harnessing water for economic purposes, there is growing statement of the importance of the function of water within ecological systems, and the dependence of all life on the direct provision of water and on the ecological services that water provides (Beder 2006; Connell 2007). The monetary and employment gains of the utilisation of waters for production purposes are posed against the longer term costs of environmental degradation. Identified losses include the loss of ecosystem services[4], environmental amenity, future incomes following unsustainable practices, and the potential costs of redress and reparation. Losses include also the opportunity costs of forgone alternative uses. This strategy seeks to interrogate the conventional benefits and gains associated with water development projects, and demands an environmental accountability in water use decisions.

Agriculture, as the primary user of water resources – an estimated 67 per cent of total water consumption (ABS 2005 in Pigram 2006) – has received critical attention. The environmental impacts of irrigation have included land degradations, increased land and water salinity, water quality problems, including turbidity and eutrophication, and loss of biodiversity and habitat (Quiggin 2001). Capital investment is diverted towards remediation and repair, including "elaborate drainage and salt disposal measures to address water logging and salinisation of irrigation areas" (Paterson 1987, p. 181–2). Consideration of the degradations

---

[4] 'Ecosystem services' are the natural processes that provide clean air and water, mediate extreme weather, renew fertility, and underpin the production of ecosystem goods (CSIRO 2002).

associated with irrigation has led to argument that irrigation, as currently practised, is not sustainable (Smith 1998). The total costs and benefits of dryland agricultural and pastoral land use in the arid and semi-arid regions have also been subject to examination. The limited contribution of agriculture to the economy is contrasted to the impacts and costs of soil loss, loss of vegetation, and the increased salinity of land and waterways (Watson 1992, Smith & Finlayson 1988). The export of agricultural goods initiates a questioning of the export of water embodied in products, 'virtual water', and the adequacy of remuneration (Pigram 2006). Drought is emphasised as a cyclical occurrence that should be budgeted for by individual water users rather that cushioned by state support and subsidy (Botterill & Fisher 2003). The continuation of some farming activity is seen to depend upon government subsidy, drought relief payments, and that land use profits are privately earned while environmental losses are publicly shared and remain largely unpaid for, transferred or postponed.

From a contemporary economic management perspective (and with reference to the Australian taxpayer), the States are subject to accountability considerations. Favourable international per capita comparisons suggest that Australia is not water poor. Rather, water shortage is the result of poor management (Edwards 2003; Young & McColl 2003). In the context of both contemporary water challenges and economic accountability considerations, the states are criticised for having provided water in a manner that has facilitated and condoned a high water use culture that does not reflect the eventual limits to supply. The use of public funds to develop water infrastructures, and the lack of profit or competition imperatives, has historically freed the state from economic accountability or economic discipline regarding water management. Until recently, the charges for water supplied by government infrastructures have been negligible, and have not reflected or generated sufficient funds to meet the cost of amortising government investments (Smith 1998). Nor have the degradations of water use been systematically accounted for, costed or charged. Generous and free/cheap provision of water is seen to have enabled unrestrained and unrestricted use, and subsidised both production and consumption activities that may not have been viable without State support. Water supplied by nature has been a free good. The supply of water, effectively at 'zero cost' (Paterson 1987) has distorted the potential for efficiencies in water use.

Environmental parameters have combined with economic considerations to challenge the capacity of technological solutions to provide for further water resources. The technocratic character of water use, in retrospect, is seen not to have considered water as a finite resource or attempted to understand the function of hydrological systems. The economic and hydrological resources are not necessarily available for new water projects, and the technical ability to harvest water potentially exceeds the capacity of the environment to accommodate the impositions of use and waste (Gleick 1993). The role of dam construction in meeting water needs has been reassessed in terms of the social and environmental impacts associated with the disruption of river systems and land use (World Commission on Dams 2000). Questions remain regarding the availability of appropriate sites, and of rainfall, to fill future dams. The costs of water harvest rise with increased power and technology expenses involved in the access of remote water supplies, including the capital intensive transformation of saline waters, or the access and relocation of remote water resources. In addition, transportation and transformation projects threaten environmental costs (WWF 2007a). Proposed water infrastructure developments are subject to evaluation in terms of environmental costs, greenhouse gas contributions and social impacts (Cullen 2006a).

Limits to water use, environmentally and politically defined, present as a critical concern for individual actors within the economic system. In the context of scarcity, contest emerges between urban and rural users, between emerging productive activities and pre-existing uses, and between uses that degrade water systems and users who depend upon access to healthy river systems. The effects of increased demand are exacerbated by the impacts of cyclical and longer term reductions in rainfall. In the context of diminishing supplies, established systems of allocation between established users are also challenged. Examples of conflict include competition between agriculture and coal-mining in the Hunter Valley (Stewart & Jones 1993); between irrigation industries and graziers in the Paroo river (Kingsford 2002); between cities and agrarian users in South Australia; and over water use regimes expressed in cities experiencing water supply limits, such as Sydney. Economic dependence on water by vested interests leads to a need to ensure the reliability of future water supplies (Stroshane 2003). Water users seek to obtain security (certainty) in their rights to use water resources. Pressure on governments to ensure access to water supplies comes from agricultural, urban and industrial users, both as a response to actual physical shortages to water supply and as a response to the social parameters introduced by the successes of the environmental lobby.

The confrontation with limits to the availability of freshwater thus presents as a punctuation in the evolution and expansion of economic activity. The realisation of water scarcity has disturbed established systems of water management and trajectories of water use, and initiated ongoing change - a process of flux and adjustment - in systems of water management. The system both seeks and is forced to adapt/adjust to new challenges. From an economic perspective, Australia has arrived at a 'mature water economy', with the emphasis changed from developing to efficiently managing water resources (Pigram 1999; Randall 1981, cited in Quiggin 2001; Young & McColl 2004). Additional resources are not easily available in cost-effective terms. The inability of water supply to satisfy competing demands presages the need for allocation decisions to be made between uses of the major inland water systems, coastal rivers and underground water resources (Freebairn 2003). Irrigation uses, urban demands, and environmental services all require consideration (Edwards 2003).

Governance systems are attempting to manage water flows and stocks whilst responding to pressure from various stakeholders to ensure agricultural, industrial, urban and environmental supplies and to protect economic outcomes. The range of interests embodied in hydrological function and water use indicate that water management is more than a technical exercise. It necessarily involves the mediation of conflicting interests. The theoretical and political process of testing systems of water allocation provides both an impetus for rethinking how water utilisation and water priorities are determined and initiates changes to water management as the state is petitioned to mediate disputes of water utilisation. The mediation of contest can be seen to be, in the context of the short-term timeframes of democratic decision making, a management challenge more immediate than sustainability and viability considerations.

Economics and water

In a concurrent development, water has been targeted as a concern for economic theory. As water has presented as a concern for economic systems, so it has also presented as an object of analysis in economic theory. The interpretation of water in terms of value generally, and as an economic good specifically, has a range of implications and practical repercussions.

The economic preoccupation with scarcity – specifically the allocation of scarce resources between competing uses – positions economic theory to comment on emerging contests over allocation. Economic theory thus lends itself neatly to questions of scarce and limited environmental resources, and provides a range of tools to revalue environmental resources and systems. Environmental economics defines the unresolved contests over environmental goods, and the external and unmet costs of environmental impacts, as problems of market failure. Three environmental services provided by the environment to the economy are identified: resource provision, the absorption of the waste products of production processes, and environmental amenity. These are economic functions because they have a positive economic value: these functions would all have positive prices if they were to be bought and sold in the market place. Environmental services are used inefficiently because the positive prices for these economic functions are not manifest: the exchanges that occur through the marketplace do not necessarily cost environmental use. This is not intrinsic to modern economies, but rather the result of the ignorance of these economic functions in the personal and social aims of individuals, groups, communities, pressure groups and politicians (Pearce & Kerry 1990). Environmental economics theory positions the market as the appropriate structure through which to effect allocation. Attention is then turned towards the incorporation of environmental considerations into economic processes. Economic instruments include the implementation of taxation and subsidy schemes, the establishment of property rights in tradeable commodities, and the corporatisation of resource delivery infrastructure (Pearce & Kerry 1990). Taxation and subsidy schemes are increasingly referred to as 'command-and-control' instruments due to the interventionist role required of government in their implementation. The property rights and corporatisation processes, in contrast, are seen to allow a greater role for markets and the expression of rational individual preferences in deciding environmental outcomes.

Water has been widely reconceived and accepted as an 'economic good' since the Dublin Conference on Water and the Environment in 1992 (Savenije 2002). The expansion and resource appetites of industrial economies focus attention on the role of contemporary trajectories of economic development in determining the journey towards capacity utilisation of water resources.[5] The role of water in economic growth, and the potential of water scarcity and diminishing quality to challenge regional economic growth, is being broached (Barbier 2004). The status afforded to water is reassessed in the context of scarcity and the need to decide distribution between competing uses.

Within the conventional conceptual economic framework, the increasing scarcity of water relative to demand is associated with an enhanced value that should be reflected in price. Water only has economic value when its supply is scarce relative to demand (Ward & Michelsen 2002). The recognition of water as an economic good has provided a growing impetus both to find the 'real' price of water and to ensure that water resources are put to their most economically efficient use. Economic theory frames water management as a question of the allocation of a scarce resource between competing users, considering imperatives for efficient and high-value use (Johansson et al 2002; Edwards 2003; Freebairn 2003; *The Economist* 2003). The water management question posed within economic method is: considering the range of possible and competing uses, what may be the best distribution and utilisation of limited water resources? Historically, because water has been a public good provided without reference to the disciplines of the market, emerging value has not been recognised. Neither have impositions upon water systems been costed or accounted for, this being a problem of

---

[5] The World Business Council for Sustainable Development recognises industrial development as "one of the major factors driving increasing water demand" (2006).

unpriced externalities. Maximising the total economic value of water has become an essential concept, yet considerable debate remains regarding how this can be achieved (Ward and Michelsen 2002, p. 426). Pricing is recognised as important, but there is a lack of consensus on an optimal water pricing policy (Johansson et al 2002, p. 175).

An alternative approach to defining the 'value' of water has looked to determine the range of alternative or non-monetary values associated with water systems. Although these approaches adopt the stated objectivity of economic/scientific method in seeking to measure values expression, they are inherently political projects in that they seek to interrogate systems of prioritising water as a disassociated economic resource. Alternative economic valuation processes emerge from the Ecological Economics project that identifies economic production as a sphere of activity embedded within the ecological domain, and therefore dependent upon functional ecosystems. Ecological economics, as a theoretical positioning in debate regarding the utilisation of environments, maintains a consistent emphasis on scale of use and constraint of economic expansion. Ecological Economic valuations indicate the comprehensive values and economic support provided by ecosystem services. Other valuation projects seek to assess the range of ways in which water contributes to human welfare in terms of cultural values or social values, and how impositions upon water systems detract from human welfare (that are not conventionally accounted for in economic processes and systems). These values may be broadly indicated or expressed as hypothetical values / shadow costs – the potential monetary value of these services if they were to be bought and sold on the market. For example, studies in relation to wetlands include the papers: 'The economic value of wetland services: a meta-analysis' (Woodward & Wui 2001); 'The value of wetlands: importance of scale and landscape setting' (Mitsch & Gosselink 2000); 'Approaches to valuing the hidden hydrological services of wetland ecosystems' (Acharya 2000); 'Ecosystems, contingent valuation and ethics: the case of wetland re-creation (Spash 2000); 'The economic valuation of saltwater marsh supporting marine recreational fishing in the south-eastern United States' (Bell 1997); 'The effect of distance on willingness to pay values: a case study of wetlands and salmon in California' (Pate & Loomis 1997); and 'Private and social returns from wetland preservation versus those from wetland conversion to agriculture' (van Vuuren & Roy 1993).

The environmental economic and ecological economic projects are not, however, exclusive. The recognition of some environmental and alternative flow requirements, combined with recognition of the finite capacity of the environment to provide flows, demands a setting of limits to water use. Within the establishment of limits, markets are signalled as the most appropriate mechanism for allocation of water resources. This suggests the potential for a water management model that establishes allocation between a range of uses, realising the highest returns across a range of water needs. This extends the economic concept of optimal allocation to incorporate multiple values. Market solutions, as a process of cap and trade, thus suggest the ability to manage and resolve the challenges presented by previously unrestrained trajectories of economic demand and the subsequent competition over water resources.

Property rights combined with market approaches are gaining policy prominence over the potential for 'command-and-control' legislation and taxation. Advocates recommend assigning property rights to previously public good or shared common property, with the establishment of markets as a system to regulate allocation. There are two prominent processes towards the establishment of property rights in water that are directed towards meeting the respective differences in urban and rural systems of water use. In relation to urban supply infrastructures, there is promotion of the privatisation/corporatisation of water supply infrastructures, with the efficiencies of private ownership and profit incentives proposed as effective forces for water management. It is expected that water prices will increase to reflect scarcity. Appropriate pricing will both encourage efficiencies in use and provide incentive for new suppliers to provide water resources. In agricultural areas with high demand for water for irrigation, the establishment of tradeable water titles and of water markets is promoted. Markets are seen to provide flexibility, physical efficiency through opportunity costs, opportunity for new market entrants, economic efficiency gains, transfer to higher value uses, the ability for inefficient users to exit from the water industry, and the potential for the government to acquire licences through market processes (Pigram 1999).

Privatisation complies with a broader ideological framework that both prioritises the market as the medium for allocative decisions, and promotes the responsibilities and incentives within private property regimes (as opposed to the interpreted anarchy of public property regimes as identified in Hardin's 1968 'Tragedy of the Commons'). The shift towards water markets as a policy instrument has been promoted by international organisations such as the UN, The World Bank, FAO and the OECD (Bjornlund 2003). The OECD has expressed commitment to the idea that when an individual/group has an ownership interest in maintaining the value of a property or resource, it will be maintained. The role of the market, as the sum of individual interactions, is promoted as preferable to the authority of government: governments are seen to be servicing their own interests and entrenched community interests, an application of public choice theory. Command-and-control policies are critiqued for costly implementation and enforcement and their potential to hamper longer-term economic development. Property rights are argued as superior to command-and-control processes in terms of flexibility, efficiency, low cost and their ability to enable rather than inhibit growth (OECD 1997, 2004).

The establishment of property rights in water presents particular challenges. Ecological considerations point to the ways in which water is not a conventional commodity. Water defies simple categorisation both in its physical properties and in its economic characteristics. Water is a mobile resource, it exists as both a stock and a flow. It takes the form of ice, liquid and vapour. Water supplies vary spatially and temporally. Hydrological systems defy political borders. Water supply is variable and uncertain. Extreme water events, such as floods and droughts are impossible to control. Water use has environmental impacts with economic repercussions that are not typically or easily incorporated into market processes or accounting systems. Defining water as commodity or capital disguises the uncontrollability of water, and the difficulties in defining partial ownership of hydrological systems. The unique characteristics of water therefore challenge the systems of resource ownership that are typically associated with stationary or quantifiable stocks and that fail to recognise natural resources in the context of complex ecological and hydrologic systems.

The distinct social relationships in and of water use further complicate the interpretation and treatment of water as a commodity. Firstly, water has public and common good characteristics. Secondly, the unique value of water as a truly essential resource is worthy of consideration. If, as proposed by Ward and Michelsen, "people will pay thousands of dollars for a quart of water if it keeps them alive" (2002, p. 443), the potential for centralised ownership suggests capacity to set prices far above a competitive intersection of supply and demand. Thirdly, concerns regarding equity to access have been raised in response to pricing arrangements (Beder 2006). Fourthly, the critique of common property regimes remains a point of dispute, with retort to the presumed inability of communal coordination and presumed optimality of individual private property. The establishment of water markets threatens to compromise existing management regimes that are defined by social imperatives. A new institutionalist economics searches for resource management regimes of a more democratic and communal organisation (Ostrom et al 1999; Quiggin 1988). Fifthly, critique addresses the costs of establishing and participating in markets. Markets and property rights are a social creation that require infrastructure, including new laws, new institutional forms, and the protection of new property arrangements. Markets may create the illusion of reduced government responsibility yet inherently require an extensive government support role in providing stable and appropriate institutions for their effective operation (Johansson et al 2002). The transaction costs of water markets, privately or publicly borne, may be significant (Connell, Dovers & Grafton 2005).

Water therefore presents as a unique commodity. In an article titled "Why water is not an ordinary economic good, or why the girl is special", Hubert Savenije proposes that while water is recognisable as an economic good, it also possesses a number of distinguishing characteristics, the combination of which makes water a special economic good (Savenije, 2002, p.741). He argues that water is essential, scarce, fugitive, an ecological system's component, bulky, non-substitutable, not freely tradable, and complex. Water is complex because it is a public good, bound by location – a complicating political factor, has high production and transaction costs, and experiences non-homogeneity in markets, macro economic interdependencies between water using activities, threat of market failures in supply, and high merit values. Therefore a complex set of economic interests needs to be taken into account. He concludes that "saying that water is an economic good does not necessarily imply that a market price needs to be paid for it to make the allocation efficient. In fact, it does not mean that it should be paid for at all" (Savenije, 2002). While water can be treated as a commodity, the production of water is unlike any other commodity As Polanyi has observed regarding land and labour (1944), water is more appropriately regarded as a ficticious commodity in that it is not produced for the market. The environmental supply of water has no relationship to the logic of the market. Unlike land and labour however, freshwater can be produced from alternative water supplies, and thus is increasingly a produced good.

Emerging water scarcity itself creates new stakeholder interests in water resources. Water presents as a business opportunity, a means to complement or replace traditional state provision of water supplies (World Business Council for Sustainable Development 2006). More radical perspectives identify water commodification as the inevitable focus of capitalist expansion. Scarcity value suggests the potential for rental, speculative, and monopoly incomes related to the private ownership or control of water resources. In addition, the ownership or control of water provides opportunity for the exercise of social and political power (Boelens, Zwarteveen & Roth 2005). Pressure on governments to privatise delivery of water services and water ownership has been exerted by corporate interest and written into trade and aid agreements (Bjornlund 2003, Johnston 2003). Accusations of poor public management and the improved management techniques of private enterprise support this agenda. From this perspective, water privatisation is both an enclosure of a previously publicly owned resource, and a process of accumulation by dispossession (Swyngedouw 2005). Struggles to retain or regain local control over water have emerged in Canada (Biro 2002), America and Bolivia (Johnston 2003), Spain (Vidal de Llobatera 2003), and South Africa (Bond 2004).

Recognition of the complexities of water as a commodity, and the potential for market dynamics to produce 'sub-optimal' social and environmental outcomes, defines the need for ongoing government monitoring and regulation of the use of markets in water management. The establishment of markets for permanent water trades are seen to require sophisticated institutional arrangements, social acceptance, and social resource capacity (Bjornlund 2003). Acknowledgement of the role required of governance bodies in implementing markets informs the reticence of some commentators to unequivocally recommend water market instruments in developing countries (Pigram 1999). Markets for permanent water have been introduced predominantly in developed countries including Australia, the USA, and Chile (Bjornlund 2003).

The purchase of economic instruments

Australia is identified at the frontier of the establishment of water markets (Bate 2006; Pigram 1999 2006; Young & McColl 2004). This puts practice ahead of experience: "arguably, policy reform is now ahead of theory and empirical analysis that is publicly available and, hence, contestable" (Young & McColl 2004, p. 4). The role of markets in water management, an approach predominantly conceived in the abstract, is now being tested.

National policy has initiated and prioritised water rights and water markets as the means to realise monetary values of water and to provide the framework for distributive decisions regarding water use, in conjunction with a raft of strategies that seek to encourage more efficient water use through research and technology development. This approach references economic method to inform interpretation of water questions and policy response. Market trade in water entitlements emerged in the early 1980s (Bjornlund 2003). The Council of Australian Governments' 1994 Water Policy Agreement committed to: address allocation of water to the environment, pricing reform, widely implement tradeable water entitlements, and clarify property rights to water (COAG 1994). The 1995 National Competition Policy linked substantial federal government payments to the states on the basis of a commitment to implement agreed reforms. This agenda was restated and progressed by the National Water Initiative 2004 (summary in

Pigram 2006). In tandem, within the Murray–Darling Basin, a 1995 moratorium on future diversions was formalised with a permanent upper limit cap in 1997, set at 1993/4 diversion entitlements (Quiggin 2001). Limits to use are being drawn, although the appropriateness and permanency of parameters are uncertain, and new ownership and allocation arrangements established. In practice, and subject to differences across states, this has entailed the formalisation of pre-existing licences to water in the form of a tradeable entitlement to a given share of water. The available share or allocation is determined on an ongoing basis subject to policy and seasonal flows.

Water trading is one aspect of a suite of strategies within emerging water policy, yet the formalisation of water property rights and markets has received a prominent focus in the implementation of water management regimes (Connell 2007; Connell, Dovers & Grafton 2005; Pigram 1999). The Minister for the Environment and Water Resources states "Water trading is a key plank of the Commonwealth's water policy blueprint, the National Water Initiative (NWI), and critical to national water reform" (Turnbull 2007a, p. 1). In the contemporary political climate, reliance on market forces and an enforceable system of property rights is preferred to rule-based and subsidised management (Pigram 1999). The adoption of property rights in water is seen to both reflect the ascendancy of the market in Australian public policy and an international trend among industrialised countries to use markets for water management (Isaac 2003). To Commonwealth and state interests, markets suggest the ability to ensure high value use and allow for continued economic growth despite resource limitations. This is arguably an important criterion to a federal government that continues to emphasise economic growth as its primary objective and responsibility (Howard 1997, 2007). The potential to propose policies that limit growth is not seen as politically feasible (M'Gonigle 1999). At the same time, it could be argued that market determination of allocations provides for political disengagement from the messy business of mediation between economic uses, although the task of formalising a division between economic and environmental flows remains contested.

The development of the market model for water distribution has been facilitated by a broad and eclectic, although not comprehensive, support.

It is important that the use of economic instruments in water management has been supported by both business representative interests and prominent environmental interests, two positions that have a history of opposition in contesting the use of natural resources and environments. Water markets have been supported by interests who perceive water management primarily as a concern for the sustainability of businesses and economic growth, and therefore a question of efficiency and allocation of a scarce resource between the competing demands of economic interests. To business interests seeking to ensure access to flows in a climate of both physical and political uncertainty, it offers some security of entitlement (Business Council of Australia and New South Wales Irrigators Council, in Geoghegan 2006). Market advocates who remain ambivalent toward the assumed merits of environmental flows can be identified (one such example is Dwyer 2006). Water markets have been supported also by a more ecologically-defined position that seeks to establish the need for environmental flows as a primary objective. This includes the Wentworth Group of Concerned Scientists (Wentworth Group 2003) and the Australian Conservation Foundation (Fisher 2004; Hechtman 2006). There is an accepted logic in the idea that water has value and therefore should be priced accordingly (e.g. Stewart & Jones 2003). From the environmental perspective, markets are recognised as both a means to ensure efficiency and appropriate pricing in the allocations assigned for production and consumption, and provide facility for governments to buy back environmental flows in over-allocated systems.

The changing terrain of water distribution

In economic terms, the effective operation of markets has been progressed. Irrigators are seen to be increasingly treating water as a commodity, another input into farming, to be bought and sold on a seasonal basis (Bjornlund 2003). However, early market exchanges have been limited, or 'thin', with problems of inefficient information flows, spatial restrictions and a range of administrative restrictions to trade (Bjornlund 2003; Crase, O'Reilly & Dollery 2000;). Water trades are occurring predominantly in temporary water rather than permanent water entitlements (Shi 2006).[6] The preference for temporary trades over permanent sales has been identified as reflecting the reluctance of entitlement holders to relinquish their claims on an increasingly valuable resource, as well as exploitation of the economic gains from resource rentals[7] (Bjornlund 2003; Freebairn 2005; Shi 2006). Some entitlement holders are using water titles as a means to remain on the land. Water itself has become a cash product (Clarke 2006). Speculative activity in water trades has been identified (Bjornlund 2003, p. 70). The uncertain future of the physical availability of 'permanent' allocations is seen to be a consideration in limiting the market in permanent titles (Bjornlund 2003). New enterprises have been established through market purchase of water entitlements, substantiating argument that water markets create opportunity to increase economic activity (Shi 2006; Young & McColl 2004)[8]. The expectation that permanent water will move to high value uses has been partially fulfilled (Bjornlund 2003). Media attention has highlighted the movement of water from small holdings to larger corporations, such as Timber Corp and Macquarie Bank (e.g., Clarke 2006; Knight 2006).[9] The consolidation of water holdings may be consistent with a general trend towards the increased scale of farming enterprises. Urban users are predicted to be competitive participants in water markets (Young, cited in Knight 2006). It should be emphasised that highest value users are those who are able to pay the most for the resource, rather than those who necessarily achieve physical efficiency or use the water for the most productive gain per unit of input.

The operation and facilitation of water markets has emerged as an area of scholarship. Maturing water markets are seen to produce more rational outcomes (Bjornlund 2002). However, "we have a long way to go before we have a fully functioning market" (Treasurer Peter Costello, in Peatling, Marriner & AAP 2006). The limited trade in permanent

---

[6] 92% of water trades in the Murray-Darling Basin, 2001/2002, were in temporary water.

[7] described in the US as water-ranching (Stroshane 2003)

[8] "[I]n the case of the wine industry for example, much of the recent expansion of grape plantings would have been impossible without water trading" (Young & McColl 2004, p. 10).

[9] The movement of water from small holdings to larger organisations has seen reduced populations in rural communities, reducing economies of scale and 'stranding' irrigation assets (Hechtman 2006).

water is seen as an impediment to market efficiency (Crase, O'Reilly & Dollery 2000). The Productivity Commission has undertaken research to assist in the implementation of water markets, with a focus on a nationally compatible market, regulatory and planning systems of management (NWI clause 23) and the facilitation of water market and trading arrangements (NWI clause 58). The Commission recommends refining and clarifying existing property rights, and relaxing or removing restrictions on who can participate in water trade (Productivity Commission 2006). A recent National Water Initiative paper has promoted the opening of markets to non-users as a means to promote efficiency (ABC 2006). The differences and complexities in titles and trading arrangements between state systems, and the need to clarify property rights, has been emphasised as requiring address if markets are to function effectively on a national basis (Brennan & Scoccimarro 1999; Crase, O'Reilly & Dollery 2000; Freebairn 2004; Shi 2006; Young & McColl 2003). The statement of need for a national coherence in water titles and administration pre-empted, and arguably provided an inevitable impetus, to the 2007 water plan that seeks to establish Commonwealth management of the Murray-Darling Basin (Howard 2007).

The environmental implications of water markets are being monitored. The outcomes of water trades demonstrate the potential to amplify the differences between natural flow regimes and extractive flow regimes (Tidsell 2001). It is recognised that more physically efficient utilisation will return less run-off to hydrological systems, and that efficiency gains in irrigated agriculture do not translate into environmental flows without management intervention (Heaney & Beare 2001; Watson 2003; Young & McColl 2003). Water markets are seen to be moving water to high value businesses rather than to crops that are efficient in environmental terms. This is interpreted as the outcome of relatively low water prices, and water remaining one factor of many in shaping agricultural decisions (e.g. Isaac 2003). The movement of water to emerging enterprises threatens additional salinity problems as new lands are developed for agricultural use. The potential remains for land-use developments, particularly forestry, to reduce water yield (Young & McColl 2003). An increasing dependence on groundwater has been recognised (Cullen 2006a). The failure to cancel unutilised and under-utilised entitlements, 'sleeper' and 'dozer' entitlements, has led to an increase in the number of active water users as these entitlements are traded and activated (Isaac 2003). The problem of economic use impacts and environmental quality continues. The need for salinity mitigation and water quality protection prompts arguments for a more comprehensive use of economic instruments to manage water quality, including the extension of property rights to externalities (Beare & Heaney 2002).

The establishment of water markets, and the associated drawing and enforcement of parameters to use emphasised by the environmental lobby, suggest a very different water management role for the states and Commonwealth – from the political and physical facilitation of access to water resources to the management of a given supply. However, governments, at both state and federal level, appear unable to concede their involvement in this historical role. There is a continued search for resources and ongoing proposals to fund further infrastructures. Examples of this process include: the establishment of a federal taskforce to examine the potential for water resources development in the tropical north of Australia (Howard 1997); the proposed 3700km pipeline from the Fitzroy River to Perth in Western Australia and the muted Clarence River diversions in NSW (Pigram 2006); Victoria's Goulburn to Melbourne pipeline and desalination plant proposals (Hughes 2007); and the desalination plant development recently approved for Sydney, NSW (AAP 2007). In addition, emphasis on pricing water is promoted as a means to stimulate private interest in the search for and development of further water resources (Dwyer 2006). Citigroup, the Business Council of Australia and Infrastructure Partnerships Australia have advocated competitive water pricing as a means to stimulate private investment in water infrastructure developments (Hepworth 2007). State governments are increasingly looking to private enterprise to invest in further infrastructure (NSW in Hepworth & Midalia 2007; WA in Burrell 2007). The introduction of demand to previously marginal water resources initiates further environmental contest.

The contest between environmental and economic flows remain and the stated objective to return an adequate level of environmental flows is yet to be realised (Lewis & Wilkinson 2007). The Australian Conservation

Foundation has raised opposition to the creation of water entitlements with unlimited tenure (Quiggin 2001). Concern has been expressed regarding the tacking of water rights onto pre-existing regimes of water use. This has been seen to consolidate existing economic interests in water: "a more immediate concern is that we may well be locking away our public water resources in private hands without any quid pro quo for the environment" (Fisher 2004, p. 25). Environmental interests have expressed dissatisfaction with limited progress towards acquiring environmental flows (Connell 2007; Cullen 2006b). This has been interpreted as a problem of political incentive in the face of an effective agricultural lobby (Fisher 2004). The economic perspective however, emphasises that achieving reductions in extractive uses is not a costless exercise (Cope no date). Securing environmental flows has two economic dimensions. The first is the costs of reclaiming flows in over-allocated catchments, and the associated need for a revenue stream. The second is the opportunity costs of not utilising available water for productive use. In the context of the costs of acquiring flows, and the opportunity costs of production forgone, environmental flows are being asked to both earn their way and prove their worth.

The acquisition of environmental flows, in a competitive market, requires targeted funds. Governments can buy water, as in the NSW Riverbank scheme. This is an increasingly expensive endeavour in the context of increases in water prices: the economic value of water can be seen to have contributed an additional dimension to the challenge of returning environmental flows (Lewis & Wilkinson 2007). The Federal Government scheme to buy back water saved through increased efficiencies has attracted minimal interest.[10] The Federal Water Resources Minister concluded that the offered price was too low: "the reality is, water is becoming more valuable and the cost of acquiring water is more likely to rise than fall" (Turnbull, in Farmonline 2007, p. 1). Alternatively, the government must compulsorily acquire entitlements or reduce allocations, and is thus subject to compensation claims (these claims may be of tenuous legality, but have a demonstrated political traction). An "across-the-board pro-rata purchase of a

---

[10] "After budgeting $200 million to purchase 200 gigalitres from irrigators, three tenders worth $765,000 for 454 megalitres of water came in under the benchmark price" (Farmonline 2007).

percentage of each water entitlement" has been recommended as a means to address the limited availability of water for sale and the potential for market distortions of a water plan voluntary buy-back proposal that is 15 times greater than the annual maximum trade in permanent entitlements (Young & McColl 2007, p. 1). The Commonwealth Water Bill 2007, introduced to parliament in August, includes commitment that water entitlements will not be compulsorily acquired. However, "the Commonwealth agrees to take on its share, together with the State Governments, of the liabilities for future reductions in water availability" (Turnbull 2007b, p.5). The participation of environmental water trusts in water markets – buying water in times of plenty when prices are lower, and selling during periods of scarcity to take advantage of higher prices – has been suggested as a means for environmental interest groups to fund their interests in acquiring environmental allocations. Alternatively, facilitating donations of water to the environments has been proposed as a cost-effective option (Young & McColl 2004).

The means to raise funds for environmental flows requires further thought. If the creation of wealth is linked to environmental transformations, as has been explored in the emerging thermodynamic/bio-economic discourse (Boulding 1966; Georgescu-Roegen 1972), or more generally within ecological economic thought (Hornborg 2005; Perez-Rincon 2005), the process of raising money itself requires a process of environmental appropriations. At the very least, the raising of funds is dependent upon a prior participation in market processes.

The opportunity costs of preserving water for the environment present significant challenges to the defence of environmental flows. More water for the environment is less water for direct production and consumption. It is estimated that the 1500 gigalitres of environmental flow indicated for a healthy and functional Murray River system, roughly translates into 150,000 hectares of irrigated agriculture (Fisher 2004). Even where flows have not been overallocated, and need to be preserved rather than returned, the preservation of environmental flows is not 'costless'. From the economic perspective, the preservation of environmental flows has opportunity costs in developments forgone.

These opportunity costs can be expected to exist in perpetuity, and will only increase as water becomes scarcer and more valuable. In both contexts, environmental flows will face ongoing expectation that they demonstrate value from use. For economic efficiency, available water resources need to be allocated to "where they are most valuable to society" (Edwards 2003, p. 196). The provision of environmental water is 'to meet human needs" and "people's demand for environmental services". (Edwards 2003, p. 197). Water savings programs will be subject to a questioning of whether "marginal benefits equal or exceed marginal costs" (Ward & Michelsen 2002, p. 426). In the face of uncertainties in ecosystem requirements, Pigram warns against 'ambit' claims and states that the environment needs to be held accountable for the water assigned to it (2006). Further: "interest groups, who are largely succeeding in acquiring substantially greater amounts of water for the environment, should now be expected 'to do better with more' – to account for the water placed under their stewardship and to service more effectively the environmental purposes specified" (Pigram 2006, p. 159). In this context, the provision of environmental flows is expected to demonstrate a clear and competitive benefit to society.

Defining environmental water use in terms of value is an extension and prioritisation of a specific conception of water that re-emphasises the need for water uses to produce gains/output. While the focus of alternative valuations entails either a redefinition or a reconceptualisation of value itself, a project to reclaim the meaning of value from a pure equation with monetary price, the contest is being played out on the terrain of economic method. The prominence of value as a means to petition for use rights suggests the dominance of utilitarian interpretations of the environment. It indicates also a complicitness, although perhaps reluctant on the part of some who participate in alternative valuation projects, with the economic concept that the most deserving water users are, by definition, those who can demonstrate the greatest utility from use. The positioning of this discussion on the home ground of economics, and the use of price as a value default, suggests an inevitable benefit to those who produce monetary gains from their water use (the home team). Within the decision making processes of the contemporary political economy, it will be an ongoing challenge for hypothetical or argued values to compete with the tangible economic gains of water utilised in productive activity.

The range of outcomes from the early experiences of water market development and operation suggest that the changes following from the establishment of water markets will be more extensive than the immediate stated objectives of water market policy. The pricing of water, and the associated changes to rights to water, appear to provide access to water to competitive economic enterprises. This process in itself will initiate a range of social and environmental adjustments. The award of environmental flows however, remains open to contest and subject to a new terrain of competition. The challenges that follow relate to the ability of environmental and longer-term sustainability interests to compete with immediate economic interests in the setting of parameters to water use.

Acknowledgements

Thanks go to Stuart Rosewarne, Leith Boully and Gavin Birch for review of drafts of this chapter.

References

Acharya G, 2000. 'Approaches to valuing the hidden hydrological services of wetland ecosystems', *Ecological Economics*, vol. 35, no. 1, October 2000, pp. 63–74 AAP (2007) 'Desalination plant gets go ahead' *Sydney Morning Herald*, July 19 2007. http://www.smh.com.au/articles/2007/07/19/1184559917447.ht ml.

Australian Broadcasting Commission, 2006. 'Water trading market should include non-users: report', 23 October, http://www.abc.net.au/news/items/200610/17771042.htm?nt.

Barbier E B, 2004. 'Water and economic growth', *Economic Record*, 80 (248), 1–16.

Bate R, 2006. *All the water in the world*, The Centre for Independent Studies, Sydney.

Beare S & Heaney A, 2002. 'Water trade and the externalities of water use in Australia', ABARE paper for Natural Resource Management Unit, AFFA, abareconomics consulting services, August.

Beder S, 2006. *Environmental principles and policies: an interdisciplinary approach* UNSW Press, Sydney.

Bell W F, 1997. 'The economic valuation of saltwater marsh supporting marine recreational fishing in the south-eastern United States', *Ecological Economics*, vol. 21, no. 3, June 1997, pp. 243–254

Biro A, 2002. 'Wet dreams: ideology and the debates over Canadian water exports' *Capitalism, Nature, Socialism*, Dec 2002, vol. 13, no. 4, pp. 29–50

Boelens R, Zwarteveen M, Roth D, 2005. 'Legal complexity in the analysis of water rights and water resources management', in Roth, D, Boelens R & Zwarteveen M, 2005. *Liquid relations: contested water rights and legal complexity*, Rutgers University Press, New Brunswick New Jersey and London.

Bond P, 2004. 'Water commodification and decommodification narratives: pricing and policy, debates from Johannesburg to Kyoto to Cancun and back', *Capitalism, Nature, Socialism*, vol. 15 no. 1 March, pp. 7–25.

Botterill L C & Fisher M (eds.), 2003. *Beyond drought: people, policy and perspectives*, CSIRO Publishing, Collingwood, Victoria.

Bjornlund H, 2003. 'Farmer participation in markets for temporary and permanent water in southeast Australia', *Agricultural Water Management* 63, pp. 57–76.

Bjornlund H, 2002. 'Are water markets maturing' Eighth Annual Pacific-Rim Real Estate Society Conference, Christchurch, New Zealand, 21–23 January 2002.

Brennan D & Scoccimarro M, 1999. 'Issues in defining property rights to improve Australian water markets', *The Australian Journal of Agricultural and Resource Economics*, vol 43, no. 1, pp. 69–89.

Boulding K, 1966. 'The economics of coming spaceship earth' reprinted with additions in Daly, H (ed.) (1980) *Economics, ecology, ethics: essays towards a steady-state economy*, pp. 253–263, Freeman, San Francisco.

Burrell A, 2007. 'WA looks at private ownership of water', *The Australian Financial Review*, 9 July 2007.

Clarke S, 2006. 'AM – Farmers sell remaining water to survive in the last-ditch hope of spring rain', ABC Online, 22 September, http://www.abc.net.au/am/content/2006/s1746114.htm.

Connell D, 2007. *Water politics in the Murray Darling basin*, The Federation Press, Sydney.

Connell D, Dovers S & Grafton Q G, 2005. 'A critical analysis of the national water initiative', *The Australasian Journal of Natural Resources Law and Policy*, vol. 10, no. 1 2005, pp. 81–107.

Coombs H C, 1990. *The return of scarcity: strategies for an economic future*, Cambridge University Press, Cambridge (England) Melbourne.

Cope D, no date. 'Water reform: who pays for the environment? Paper prepared for the National Competition Council, Deborah Cope, Principal, Pirac Economics, http://www.ncc.gov.au/pdf/PIReWa-008b.pdf

Council of Australian Governments (COAG), 1994. 'A Water Resource Policy', COAG.

Council of Australian Governments (COAG), 2004 'Intergovernmental agreement on a national water initiative', COAG.

Crase L, O'Reilly & Dollery B, 2000. 'Water markets as a vehicle for water reform: the case of New South Wales', *The Australian Journal of Agricultural and Resource Economics*, vol. 44, no. 2, pp. 299–321.

CSIRO, 2002. 'The law and ecological services' Media Release – Ref 2002/207 – Oct 22, 2002 http://www.csiro.au/files/mediaRelease/mr2002/Prsalzman.htm.

Cullen P, 2006a. 'Flying blind – the disconnect between groundwater and policy', Peter Cullen, National Water Commission, 10th Murray-Darling Basin Groundwater Workshop, Canberra. 19 Sept 2006. http://www.wentworthgroup.org/docs/Flying_Blind_Groundwate r_&_Policy.pdf.

Cullen P, 2006b. 'Running on empty – the risk of continuing to dither while the empty light is flashing'. Occasional Paper South Australian Centre for Economic Studies, Adelaide, Lunchtime Address November 23rd 2006 http://www.wentworthgroup.org/ docs/Running_on_Empty_PCullen1.pdf.

Davidson B R, 1965. *The northern myth: a study of the physical and economic limits to agricultural and pastoral development in tropical Australia*, Melbourne University Press, Cambridge University Press, London and New York.

Deane P, 1978. *The evolution of economic ideas*, Cambridge University Press, Cambridge, New York.

Dwyer T, 2006. 'Urban water policy: in need of economics' Agenda, vol. 13, 2006, pp 3–16.

Edwards G, 2003. 'Water policy: setting the scene' *The Australian Economic Review*, vol. 36, no. 2, pp. 193–202.

Ekins P, Folke C & Groot R, 2003. 'Identifying critical natural capital' *Ecological Economics*, vol. 44, no. 2–3, pp. 3–4.

Farmonline (2007) 'Just three willing sellers for Murray water buyback', 31 May, http://www.farmonline.com.au/news_daily.asp?ag_id= 42735.

Fisher T, 2004. 'Water sustainability or sell-out?, the national water initiative in perspective' *Australian Options*, Autumn 2004.

Freebairn J, 2003. 'Principles for the allocation of scarce water', *The Australian Economic Review*, vol. 36, no.2, pp. 203–12

Galaz V R, undated. 'Does the EC water framework directive build resilience? Harnessing socio-ecological complexity in water management' Policy Paper by 'The Resilience and Freshwater Initiative', Swedish Water House, Centre for Transdisciplinary Environmental Research, Stockholm University http://www.resalliance.org/files/1133262688_swedishwaterhouser esiliencepolicypaper1.pdf.

Georgescu-Roegen N, 1972. 'Energy and economic myths', in Georgescu-Roegen, *Energy and economic myths: institutional and analytical essays*, pp. 3–36, Pergamon, New York.

Gleick P, 1993. *Water in crisis: a guide to the world's fresh water resources*, Oxford University Press, Melbourne.

Geoghegan A, 2006. 'Business Council urges water price increase', ABC Online 22 September 2006, http://www.abc.net.au/water/stories/s1743849.htm.

Hall-Wallace, M, Scott-Walker C, Kendall L & Schaller C, 2003. *Exploring water resources: GIS investigations for the earth sciences*, Brooks/Cole, Canada.

Hardin G, 1968. 'The tragedy of the commons', *Science*, vol. 162, pp. 1243.

Heaney A & Beare S, 2001. 'Water trade and irrigation: defining property rights to return flows', *Australian Commodities*, vol. 8, no. 2, June 2001.

Hechtman M, 2006. 'Squeezing the best out of every last drop', *The Australian Financial Review*, Thursday 27 July, p. 12.

Hennessy K, Page C, Durack P & Bathols J, 2006. 'Climate change projections for Victoria', CSIRO marine and atmospheric research, CSIRO, Aspendale, Victoria.

Hepworth A, 2007. 'Pricing, competition reforms hold the most water', *The Australian Financial Review*, 23 July.

Hepworth A & Midalia A, 2007. 'Water pricing "needs debate"' *The Australian Financial Review*, 16 July 2007.

Hornborg A, 2005. 'Footprints in the cotton fields: the industrial revolution as time-space appropriation and environmental load displacement' *Ecological Economics*.

Howard J, 1997. 'Investing for growth', Address by the Prime Minister, the Hon John Howard MP, National Press Club, Canberra 8 December.

Howard J, 2007. A national plan for water security, 25 January.

Hughes D, 2007. 'Desalination plant may be state's biggest PPP' *The Australian Financial Review*, 20 June.

Hutton D & Connors L, 1999. *A history of the Australian environment movement*, The Press Syndicate of the University of Cambridge, UK.

Isaac M, 2003. 'The political economy of water reform feasibility in Australia', *Water Science and Technology: Water Supply*, vol. 3, no. 1–2, pp395–404, IWA Publishing.

Johansson R C, Tsur Y, Roe T L, Doukkali R & Dinar A, 2002. 'Pricing irrigation water: a review of theory and practice', Water Policy 4, pp. 173–199.

Johnston B, 2003. 'The political ecology of water: an introduction', *Capitalism, Nature, Socialism*, vol. 14, no. 3, September, pp. 73–90.

Kingsford R T, 2002. 'Inland rivers and floodplains: fact sheet 8', Land and Water Australia, Canberra, http://www.rivers.gov.au/acrobat/facts08.pdf.

Knight B, 2006. 'High prices tempt farmers to sell water', ABC TV Program transcript, 7.30 Report, 19 September, http://www.abc.net.au/7.30/content/2006/s1744867.htm.

Lewis D & Wilkinson M, 2007. 'Licence to spill is a big water fight' *Sydney Morning Herald*, June 30.

M'Gonigle R M, 1999. 'Ecological economics and political ecology: towards a necessary synthesis' *Ecological Economics*, vol. 28, pp. 11–26.

Mitsch W J & Gosselink J G, 2000. 'The value of wetlands: importance of scale and landscape setting', *Ecological Economics*, vol. 35, no. 1, October, pp. 25–33.

National Water Initiative, 2004. hhtp://www.pmc.gov.au/nwi/index.cfm.

OECD, 2004. Recommendation of the Council on the use of economic instruments in promoting the conservation and sustainable use of biodiversity 21 April, – C(2004)81 http://webdomino1.oecd.org/horizontal/oecdacts.nsf/Display/FC32046F0ED8F9E5C125729700 4784DF?OpenDocument.

OECD, 1997. 'Policy responses and directions', global environment outlook, United Nations Environment Programme, Global state of the environment report, http://www.unep.org/Geo/geo1/ch/ch3_2.htm.

Ostrom E, Burger J, Field C B, Norgaard R B & Policansky D, 1999. 'Revisiting the commons: local lessons, global challenges' *Science*, 284.5412, p. 278(1).

Pate J & Loomis J, 1997. 'The effect of distance on willingness to pay values: a case study of wetlands and salmon in California', *Ecological Economics*, vol. 20, no. 3, March, pp. 199–207.

Paterson J, 1987. 'The privatisation issue: water utilities', in Abelson P (ed.), *Privatisation: An Australian Perspective*, Australian Professional Publications, Mosman, NSW.

Pearce D W & Kerry T R, 1990. *Economics of natural resources and the environment*, Harvester Wheatsheaf, Great Britain.

Pearce F, 2006. *When the rivers run dry: what happens when the water runs out?* Doubleday.

Peatling S & Marriner C, 2006. 'Costello pushes for water market to end rationing' *Sydney Morning Herald*, November 2.

Perez-Rincon M A, 2005. 'Columbian international trade from a physical perspective: towards an ecological "Prebisch thesis"', *Ecological Economics*, vol. 59, pp. 519–529.

Pigram J J, 1999. 'Tradeable water rights: the Australian experience', Taiwan Institute for Economic Research, Taipei, 21 June.

Pigram J J, 2006. *Australia's water resources: from use to management*, CSIRO Publishing, Collingwood, Victoria.

Pimentel D, Berger B, Filiberto D, Newton M, Wolfe B, Karabinakis E, Clark S, Poon E, Abbett E & Nandagopal S, 2004. 'Water resources: agricultural and environmental issues' *BioScience*, vol. 54, no. 10.

Polanyi K, 1944. *The great transformation*, Farrar and Rhinehart, New York.

Powell J M, 1997. 'Enterprise and dependency: water management in Australia', in Griffiths T & Robin L, *Ecology and empire: environmental history of settler societies*, Melbourne University Press, pp. 102–121

Powell J M, 2000. 'Water management and the geographical imagination', in Dovers S (ed.), *Environmental history and policy: still settling Australia*, Oxford University Press, South Melbourne Victoria.

Productivity Commission, 2006. 'Rural water use and the environment: the role of market mechanisms', Productivity Commission Research Report, Australian Government, 11 August.

Quiggin J, 1988. 'Private and common property rights in the economics of the environment' *Journal of Economic Issues*, vol. 22, no. 4, pp. 1071–1087.

Quiggin J, 2001. 'Environmental economics and the Murray-Darling river system', *The Australian Journal of Agricultural and Resource Economics*, vol. 45, no. 1, pp. 67–94.

Savenije H HG, 2002. 'Why water is not an ordinary economic good, or why the girl is special', *Physics and Chemistry of the Earth* 27, pp. 741–744.

Shi T, 2006. 'Simplifying complexity: rationalising water entitlements in the Southern Connected River Murray System, Australia' *Agricultural Water Management*, vol. 86, pp. 229–239.

Smith D I, 1998. *Water in Australia: resources and management*, Oxford University Press, Melbourne .

Smith D I & Finlayson B, 'Water in Australia: its role in environmental degradation', in (eds.) Heathcote R L & Mabutt J A, 1988. *Land Water and People: Geographical Essays in Australian Resource Management*, Allen and Unwin, Sydney.

Spash C L, 2000. 'Ecosystems, contingent valuation and ethics: the case of wetland re-creation', *Ecological Economics*, vol. 34, no. 2, pp. 195–215.

Stewart J & Jones G, 2003. *Renegotiating the environment: the power of politics* The Federation Press.

Stroshane T, 2003. 'Water and technological politics in California', *Capitalism, Nature,* Socialism, vol. 14, no. 2, pp. 34–76.

Swyngedouw E, 2005. 'Dispossessing H$_2$O: the contested terrain of water privatization', *Capitalism, Nature, Socialism,* vol. 16, no. 1.

The Economist, 2003. 'Priceless', *The Economist*, vol. 368, no. 8333, p. 3–5.

Tidsell J G, 2001. 'The environmental impact of water markets: an Australian case-study', *Journal of Environmental Management,* vol. 62, pp. 113–120.

Turnbull M, 2007a. 'Government invests millions to further develop water trade', media release, The Hon Malcolm Turnbull MP, Minister for the Environment and Water Resources, 7 March.

Turnbull M, 2007b. 'Water Bill 2007: Speech, the Hon Malcolm Turnbull MP, Minister for the Environment and Water Resources', 8 August http://www.environment.gov.au/minister/env/2007/pubs/tr08aug07.pdf.

Ward F A & Michelsen A, 2002. 'The economic value of water in agriculture: concepts and policy application', *Water Policy* 4, vol. 4, pp. 423–446.

van Vuuren W & Roy P, 1993. 'Private and social returns from wetland preservation versus those from wetland conversion to agriculture', *Ecological Economics*, vol. 8, no. 3, pp. 289–305.

Vidal de Llobatera N, 2003. 'Water wars in Spain', *Capitalism, Nature, Socialism,* vol. 14, no. 3, pp. 159–161.

Watson A, 2003. 'Approaches to increasing river flows', *The Australian Economic Review*, vol. 36, no. 2, pp. 213–24.

Watson C, 1992. 'An ecologically unsustainable agriculture', in Lawrence G, Vanclay F & Furze B (eds.), *Agriculture, environment and society: contemporary issues for Australia*, Macmillan, South Melbourne.

Wentworth Group of Concerned Scientists, 2003. *Blueprint for a national water plan*, World Wild Life Fund Australia, Sydney, 31 July.

Woodward R T & Wui Y, 2001. 'The economic value of wetland services: a meta-analysis', *Ecological Economics*, vol. 37, no. 2, pp. 257–270.

World Business Council for Sustainable Development, 2006. 'Business in the world of water: WBCSD water scenarios to 2025', http://www.wbcsd.org/DocRoot/Q87vukbkb5fNnpbkbLUu/h20 -scenarios.pdf.

World Commission on Dams, 2000. *Dams and development: a new framework for decision*-making, Earthscan, London.

WWF, 2007a. 'World's top 10 rivers at risk', Wong C M, Williams C E, Pittock J, Collier U & Schelle P, WWF International. Gland, Switzerland. March.

WWF, 2007b. 'Making water: desalination: option or distraction for a thirsty world', WWF Global Freshwater Programme, Phil Dickie, June.

WWF, 2007c. 'Pipedreams?: Interbasin water transfers and water shortages', WWF Global Freshwater Programme, June.

Young M D & McColl J C, 2003. 'Robust reform: the case for a new water entitlement system for Australia', Policy Forum: Water Pricing and Availability, *The Australian Economic Review*, vol. 36, no. 2, pp. 225–34.

Young M D & McColl J C, 2004. 'The right to water: 'ownership' and responsibility', *Dialogue*, vol. 23, no. 3, pp. 4–18.

Young M D & McColl J C, 2007. 'The unmentionable option: is there a place for an across-the-board purchase?', Droplets no. 8, 22 July 2007, the University of Adelaide, http://www.myoung.net.au/ water/droplets/Over_allocation.doc.

Part 2
Scientific viewpoints

6

Management of water resources under uncertainty: what does the future hold?

R. Willem Vervoort

Abstract

Current predictions indicate that the climate in Australia will become more variable and extreme. This will increase pressure on fragile natural resources and sound water resource management will become increasingly important. Forecasting is therefore essential in both agriculture and natural resource management. Is the current hydrological science up to this task and what tools are available for Australia? Much of the current hydrological knowledge is grounded in the work on perennial and humid systems with virtually no real 'Australian hydrology', despite evidence of the unique nature of our semi-arid river systems. While simulation models have become ubiquitous in hydrological science, most are used for so-called backcasting, rather than forecasting. This means simulations are run based on existing daily climate data as future daily predictions are often unavailable and uncertain. Additionally, there is still a significant gap with respect to the data needs of distributed models and the actually available natural resource data. Models with fewer parameters have been advocated, taking full advantage of the information in the available streamflow data. However, the associated simplifications and assumptions also introduce model uncertainties, which should be based on sound systems knowledge. It is unclear how such uncertainties would propagate if the models are used for forecasting rather than backcasting and perturbed under different management scenarios. Research into the temporal variability of model parameters, combined with probabilistic approaches to capture the non-linearity and variability of the Australian hydrological system will increase the ability to manage the system into the future.

Introduction

The Australian climate is recognised as one of the most variable in the world (Meinke et al 2003). Given that stream flow is an expression of the rainfall signal, Australian stream flow is also among the most variable in the world (McMahon et al 1992). The latest International Panel of Climate Change assessment foreshadows a significant decrease in water availability in Eastern Australia (IPCC 2007), and the most recent national climate change predictions indicate that the Australian climate will also become more variable (Preston & Jones 2006; Whetton et al 1993). There is also empirical evidence that droughts are becoming more severe, mainly due to changes in temperature (Nicholls 2004). The higher variability in climate implies that increased skill would be needed in forecasting for agricultural production and natural resource planning (Meinke & Stone 2005). Prediction of streamflow, for irrigation and drinking water management, and soil moisture balances, for crop production and irrigation efficiency, will have to be improved. The current drought and its impact on urban and rural water supplies (such as in Goulburn and on the Murray River) indicates that such forward planning is desperately needed. However, the question is on what hydrological scientific information is this forward thinking going to be based? For streamflow and the soil moisture balance, rainfall is the primary forcing variable, but it is the translation that makes prediction of the secondary variables difficult (Kundzewicz & Mata 2007). There is additional difficulty in defining river types, conditions and climatic events. For example, a concept such as drought is not easily defined (Alley 1984; Dracup, Lee & Paulson 1980), and this means that the prediction of drought with increasing variability will be even more difficult.

Much has already been produced in relation to the topic of climate change by colleagues in the field of meteorology and climatology, but it appears that little has been flowing on into the areas of hydrology and agrohydrology. This means that where climatological studies have combined with cropping and hydrological predictions, models have been used 'as is' (i.e. Chiew & McMahon 2002; Meinke & Stone 2005), and little time has been spent on reassessing the assumptions underlying the models. This chapter will concentrate on an investigation into the nature of hydrological knowledge in Australia and whether this allows us to face future challenges. There is no attempt to review all the literature on this topic. The work mainly focuses on the ability to make hydrological predictions using simulation models under a changing climate.

Australian hydrology

The hydrology of Australia has been identified as being unique in the world (McMahon et al 1992) and is characterised by very low runoff coefficients and high coefficients of variation. Following the classification made by Uys and O'Keeffe (1997), most Australian rivers are episodic, ephemeral or non-seasonal variable, meaning that they can be dry for any length of time during the year. This uniqueness is partly driven by the fact that the Australian environment is mostly arid and semi-arid, which leads to strongly non-linear and highly variable systems. These systems have not been highlighted as much in the hydrological literature as their perennial humid variant. This might be partly due to the difficulty of the topic, partly due to the spatial distribution of hydrologists and partly due to the fact that water resource management of humid rivers is an easier target. While Australian literature has very early recognised that this type of hydrology was different and dominated in many areas of Australia (Pilgrim, Chapman & Doran 1988; Srikanthan & McMahon 1980b; Watkins 1969), this has not led to a significant body of hydrological work, specifically aimed at 'Australian Hydrology'.

The major thinking in terms of hydrology and the structure of models is based on ideas developed between 1940 and 1960 in the USA and Great Britain (e.g. Beven 2004; Dunne & Black 1970; Freeze and Harlan 1969). The structure of most hydrological models and conceptualised systems can therefore easily be traced back to the work of Horton, Dunne and Freeze and possibly Klemes (Klemes 1978). Much of the traditional hydrology highlights the importance of groundwater driven baseflow (Beven 2001), a component which delivers the persistence and continuity in much of the perennial streamflow. In contrast, semi-arid hydrology is characterised by a rapid response of the streamflow to rainfall and only very little persistence (Fig. 6.1). Most Australian rivers are therefore characterised by long periods of no-flow, indicating that the groundwater input is negligible or inconsistent (McMahon & Finlayson 2003). Such a lack of persistence (or baseflow) creates a river system in which streamflow seems almost random and this makes prediction more of a challenge (Pilgrim, Chapman & Doran 1988; Srikanthan and McMahon 1980a; Srikanthan & McMahon 1980b). Most of the hydrological literature discussing Australian catchments builds on

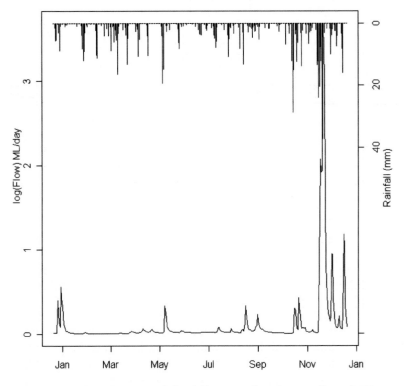

Figure 6.1 Logarithms base 10 of the daily streamflow in megaliters (ML) per day (left axis) and rainfall in mm (right axis) for a semi-arid catchment in northen NSW. Streamflow responds quickly to rainfall, but is a somewhat subdued and delayed reflection of the rainfall. Rainfall is the primary forcing variable, while streamflow is the secondary variable. The flow is plotted on a log scale which exaggerates the low flow behaviour.

the concepts derived from the US and Europe and applies these to the Australian environment. This means that often papers emphasise the contribution of groundwater to the stream flow (e.g. Bari & Smettem 2006; Farmer, Sivapalan & Jothityangkoon 2003; Keith 2004; McMahon & Finlayson 2003; Peck & Hatton 2003; Vaze et al 2004), even though this is unlikely in a semi-arid environment (Pilgrim, Chapman & Doran 1988). Australian books aimed at hydrological practitioners also spend considerable time on the topic of 'baseflow separation' and little discussion on semi-arid processes (Grayson et al 1996; Salama 1998; Zhang, Walker & Flemming 2002).

There are two main issues which make semi-arid hydrology particularly challenging:

- The highly non-linear response of runoff to rainfall. Depending on the moisture status of the catchment, a similar amount of rainfall can generate totally different levels of runoff (Pilgrim, Walker & Doran 1988). This leads to difficulties in simulating rainfall runoff response.

- The nature and variability of the transmission losses (Dunkerley & Brown 1999; Knighton & Nanson 1994; Lange 2005). This leads to difficulty in simulating the routing of streams through a catchment.

On the other hand, there is a body of work, mainly related to the ecology and geomorphology of rivers in semi-arid regions of Australia, that recognises the variability and unpredictability of flow (Costelloe et al 2003; Dunkerley & Brown 1999; Knighton & Nanson 1994, 2001; Thoms & Sheldon 2000; Young, Brandis & Kingsford 2006). Other authors have highlighted the unique connection in time between streamflow and the El-Niño Southern Oscillation signal (ENSO), particularly in south eastern Australia (Chiew et al 1998; Piechota et al 1998). The ENSO is related to the southern oscillation index (SOI) and the annual fluctuation in temperature of the ocean water of the coast of South America. High ocean temperatures near South America are related to negative SOI indices and are generally related to dry years or drought conditions in Australia and vice versa (see http://www.bom.gov.au/climate/enso/). As a result, the amount of streamflow appears to follow the SOI signal up and down with about a 3-month lag (Chiew et al 1998; Piechota et al 1998). However, all stations used for the above-mentioned research were relatively close to the ocean in the zone defined as humid (Watkins 1969), with no stations in the more arid interior. If the aridity and with it the variability of the rainfall increases, drought signatures persist longer in soil moisture (Entekhabi, Rodriguez-Iturbe & Bras 1992). As riverflow will only occur at high soil moisture levels (i.e. there has to be 'too much' water) this would decrease the connection to the ENSO signal, meaning the river flows would either not follow this signal as strongly, or not at all.

Overall, it seems that the uniqueness of Australian hydrology is recognised, but that researchers have struggled to come to terms with these difficulties in terms of conceptual models and predictions. Development of future management will need to be based on a good understanding of the hydrological system. Further research into semi-arid hydrological systems and their behaviour under a range of conditions appears to be an important need for Australia.

Simulation models and forecasting

To be able to develop management decisions, simulation models are key as they allow predictions into the future. There has been much debate in hydrological science on how well models actually predict the behaviour of a system and the uncertainty that is related to the predictions of models (Beven 2002; Kirchner 2006; Silberstein 2006). In general, the conclusion is that while models are not perfect, they are the best possible means of studying systems. Basically, hydrological models are based on the conceptual image a scientist has of the catchment and this is translated into a set of mathematical equations and computer codes. The model needs three types of data: the first are boundary conditions and initial conditions, the second are parameters, which are generally considered to be time-invariant and define the internal processes in the system; the third are variables, which force the behaviour of the model (such as rainfall and potential evaporation). The model output is then compared against observed data and the parameters in the model are adjusted (this is the process of model calibration) to get the best possible match between observed and predicted data.

Hydrological models aim to forecast the variable of interest (in most cases stream flow or groundwater) for management purposes. This means they attempt to look into the future to see how different actions will influence the variable. Interestingly, most scenarios and hydrological models only backcast (or hindcast) that is; the forcing variables (i.e. rainfall) tend to be based on existing measurements, with the argument that these data are more reliable (Stauffacher et al 2003; Tuteja et al 2003; Vertessy et al 1993). This means that the models tend to simulate a different realisation of the current or historic time, rather than look into the future. This approach appears to be the most common in analyses of management impact on stream flow.

A different approach is taken by most research interested in climate change. In those cases the output of global circulation models (GCM) is downscaled to the scale of interest and the different climate scenarios are pushed through hydrological models (Jones et al 2006), often calibrated earlier using historical data (e.g. Chiew et al 1995). While this seems a better approach, as it recognises the fact that we cannot use the current climate to predict future impacts, it still has some problems. One important issue is that the downscaled GCM data for the future is not very accurate and daily estimates are difficult to obtain (Chiew 2006).

Time invariance of parameters

Another issue relates to the underlying assumptions on which hydrological models are based. Different rainfall runoff model structures have different responses to changes in rainfall (Boorman & Sefton 1997; Jones et al 2006). Depending on how the conceptual rainfall-runoff model is structured and how this is translated into code, the runoff response to rainfall will differ. Apart from the more complex distributed groundwater and surface water models, most hydrological models consider parameters to be time invariant. This means the 'calibrated' parameter values of the model will be based on historic data, and assumed to undergo no change into the future. However, the parameters in hydrological models are generally coupled to some conceptual representation of the soil or vegetation system or the routing parameters in the catchment. Studies to investigate the sensitivity and uncertainty of parameters help explain some of the model outcomes (Boorman and Sefton 1997; Jones et al 2006), but this does not recognise a further problem (Boorman & Sefton 1997; Chiew et al 1995), which is caused by the coupling and feedbacks between climate, vegetation, soil moisture and streamflow.

Because soil moisture and stream flow are dependent secondary variables (Fig 6.1), the behaviour is dependent on changes in vegetation and climate. The work by Eagleson and Entekhabi (Eagleson 1978; Eagleson & Segarra 1985; Entekhabi, Rodriguez-Iturbe & Bras 1992) has highlighted that such feedback loops can be strong, and this would undoubtedly influence results (Chiew et al 1995; Farmer, Sivapalan & Jothityangkoon 2003). What this means is that it is highly unlikely that parameters are time invariant, and this is often demonstrated during calibration and validation (e.g. Kirchner 2006). During calibration, the model parameters are in fact adjusted to the 'mean' value of the time series of the 'true' parameters, or in other words, the calibrated parameters can be seen as the expected value of the parameter distribution. While this is recognised in model calibration and is the basis of the thinking behind equifinality (Beven 2002), the implications of this for forecasting under climate change scenarios seem to be less recognised. For forecasting under changed climate the variability of the parameters in time needs to be predicted.

Of course, it is difficult to predict how model parameters will change into the future. I am not advocating that an 'evolutionary model' should be created that will adapt to changes. Such a model would be too complex and the number of relationships and parameters within the model would not allow a calibration or validation (Kirchner 2006). However, as a minimum requirement, long-term forecasts should analyse whether the distribution of parameters during the calibration period will be the same as the distribution during the forecast period (e.g. Evans & Schreider 2002). Given the complexity in the catchment scale processes and the number of feedback loops, this will probably not be true.

Research into the variability of model parameters in time, their sensitivity to climatic and weather indices and their biophysical explanation has so far not been extensively attempted. The work by Evans and Schreider (2002) and Wilby (2005) are possibly the only papers making an attempt. The analysis by Evans and Schreider (2002) (which found no significant change in parameters) was limited to only one catchment on the coastal fringe in Western Australia, while their climate change modelling included six catchments. In contrast, the work by Wilby (2005) is more thorough, but the work was done on the Thames River in England.

What is needed are relationships that will predict changes in the model parameters with time, climate or weather, such as southern oscillation index (SOI), rainfall, temperature and carbon dioxide (CO_2) levels. This would thus extend the more common sensitivity analysis to actual predictive relationships. It seems somewhat contradictory: to use a model to predict the parameters of a model. However, empirical relationships, kriging, pedotransfer functions (McBratney et al 2002) and meta modelling (Haberlandt, Krysanova & Bardossy 2002) are already established approaches to derive or integrate parameters for simulation modelling. Though these methods mostly predict spatial model parameters, it justifies the study of a similar approach in time-dependent parameters. This explicitly recognises the dynamic nature of many of the soil and vegetation parameters and their influence on the hydrology of a catchment.

Distributed models and data

In semi-arid and arid catchments, simulation modelling is made difficult by the earlier mentioned non-linearities. For example, while the long-term non-linearity in rainfall-runoff can sometimes be accounted for by equating the mass balances (Jakeman & Hornberger 1993), this would not account for the possible dynamic nature of such a non-linearity. This can only be accounted for by explicitly modelling the water balance and drying in the catchment, such as by using and predicting the catchment moisture balance (Croke & Jakeman 2004; Evans & Jakeman 1998).

One approach to improve the modelling outcomes in arid and semi-arid catchments would be to increase the complexity of the model and to explicitly include the different processes. This is the direction in which many hydrological models have gone, following the concepts developed by Freeze and Harlan (1969). There are, however, difficulties with this: such an increase in complexity has to be matched with an equivalent increase in data available for parameterisation, calibration and validation. While some aspects can be included with few additional parameters (Croke & Jakeman 2004), more complex interactions and processes would require more data.

The difficulty is that Australia and semi-arid areas in general are relatively data poor. Again, this is partly due to the extensive nature of the human activities in such areas, which means they are less densely populated and economically less important. In addition, the large land mass of Australia has also limited data collection, purely due to the related costs. Only in recent years, with the development and availability of satellite and remote sensing data, do we see an increase in data availability. However, the relationships between remotely sensed data and hydrologically important variables are still tenuous (Schmugge et al 2002; Western et al 1999). Increased calibration and validation data in the form of streamflow is also difficult as most gauge records are not long enough to cover all variability. The fact that zero flows cannot be used as calibration data and that these occur frequently does not help the situation (Pilgrim, Chapman & Doran 1988).

Complexity or simplicity

There are generally two reasons for increasing the complexity in a model. The first is to increase the accuracy of the predictions; the second is to gain more insight into the processes. In the context of climate change and future predictions, the first seems more important. However, a range of authors have argued, and demonstrated, that increased complexity does not equate to increased accuracy of prediction (e.g. Beven 2001; Grayson, Moore & McMahon 1992; Jakeman & Hornberger 1993; Silberstein 2006; Sivapalan 2003). This has led to several researchers arguing for a so-called 'top-down' approach, which starts with a basic model of the catchment and increases in complexity when necessary (Farmer, Sivapalan & Jothityangkoon 2003; Sivapalan et al 2003; Young 2003), purely based on the information in the flow data set. This is attractive in terms of decreasing the need for parameters and delivering statistically sound predictions and their uncertainties. In addition, each increase in complexity should deliver additional information about the behaviour of the catchment (Sivapalan 2003).

While we can use statistics, such as the Akaike Information Criterion to maximise the parsimony in models, this comes at a cost not quantified in the statistic. This assumes that the understanding of the hydrological processes is sufficient to develop conceptual models. The simpler models might include conceptual simplification, which might or might not represent the true complexity and behaviour of the system. If this is not the case then calibration is no more than extensive curve fitting, which lowers the confidence in the outcomes. While the model might be more parsimonious in the calibration period and fit the data better, this does not always translate to a validation period (Refsgaard & Henriksen 2004). This can often be seen in the difficulty in validating models; while a model can often be well calibrated, validation is not easily achieved (Refsgaard & Henriksen 2004). Understandably, if the model is subsequently perturbed with quite different climate data from a climate change scenario, there is no guarantee that the historical parameter data are valid for the future periods (e.g. Boorman & Sefton 1997; Wilby 2005). Many of the papers using the "top-down" approach are limited to calibration (e.g. Farmer, Sivapalan & Jothityangkoon 2003; Jothityangkoon, Sivapalan & Farmer 2001; Son & Sivapalan 2007), although the last paper uses a range of different data (such as water quality and quantity). Only solid conceptual understanding will allow simplification of complex models, but conversely the understanding can only be achieved using more complex and data-rich models, and this needs to be regularly checked and updated.

Example 1: Soil moisture balances

Part of the inspiration for this chapter was given by a debate about the occurrence of drought and the definition of drought in northern NSW. The debate focussed on the question whether it was the rainfall deficiency or the rainfall variability and timing that defined the occurrence of drought. From an agricultural or natural resource planning perspective the latter is more important than the former. This means that the definition of drought is somewhat nebulous and the future prediction of drought even more so. The literature is quite similarly undecided about the definition of drought (Alley 1984; Byun & Wilhite 1999; Dracup, Lee & Paulson 1980; Hisdal & Tallaksen 2000; Whetton et al 1993) and different calculations procedures have been suggested to calculate the occurrence of drought. These procedures differ depending on the perspective, for example, we can define a hydrological, an agricultural and a socioeconomic drought (Dracup, Lee & Paulson 1980). An 'exceptional circumstances', declaration by the federal and state governments in Australia can be seen as a declaration of socioeconomic drought (Donnelly, Freer & Moore 1998).

For future agricultural management, it seems most important to focus on the probability (likelihood) of a soil moisture deficiency at critical times. Soil moisture deficiency has often been suggested as a more objective agricultural drought criterion than rainfall deficiency, and calculation examples have been developed (Byun & Wilhite 1999; Hisdal & Tallaksen 2000). The well-known Palmer Drought Index is also based on some sort of soil water balance (Alley 1984). The problem in this case is the issue of regionalisation. While it is not difficult to calculate the changes in soil moisture over time at a point in the landscape, it becomes difficult to extend these results to a larger region or across regions (as the Palmer drought index attempts) as spatial variability of soils and vegetation would affect the results. By using a probabilistic system, such differences can, of course, be accounted for through the related uncertainty.

The calculation of statistical moisture distributions is not new; in fact there are a series of papers dealing with this concept beginning with Eagleson (1978). The concept has later been extended (Entekhabi, Rodriguez-Iturbe & Bras 1992; Laio et al 2001; Milly 2001; Rodriguez-Iturbe 2000) to allow calculation of crossing probabilities and plant water stress. The advantage of these approaches is that they are based on an analytical model and this allows direct calculations of distribution of values (the probability density function) and the mean and variance of the variable in question. These properties give a summary of the values, the probability density function gives a graphical overview of the distribution of values, which can also be described by such statistical parameters as the mean, variance and skewness. It also allows the calculation of the likelihood (probability) that something might or might not occur. In this section, an example of the calculation of the probability of a certain soil moisture status will be given for two different soils in two locations in NSW.

Methods

Two rainfall datasets from 1901–1998 were extracted from Rainman V4.3 (Queensland DPI, Brisbane, QLD) for a site in the north west of New South Wales (NSW) (Warialda Creek station 418016) and a site in central west NSW (Lachlan River station 412063). Monthly evaporation data were obtained from the Bureau of Meteorology website (http://www.bom.gov.au). The two sites have some differences in their distributions of rainfall and evaporation (Table 6.1), with the Lachlan site being slightly higher in rainfall and daily evaporation, but with a narrower and less skewed distribution.

Table 6.1 Statistics of rainfall and evaporation for Warialda and Lachlan stations used in example 1

	Warialda	Lachlan
Mean daily rainfall depth	1.85	1.95
Mean dry spell length	0.27	0.38
Variance daily rainfall depth	33.2	26.7
Skew daily rainfall depth	6.58	5.61
Mean daily Evaporation	2.73	3.12
Variance daily Evaporation	2.14	1.97

A soil moisture balance model, such as suggested by Milly (2001), was used to calculate the daily 'relative' soil saturation (scale of 0 to 1) for both locations. The relative soil saturation (s) is defined as:

$$s = \frac{\theta - \theta_w}{\theta_s - \theta_w} \tag{1}$$

Where, θ is the soil water content, θ_w is the water content at the wilting point and θ_s is the saturated water content. This was used to derive the numerical probability density function of the relative soil saturation for both locations on two representative soil types (medium light clay and clay) and two different profile depths (Zr) (Table 6.2). This means, daily values of soil moisture were calculated for 96 climate years and these were summarised in the probability density function.

Table 6.2 Parameters for the Milly (2001) soil moisture balance model for the medium light clay (MLC) and clay used.

	Medium light clay (MLC)	Clay
Zr (mm)	500, 1000	500, 1000
N	0.43	0.37
s1	0.86	0.72

Note: The parameter Zr represents the root or profile depth, n is the porosity and s1 is the soil saturation at which runoff occurs.

The rainfall datasets were also used to derive the mean dry-spell length and the mean rainfall depth assuming the rainfall events follow a Poisson distribution (Rodriguez-Iturbe, Gupta & Waymire 1984) (Table 6.1). This is then used to derive the theoretical probability density function of the relative soil saturation (Milly 2001). In this case, the daily values were not actually calculated as the values for the probability density function can be calculated directly.

Results

All the probability densities functions (pdfs) for the relative soil saturation indicated a strong peak (maximum) at the dry end (Fig. 6.2). This means that the soil is 'most likely' very dry. Note that 0 does not mean that the soil is bone dry, rather in this model it indicates that the soil is at the dry end of the soil saturation spectrum (wilting point) and water available for plants will be very limited. The strong peak at the dry end would be expected, given that both these areas can be classified as semi-arid.

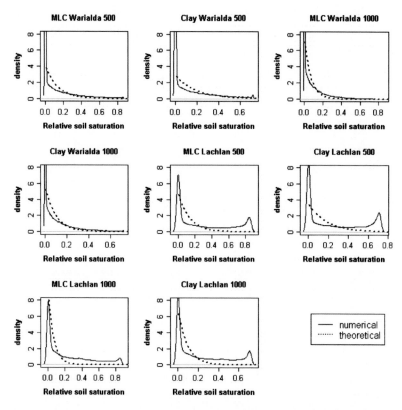

Figure 6.2 Numerical and theoretical probability density functions (pdfs) for the two locations, different soil types and different root depths. The y-axis gives the relative frequency of occurrence with large values indicating more probable values. A large peak (maximum) can be observed at the dry end (around zero), particularly for Warialda, but particularly the graphs for the Lachlan location indicate a bimodal structure, with a second (smaller) peak near saturation, indicating two preferred soil moisture states (Western, Blöschl & Grayson 2001).

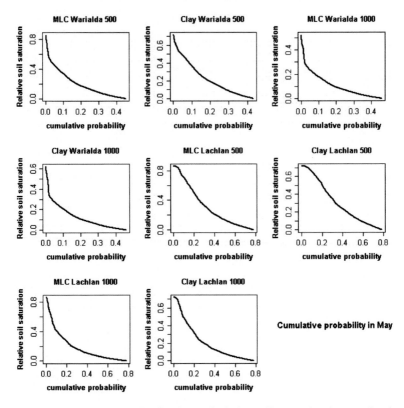

Figure 6.3 Cumulative distributions of relative soil saturation in May for the two locations and different soils and root depths. The results indicate that there is generally a low probability that the relative soil saturation would be above 0.5 (or half full moisture profile) at both locations.

The theoretical pdfs are even more skewed than the numerical pdfs, meaning that they indicate even stronger the fact that the soils are 'most likely' dry. The means and variances of the numerical distributions are much higher than the theoretical distributions, indicating that the theoretical distributions probably underestimate the probabilities (likelihood) of the soil being wet and overestimate the probability associated with the dry end. However, overall the shape of the theoretical pdfs is similar to the numerical pdfs, particular for the Warialda location.

Interestingly, the Lachlan distributions are bimodal with a second (smaller) peak occurring at the wet end (Fig. 6.2). This indicates that the soil will also be at the wet end for significant intervals, but does not spend much time at the intermediate levels (Western, Blöschl & Grayson 2001). Similar responses for a semi-arid climate have also been indicated by Entekhabi, Rodriguez-Iturbe & Bras (1992) and this has been related to the fact that a significant shock is needed to move from a drought (low moisture) to a wetter regime and vice versa. The results indicate that the Warialda location is less likely to have significant soil moisture during the year and is more likely to have a dry profile. Overall the results indicate that, based on the data of the last century, the soil in Warialda has been more often dry than wet, while the Lachlan soils had a bit higher likelihood of having some soil moisture and this is also reflected in the means of the distributions (Table 6.3). This has, of course, serious implications for agricultural management. The theoretical means agree better with the numerical results in the drier location (Warialda, Table 3), again indicating the underestimation of the soil saturation. The fact that the numerical pdfs in the drier location agree reasonably with the theoretical pdfs means that the theoretical pdfs could also be used to calculate broad statistics for the average relative soil saturation status.

Table 6.3 Statistics for the numerical and theoretical pdfs for the different soil types and root depths at the Warialda and Lachlan stations.

	Soil	Zr	Mean numerical	Mean theoretical	Variance numerical	Variance theoretical
Warialda	MLC	500	0.12	0.07	0.04	0.014
	Clay	500	0.12	0.10	0.03	0.025
	MLC	1000	0.08	0.04	0.02	0.003
	Clay	1000	0.08	0.05	0.02	0.007
Lachlan	MLC	500	0.34	0.08	0.11	0.014
	Clay	500	0.30	0.11	0.08	0.026
	MLC	1000	0.29	0.04	0.08	0.004
	Clay	1000	0.27	0.06	0.07	0.007

Note: MLC is medium light clay, Zr is the root depth.

The same results can also be analysed using a cumulative distribution. This allows the estimation of the probability of having a certain soil saturation level (for example needed for planting crops or to estimate runoff potential of predicted rainfall) for the different soils. In relation to planting crops, the most crucial time for wheat production is the soil moisture status in May, when most growers would like a full- or half-full soil moisture profile for planting. Using the data from the soil moisture balance and plotting the cumulative probabilities of relative soil saturation for the month of May, it is clear that the prospects of having sufficient moisture for wheat planting (i.e. 50% full or higher, or above 0.5 on the y-axis) are in fact quite slim (Fig. 6.4). Probabilities are generally small (below 20%), indicating that, in essence, sufficient soil moisture for planting can only be expected one in five years. Given the limited number of soils and the simple soil moisture model applied, this is of course a somewhat uncertain estimate.

The analysis however indicates two major points. The bimodal behaviour indicates that the soil moisture status basically revolves around two states, one wet and one dry (i.e. Western, Blöschl & Grayson 2001). Significant weather changes (such as a 'La Niña' or 'El Niño' event) are needed to move from one state to the other. This also means that after a prolonged dry period, there remains a significant probability of returning to the dry soil moisture status even after some rain. Secondly, the use of the cumulative probability distribution allows an assessment of the 'average' risk for agricultural production in the area. It indicates the probability of a certain moisture profile in the future, purely based on the historical climate data and the soil properties.

Under climate change, the distributions would of course shift, but as the model does not involve any calibration, but is based on the 'average' soil characteristics in the area, there would be little change in the soil parameters. The difficulty of generating representative daily rainfall data from climate change scenarios to drive the model remains (Chiew 2006). However, while in this case the rainfall amount, as well as the daily distribution is important, a stochastic realisation of the rainfall data would be sufficient.

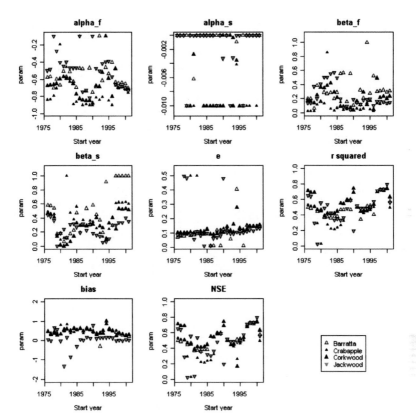

Figure 6.4 Variation in calibrated parameters for five-year moving windows for four of the catchments in the Karuah Hydrology Research catchments from 1976 to 2005. Parameters are plotted against the start year of the moving window. Some of the parameters are clearly highly variable in time, while others are relatively stable.

Example 2: Temporal variability of model parameters

NSW State Forests has a long-term monitoring program on a series of research catchments on the mid-north coast of NSW, near Chichester on the headwaters of the Telegherry River. These catchments, the

Karuah Hydrology Research, were originally set up to study the effect of logging on catchment water yields (Cornish 1993). Some of the catchments were logged in 1983, while others have never been logged (Cornish 1993). Two earlier papers describe the changes in the catchment water yield and the changes in evapotranspiration as a result of the logging treatments (Cornish 1993; Cornish & Vertessy 2001). This example will not research that aspect, but the good quality streamflow data for the catchments, which is available from 1976 to 2005, creates an opportunity to study the temporal variability of parameters in a rainfall-runoff model.

Methods

The data were subdivided into five-year moving windows and a rainfall runoff model, the CMD version of IHACRES (Croke & Jakeman 2004; Evans & Jakeman 1998), was used to predict the streamflow over each period for the first four catchments. Of these, three have been logged, while the Crabapple catchment has never been logged (Cornish 1993). Maximum temperature was used as a proxy for potential evaporation (Croke & Jakeman 2004; Evans & Schreider 2002) and rainfall was sourced from the nearby Chichester dam weather station. The CMD version of the IHACRES model has a total of eight parameters that describe the streamflow response of the catchment. Three of the parameters can be readily fixed (Croke and Jakeman 2004) and these are: f, which is the ratio between the flow and the stress thresholds, $d1$ (mm), which is the flow threshold and n, the balance between the two linear segments of the drainage equation. Of the other five parameters, four describe the balance between quick flow (f) (generally direct runoff) and slow flow (s) (often groundwater input): alpha f and alpha s, the decay parameters (unitless) for the quick and slow flow and beta f and beta s, parameters (unitless) which determine the fractions of quick and slow flow in the final output (for a full description see Croke & Jakeman 2004). The final parameter is e (unitless or mm/$^\circ$C), which determines the transformation of the daily evaporation (or daily maximum temperature) to evapotranspiration.

Following the suggestions by Croke and Jakeman (2004), the last five mentioned parameters were calibrated (Table 6.4) using a five-year moving window over the data (i.e. 1976–1981, 1977–1982, 1978–1983, etc.). This means 26 five-year datasets were used, which all partly overlapped with their neighbours. Parameter uncertainty was not analysed here, but this could add additional complexity (Wilby 2005). The parameters were calibrated by matching the observed flow data to the predicted flow data and by maximising the Nash-Sutcliffe Efficiency (NSE). The NSE is a standard measure for goodness of fit in hydrology and is defined as 1 minus the ratio of the variance of the observed minus predicted data divided by the variance of the observed data (Beven 2001):

$$NSE = 1 - \frac{\sigma_e}{\sigma_o} \qquad (2)$$

Values of NSE close to 1 indicate a good fit, while 0 or negative values indicate that the model is no better than fitting the average value.

Table 6.4 Overview of calibration parameters for the CMD IHACRES model.

Parameter	Initial value	Upper bound	Lower bound
alpha f (-)	-0.7	-0.1	-1
alpha s (-)	-0.01	-1E-10	-0.01
beta f (-)	0.5	1	0.001
beta s (-)	0.5	1	0.001
e (mm ^{o}C^{-1})	0.15	1	0.01
f	0.93	Fixed	
$d1$ (mm)	200	Fixed	
n	0.1	Fixed	

Note: The f (ratio of the flow and stress thresholds, $d1$ (the flow threshold) and n (the balance between the two linear segments of the drainage equation) parameters were fixed (Croke & Jakeman 2004).

Results

Some of the calibrations of the model were not very good with NSE values ranging from negative (indicating no fit) to 0.79 (indicating a good fit) (Fig 6.4). This 'goodness of fit' is also expressed by the r-squared (which indicates the correlation between observed and predicted) and the bias (in mm, which indicates how much the model over or under predicts) (Fig. 6.4). However most of the fitted parameters indicate temporal variability (Fig. 6.4). Given that some of the calibration results were quite low, it means that the results of this study should be interpreted with some caution.

The variation in some of the parameters (such as the quick flow parameters, alpha f and beta f) is quite substantial (Fig. 6.4). In practice this would translate in varying amounts of quick flow (or streamflow which quickly responds to rainfall) being predicted over time. This variation is no different for the catchments which were logged and the catchment which was not logged (Crabapple). The lowest variance is in the Barrata catchment, which also had the lowest change in water yield following logging (Cornish 1993). In contrast, the unlogged Crabapple catchment has the highest variation. This already indicates that the assumption of temporal parameter stability is clearly untenable, even without the land use effects included in these data. Similar variation in parameters in time in rainfall-runoff modelling were also found in a calibration and validation example for the Thames River (Wilby 2005) and is often encountered when attempting to validate models, indicating that this result is not isolated.

Some interesting points can be observed from the data. The variance is largest in the quick flow parameters alpha f and beta f, which describe how fast and what fraction of the runoff directly responds to rainfall. The variation in the alpha s parameter is the lowest, but this might be partly caused by the fact that the parameter was only allowed to vary over a small range during the calibration (Table 6.4).

Another interesting fact is the low calibration results obtained for all catchments in the 1980s (around 1985). This was the period that most of the catchments were logged (Cornish 1993), but it also includes the drought in that period (1980) and the period right after, which included high flows (1983–1985) (Cornish 1993). During this period, the model has difficulty in predicting the observed data in all catchments, including the catchment that was not logged. The low calibration results (and related change in the alpha f and beta s parameters) could be caused by a wide range of landscape and climate properties, and this in itself would be an indication of parameter variability in time (Fig. 6.4). It could also be a case of measurement uncertainty, with the results reflecting possible inaccuracies in the data in that period, as the logging activities might have disturbed some of the measurements.

Interestingly, a slight positive trend with time can be observed in the e parameter (Fig. 6.4). This parameter is related to evapotranspiration from the catchment (Croke and Jakeman 2004), with increasing e indicating an increase in the predicted evapotranspiration. The slow increase after logging in 1983 is not surprising, as the regrowth would increase evapotranspiration (Cornish 1993). However the e parameter for the unlogged Crabapple catchment also increases and the increase is over the whole period of measurement (both before and after logging), which would not be expected. The results are therefore possibly some indication of climate effects at a much longer time scale. This could indicate that temporal parameter variability itself can be a tool for investigating long-term climatic trends or cycles.

Summary and discussion

Climate change will create some significant challenges for Australia in terms of water, natural resources and agricultural management. These challenges will have to be anticipated to be managed, and this anticipation can best be based on solid simulation modelling results as these offer the best possibility to predict the future. However there are some significant gaps in our current modelling capabilities. Many of those have been highlighted by other authors and have only been summarised in this chapter (Beven 2002; Chiew 2006; Kirchner 2006; Silberstein 2006). As a result, models are often calibrated, but not validated and most models are used in a back- or hind-casting manner which does not enable reliable predictions into the future for two reasons: the climate data are not representative of the future; and the parameters in the model cannot be assumed to be time invariant into the future (see example 2).

The problem is further exacerbated in Australia due to the low data availability in large areas and the non-linearities in the semi-arid system. Semi-arid hydrology and 'Australian hydrology' have, in addition, not been studied in a coordinated and focussed manner, with much of the current hydrological knowledge in Australia still strongly grounded in humid US and European theory. This appears to neglect the unique nature of the Australian systems.

For management purposes and due to data paucity, simplified models (Stauffacher et al 2003) have been advocated in Australia and this should also enable better calibration and lower parameter uncertainty (Sivapalan 2003; Young 2003). However, simplification of models can only occur if such simplification is valid and robust, based on the best possible conceptual models, and will account for most variability in the systems. The best example of a successful simplification is probably the so-called 'Zhang curves', which are relationships between rainfall and evapotranspiration for different vegetation types (Zhang, Dawes & Walker 2001). These curves are based on a thorough understanding of the underlying conceptual model, and give a quick estimate of the elements of the hydrological balance, such as deep drainage and runoff. Danger occurs when conceptual models are based on theory developed elsewhere, which is not checked against local observations. Too much simplification will mostly just deliver the long term expected value. Since 'variability' is the key word in Australian hydrology this may be problematic.

Overall, this seems to suggest that there are some significant difficulties in terms of using models for making predictions of future trends in water, natural resources and agriculture for Australia. The tools are still lacking, but there are also some deeper conceptual difficulties related to semi-arid hydrology, which partly relate to social training and distribution of hydrologists. Development of a uniquely Australian hydrological science which focuses specifically on the particular issues of semi-arid hydrology and is supported by a strong data collection program (Silberstein 2006) appears to be a prime need for the future.

Risk and probability are important concepts for future management. Being able to assess the risk or probability of success of certain management activities will assist in making policy decisions. Particularly in the case of highly variable properties, such as soil moisture or streamflow, probabilistic approaches can give a better indication of the most likely magnitudes of a property. In the case of soil moisture (example 1) it can be used to assess the probability of having sufficient moisture for planting or for completing a crop. The cumulative probability curve in the example clearly indicates that 'dry' is the norm, rather than the exception.

Future predictions with models hinge on the ability of the model to capture the main dynamics and feedbacks of the catchment under changing climate. One of the problems with forward prediction, real forecasting, is that any uncertainty in the conceptual model will be propagated in the forecast, even if the model is calibrated on historic data. This means that forecasting validation is essential, and should in particular cover a data set with a different variability to the calibration set. However, this is seldom done in practice, either due to unavailability of the validation data, or because it is just too difficult. What is demonstrated in example 2 is that assuming that parameters are variable in time might assist in developing better calibration and validation of models. Given the semi-arid character of the Australian hydrology and its strong non-linear response to rainfall, temporal variability of model parameters would be logical and the runoff response would be highly likely to change under different climatic conditions due to the strong vegetation response in semi-arid systems and the strong feedback between vegetation and hydrology. However, if there is a trend in the data with time, land use or with climate indices, then this might be translated into temporal variability of the parameters. This can be used to derive relationships, which can be applied in climate change scenarios. What isn't researched here is the interaction between parameter uncertainty and temporal parameter variability. Note that the former has been researched extensively, but the second has not attracted attention. The question is whether using time variant parameters will reduce parameter uncertainty. This will be the topic of further research in this area.

Conclusions

Climate change is creating some significant challenges in hydrology and these challenges are made even more difficult due to the unique non-linearity and high variability of the processes in Australian semi-arid systems. Development of a strong branch of Australian hydrology to focus on the specifics of such systems is needed. Two areas of further research in this context have been identified. Firstly, continuing to develop probabilistic approaches which can be translated easily into risk for management purposes and, secondly, investigating parameter variability in time and uncertainty in rainfall-runoff and other hydrological models to better manage the dynamics of semi-arid systems. Both of these are needed to develop credible scenarios for natural resource management under climate uncertainty.

Acknowledgements

The author would like to acknowledge Dr Ashley Webb from NSW State Forests for kindly sharing the data from the Karuah Hydrology Research, Floris van Ogtrop for fruitful discussions on these topics and Zara Farrell and Leah McKinnon at the BRG CMA for asking critical questions about drought and soil moisture balances.

References

Alley W M, 1984. The Palmer drought severity index: limitations and assumptions. *Journal of Climate and Applied Meteorology*, vol. 23, pp. 1100–1109.

Bari M A, Smettem KJ 2006. 'A conceptual model of daily water balance following partial clearing from forest to pasture', *Hydrology and Earth Systems Sciences*, vol. 10, pp. 321–337.

Beven K J, 2001. '*Rainfall-runoff modelling: the primer*', John Wiley & Sons, Chichester.

Beven K J, 2002. 'Towards and alternative blueprint for a physically based digitally simulated hydrologic response modelling system', *Hydrological Processes*, vol. 16, pp. 189–206.

Beven K J, 2004. 'Robert E. Horton's perceptual model of infiltration processes', *Hydrological Processes*, vol. 18, pp. 3447–3460.

Boorman D B & Sefton C E M, 1997. 'Recognising the uncertainty in the quantification of the effects of climate change on hydrological response', *Climatic change*, vol. 35, pp. 415–434.

Byun H R & Wilhite D A, 1999. 'Objective Quantification of Drought Severity and Duration', *Journal of Climate*, vol. 12, pp. 2747–2756.

Chiew F H S, 2006. 'An overview of methods for estimating climate change impact on runoff', in '3rd Hydrology and Water Resources Symposium', Launceston, TAS.

Chiew F H S & McMahon T A, 2002. 'Modelling the impact of climate change on Australian streamflow', *Hydrological Processes*, vol. 16, pp. 1235–1245.

Chiew F H S, Piechota T C, Dracup J A & McMahon T A, 1998. 'El Nino/Southern Oscillation and Australian rainfall, streamflow and drought: links and potential for forecasting', *Journal of Hydrology*, vol. 204, pp. 138–149.

Chiew F H S, Whetton P H, McMahon T A & Pittock A B, 1995. 'Simulation of the impacts of climate change on runoff and soil moisture in Australian catchments', *Journal of Hydrology* vol. 167, pp. 121–147.

Cornish P M, 1993. 'The effects of logging and forest regeneration on water yields in a moist eucalypt forest in New South Wales, Australia', *Journal of Hydrology*, vol. 150, pp. 301–322.

Cornish P M & Vertessy R A 2001. 'Forest age-induced changes in evapotranspiration and water yield in a eucalypt forest', *Journal of Hydrology*, vol. 242, pp. 43–63.

Costelloe J F, Grayson R B, Argent R M & McMahon T A, 2003. 'Modelling the flow regime of an arid zone floodplain river, Diamantina River, Australia', *Environmental Modelling & Software*, vol. 18, pp. 693–703.

Croke B F W & Jakeman A J, 2004. 'A catchment moisture deficit module for the IHACRES rainfall-runoff model', *Environmental Modelling & Software*, vol. 19, pp. 1–5.

Donnelly J R, Freer M & Moore A D, 1998. 'Using the GrassGro decision support tool to evaluate some objective criteria for the definition of exceptional drought' *Agricultural Systems*, vol. 57, pp. 301–313.

Dracup J A, Lee K S & Paulson Jr. E G, 1980. 'On the definition of droughts', *Water Resources Research*, vol. 16, pop. 297–302.

Dunkerley D & Brown K, 1999. 'Flow behaviour, suspended sediment transport and transmission losses in a small sub bank full flow event in an Australian desert stream', *Hydrological Processes*, vol. 13, pp. 1577–1588.

Dunne T & Black R D 1970. 'An experimental investigation of runoff production in permeable soils', *Water Resources Research*, vol. 6, pp. 478–490.

Eagleson P S, 1978. 'Climate, Soil and Vegetation: 1. Introduction to water balance dynamics', *Water Resources Research*, vol. 14, pp. 705–712.

Eagleson P S & Segarra R I, 1985. 'Water-limited equilibrium of Savanna vegetation systems', *Water Resources Research*, vol. 21, pp. 1483–1493.

Entekhabi D, Rodriguez-Iturbe I & Bras R L, 1992. 'Variability in large-scale water balance with land surface-atmosphere interaction', *Journal of Climate*, vol. 5, pp. 798–813.

Evans J P & Jakeman A J, 1998. 'Development of a simple, catchment-scale, rainfall-evapotranspiration-runoff model', *Environmental Modelling and Software*, vol. 13, pp. 385–393.

Evans J & Schreider S, 2002. 'Hydrological Impacts of Climate Change on Inflows to Perth, Australia', *Climatic change*, vol. 55, pp. 361–393.

Farmer D, Sivapalan M & Jothityangkoon C, 2003. 'Climate, soil, and vegetation controls upon the variability of water balance in temperate and semiarid landscapes: downward approach to water balance analysis', *Water Resources Research*, vol. 39, p. 1035.

Freeze R A & Harlan R L, 1969. 'Blueprint for a physically-based, digitally-simulated hydrologic response model', *Journal of Hydrology*, vol. 9, pp. 237–258.

Grayson R B, Argent R M, Nathan R J, McMahon T A & Mein R G, 1996. 'Hydrological recipes. Estimation techniques in Australian hydrology', CRC for Catchment Hydrology. Melbourne.

Grayson R B, Moore I D & McMahon T A, 1992. 'Physically based hydrologic modeling 2. Is the concept realistic', *Water Resources Research*, vol. 28, pp. 2659–2666.

Haberlandt U, Krysanova V & Bardossy A, 2002. 'Assessment of nitrogen leaching from arable land in large river basins: Part II: regionalisation using fuzzy rule based modelling', *Ecological Modelling*, vol. 150, pp. 277–294.

Hisdal H & Tallaksen L M, 2000. *Drought event definition*, Department of Geophysics, University of Oslo, Technical report no. 6, Blindern, Oslo, Norway.

IPCC, 2007. 'Climate change 2007: impacts, adaptation and vulnerability. Summary for policy makers', IPCC Secretariat, Geneva.

Jakeman A J & Hornberger G M, 1993. 'How much complexity is warranted in a rainfall-runoff model', *Water Resources Research*, vol. 29, pp. 2637–2649.

Jones R N, Chiew F H S, Boughton W C & Zhang L, 2006. 'Estimating the sensitivity of mean annual runoff to climate change using selected hydrological models', *Advances in Water Resources*, vol. 29, pp. 1419–1429.

Jothityangkoon C, Sivapalan M & Farmer D L, 2001. 'Process controls of water balance variability in a large semi-arid catchment: downward approach to hydrological model development', *Journal of Hydrology*, vol. 254, pp. 174–198.

Keith B, 2004. 'Robert E. Horton's perceptual model of infiltration processes', *Hydrological Processes*, vol. 18, pp. 3447–3460.

Kirchner J W, 2006. 'Getting the right answers for the right reasons: linking measurements, analyses and models to advance the science of hydrology', *Water Resources Research*, vol. 42, W03S04.

Klemes V, 1978. 'Physically based stochastic hydrologic analysis', *Advances in Hydroscience*, vol. 11, pp. 285–356.

Knighton A D & Nanson G C, 1994. 'Flow transmission along an arid zone anastomising river, Cooper Creek, Australia', *Hydrological Processes*, vol. 8, pp. 137–154.

Knighton A D & Nanson G C, 2001. 'An even-based approach to the hydrology of arid zone rivers in the Channel Country of Australia', *Journal of Hydrology*, vol. 254, pp. 102–123.

Kundzewicz Z W & Mata L J, 2007. 'Concept paper on cross-cutting theme: WATER', IPCC, Geneva.

Laio F, Porporato A, Ridolfi L & Rodriguez-Iturbe I, 2001. 'Plants in water-controlled ecosystems: active role in hydrologic processes and response to water stress: II. probabilistic soil moisture dynamics', *Advances in Water Resources*, vol. 24, pp. 707–723.

Lange J, 2005. 'Dynamics of transmission losses in a large arid stream channel', *Journal of Hydrology*, vol. 306, pp. 112–126.

McBratney A B, Minasny B, Cattle S R & Vervoort R W, 2002. 'From pedotransfer functions to soil inference systems', *Geoderma*, vol. 109, pp. 41–73.

McMahon T A & Finlayson B L, 2003. 'Droughts and anti-droughts: the low flow hydrology of Australian rivers', *Freshwater Biol*, vol. 48, pp. 1147–1160.

McMahon T A, Finlayson B L, Haines A T & Srikanthan R, 1992. *Global runoff – Contintental comparisons of annual flows and peak discharges*, Catena-verlag, Cremlingen-Destedt, Germany.

Meinke H & Stone R, 2005. 'Seasonal and inter-annual climate forecasting: the new tool for increasing preparedness to climate variability and change in agricultural planning and operations', *Climatic change*, vol. 70, pp. 221–253.

Meinke H, Wright W, Hayman P & Stephens D, 2003. 'Managing cropping systems in variable climates', in Pratley J E (ed.), *Principles of field crop production*, pp. 26–77, Oxford University Press, Oxford.

Milly P C D, 2001. 'A minimalist probabilistic description of root zone soil water', *Water Resources Research*, vol. 37, pp. 457–463.

Nicholls N, 2004. 'The changing nature of Australian droughts', *Climatic change*, vol. 63, pp. 323–336.

Peck A J & Hatton T, 2003. 'Salinity and the discharge of salts from catchments in Australia' *Journal of Hydrology*, vol. 272, pp. 191–202.

Piechota T C, Chiew F H S, Dracup J A & McMahon T A, 1998. 'Seasonal streamflow forecasting in eastern Australia and the El-

Nino-Southern Oscillation', *Water Resources Research*, vol. 34, pp. 3035–3044.

Pilgrim D H, Chapman T G & Doran D G, 1988. 'Problems of rainfall-runoff modelling in arid and semiarid regions', *Hydrological Sciences Journal*, vol. 33, pp. 379–400.

Preston B L & Jones R N, 2006. *Climate change impacts on Australia and the benefits of early action to reduce global greenhouse gas emissions*, CSIRO Maritime and Atmospheric Research, Aspendale, Victoria.

Refsgaard J C & Henriksen H J, 2004. 'Modelling guidelines – terminology and guiding principles', *Advances in Water Resources*, vol. 27, pp. 71–82.

Rodriguez-Iturbe I, 2000. 'Ecohydrology: a hydrologic perspective of climate-soil-vegetation dynamics', *Water Resources Research*, vol. 36, pp. 3–9.

Rodriguez-Iturbe I, Gupta V K & Waymire E, 1984. 'Scale considerations in the modelling of temporal rainfall', *Water Resources Research*, vol. 20, pp. 1611–1619.

Salama R B, 1998. 'Part 1. Physical and chemical techniques for discharge studies', CSIRO Publishing, Collingwood, Victoria.

Schmugge T J, Kustas W P, Ritchie J C, Jackson T J & Rango A, 2002. 'Remote sensing in hydrology', *Advances in Water Resources*, vol. 25, pp. 1367–1385.

Silberstein R P, 2006. 'Hydrological models are so good, do we still need data?', *Environmental Modelling & Software*, vol. 21, pp. 1340–1352.

Sivapalan M, 2003. 'Process complexity at the hillslope scale, process simplicity at the watershed scale: is there a connection?', *Hydrological Processes*, vol. 17, pp. 1037–1041.

Sivapalan M, Blöschl G, Zhang L & Vertessy R A, 2003. 'Downward approach to hydrological prediction', *Hydrological Processes*, vol. 17, pp. 2101–2111.

Son K & Sivapalan M, 2007. 'Improving model structure and reducing parameter uncertainty in conceptual water balance models through the use of auxiliary data', *Water Resources Research*, vol. 43, W01415.

Srikanthan R & McMahon T A, 1980a. 'Stochastic generation of monthly flows for ephemeral streams', *Journal of Hydrology*, vol. 47, pp. 19–40.

Srikanthan R & McMahon T A, 1980b. 'Stochastic time series modelling of arid zone streamflows', *Hydrological sciences bulletin*, vol. 25, pp. 423–434.

Stauffacher M, Walker G, Dawes W, Zhang L & Dyce P, 2003. 'Dryland salinity management: can simple catchment-scale models provide reliable answers? An Australian case study', CSIRO L&W, 27/03, Canberra.

Thoms M C & Sheldon F, 2000. 'Lowland rivers: an Australian introduction', *Regulated rivers: research and management*, vol. 16, pp. 375–383.

Tuteja N K, Beale G T H, et al., 2003. 'Predicting the effects of landuse change on water and salt balance – a case study of a catchment affected by dryland salinity in NSW, Australia', *Journal of Hydrology*, vol. 283, pp. 67–90.

Uys M C & O'Keeffe J H, 1997. 'Simple words and fuzzy zones: early directions for temporary river research in South Africa', *Environmental Management*, vol. 21, pp. 517–531.

Vaze J, Barnett P, Beale G T H, Dawes W, Evans R, Tuteja N K, Murphy B, Geeves G & Miller M, 2004. 'Modelling the effects of land-use change on water and salt delivery from a catchment affected by dryland salinity in south-east Australia', *Hydrological Processes*, vol. 18, pp. 1613–1637.

Vertessy R A, Hatton T J, O'Shaughnessy P J & Jayasuriya M D A, 1993. 'Predicting water yield from a mountain ash forest catchment using a terrain analysis based catchment model', *Journal of Hydrology*, vol. 150, pp. 665–700.

Watkins J R, 1969. 'The definition of the terms hydrologically arid and humid for Australia', *Journal of Hydrology*, vol. 9, pp. 167–181.

Western A W, Blöschl G & Grayson R B, 2001. 'Toward capturing hydrologically significant connectivity in spatial patterns', *Water Resources Research*, vol. 37, pp. 83–97.

Western A W, Grayson R B, Blöschl G, Willgoose G R & McMahon T A, 1999. 'Observed spatial organization of soil moisture and its relation to terrain indices', *Water Resources Research*, vol. 35, pp. 797–810.

Whetton P H, Fowler A M, Haylock M R & Pittock A B, 1993. 'Implications of climate change due to the enhanced greenhouse effect on floods and droughts in Australia', *Climatic change*, vol. 25, pp. 289–317.

Wilby R L, 2005. 'Uncertainty in water resource model parameters used for climate change impact assessment', *Hydrological Processes*, vol. 19, pp. 3201–3219.

Young P, 2003. 'Top-down and data-based mechanistic modelling of rainfall-flow dynamics at the catchment scale', *Hydrological Processes*, vol. 17, pp. 2195–2217.

Young W, Brandis K & Kingsford R, 2006. 'Modelling monthly streamflows in two Australian dryland rivers: matching model complexity to spatial scale and data availability', *Journal of Hydrology*, vol. 331, pp. 242–256.

Zhang L, Dawes W R & Walker G R, 2001. 'Response of mean annual evapotranspiration to vegetation changes a catchment scale', *Water Resources Research*, vol. 37, pp. 701–708.

Zhang L, Walker G R & Fleming M, 2002. 'Surface water balance for recharge estimation', CSIRO publishing, Collingwood, Victoria.

7

A short geological and environmental history of the Sydney estuary, Australia

Gavin Birch

Abstract

Sydney is blessed with one of the most beautiful harbours in the world. However, like many large, capital ports world-wide, this environment has been exposed to relentless stress due to a rapidly increasing population density and extensive residential, commercial and industrial expansion. In this chapter, we explain why the coastal zone is such an important environment, especially for the people of Australia, and describe changes to the Sydney estuary as an example of environmental transformation due to anthropogenic pressure. The geologic development of the Sydney estuary is briefly traced, showing how the feature was eroded into the Hawkesbury Sandstone, mainly during low sea levels of the glacial periods. The estuary and its catchment changed soon after Captain Philip landed in Sydney Cove. Early land clearing increased sedimentation in the waterway and rapid industrial growth, located mainly on the waterfront, resulted in increasing contamination of the estuary. At the University of Sydney, a novel collaboration between urban geographers working on changes in historical cadastral records of the city and environmental chemists studying estuarine sediments, have shown that as urbanisation and industrialisation spread through the catchment, so did the level and spatial extent of contamination in the estuary. The area of the estuary has been reduced by 22 per cent over 220 years of almost constant reclamation, resulting in ecological modification and possible additional contamination. The present contaminant status of the waterway is described in the concluding part of the chapter and a plea is made for a new effort for remediation and restoration of this iconic environment.

Introduction

Much of the character, and indeed the beauty, of Sydney can be attributed to its estuaries. Four deeply-incised, flooded valleys dissect the raised coastal margin of the region producing one of the longest coastlines of any capital city in the world. These beautiful waterways have 'injected' a maritime character deep into the heartland of suburban Sydney and have provided an extensive shoreline along which many beautiful historic homesteads have been built. These attributes have been vital in the development of Sydney into one of the most beautiful cities in the world.

These waterways have also provided excellent harbours for international trade and thus the city is at the intersection of domestic and international transport. Because of its locality, Sydney has attracted people and industry from many far off lands. The population of Sydney has grown rapidly since the Second World War and now exceeds four million – almost one quarter of the total population of Australia. The waterways have provided easy access for raw materials and export of produce and have supplied coolant for machinery, but they have also acted as a convenient receptacle for waste. All sewage and industrial waste was discharged directly into the estuaries until 1898 when three major coastal outfalls were constructed to disgorge effluent directly into the surf zone offshore from Sydney. Only in 1972 was discharge into the estuaries controlled by the Clean Waterways Act and, since 1990, sewage has been dispersed into the sea about four kilometres from the coast in approximately 80 metres of water (Birch 2000).

Australian population

Australia is a vast island continent with an area of almost 6 million km^2 and a population of just 21 million. This extremely low average population density is deceptive as vast areas of internal desert and bushland are virtually uninhabited and over 85 per cent of the population live in the coastal zone (Zann 1996). Moreover, Australia is one of the most urbanised countries in the world with 67 per cent of the national population living in one of the eight state and territory capital cities, all of which, except for Canberra, are located on the coast (Phillips, et al 1992). Even the 'coastal zone', which is defined as a section of land three kilometres wide running parallel to the coastline, has an extremely uneven population distribution: 82 per cent of the coastal fringe population live in just 1170 km, or 3.9 per cent, of coastline with 72 per cent of coast having zero population (McDonald et al 1993).

Australian estuaries

Coastal ecosystems support a variety of vital biological, economic and cultural functions; however, these systems are under considerable and increasing stress due to rapid urban and industrial development. Estuaries, in particular, are being threatened from increasing human intervention due to changes in water circulation, sedimentation, habitat loss, decline in native species and contamination by heavy metals, organochlorine compounds and polycyclic aromatic hydrocarbons. Environmental degradation appears to be an inevitable consequence of urbanisation and industrialisation.

Port Jackson

The waterway has a complicated geological and human history and even the naming of the estuary is difficult. Roy (1981) includes Middle Harbour, Port Jackson, and the Lane Cove and Parramatta Rivers in the definition of 'Sydney Harbour', whereas others confine the meaning to the central harbour area, including Circular Quay, Darling Harbour and White, Rozelle and Blackwattle Bays (McLoughlin 2000). 'Sydney estuary' will be used in the present text to include all of the above locations, including Duck River, and tributaries up to the fresh water limit and to the weirs on the Duck and Parramatta Rivers.

Port Jackson is one of 80 recognised harbours and 970 estuaries on the Australian seaboard (NLWA 2002). The estuary is approximately 30 km long, 2 km wide and occupies about 50 km^2, whereas the total catchment is about ten times the surface area of the estuary (500 km^2). Eighty-six per cent of the Port Jackson catchment is urbanised and/or industrialised. Sensitivity to environmental harm is given by the relationship between the area of the estuary and that of the catchment. The Sydney estuary should have a low sensitivity to anthropogenic effect, however that is overwhelmed by the huge proportion of the catchment that is urbanised (86%), as will be seen in the following discourse.

The central east coast of Australia is micro-tidal and Port Jackson experiences a maximum 2.1 metre tidal range. Flushing times increase from three to seven days in the lower harbour to seven to ten days in the upper estuary. With such a small catchment, only a small quantity of fresh water enters the estuary under normal conditions and Port Jackson is almost completely saline. However, during heavy rainfall, large volumes of fresh water are delivered to the estuary quickly due to the short length of rivers. At these times, water in the harbour becomes stratified with a one to two metre thick layer of turbid, buoyant, fresh water at the surface and salty water below. These conditions for low- and high-rainfall periods are unusual for estuaries, which are typically more mixed with fresh and saline water.

Geological history

Permo-Triassic era

Port Jackson is located in the Sydney Basin which is Permian to Triassic age (300–220 million years). The most distinctive feature of the Port Jackson catchment is the beautiful outcrops of Hawkesbury Sandstone into which the estuary is dissected. Most of the high land in the outer catchment is comprised of Ashfield Shale which overlies the Hawkesbury Sandstone. The configuration of Port Jackson drainage system, the orientation of bays and shoreline are all controlled by underlying geological structures.

The Sydney estuary is a drowned river valley, which is eroded up to 85 metres into the Hawkesbury Sandstone. However, the origin and evolution of such a large river valley compared to its small catchment area has always been difficult to explain. Possibly the Parramatta River was once considerably larger than it is today and extended westwards to be connected to the Nepean River. Perhaps the Nepean River was later 'captured' by the Hawkesbury River leaving the Parramatta River considerably reduced in size (Liu 1989). This history may explain the unusually deep erosion associated with what is currently a small catchment.

The ancient river, which is now Port Jackson, was an old, mature river that meandered across a flat plain 80 million years ago. During periods of uplift, the river eroded down into the elevated coastal plain forming steep-sided banks and at times cut through some of the meanders. During interglacial periods, sea level rises and the 'river' is flooded, leaving the breached meanders as islands, of which there are 14 under present sea level conditions. The great depth to bedrock in Port Jackson is attributed to the incision by the rejuvenated paleo-Port Jackson stream associated with uplift during and related to sea floor spreading when the Australian plate moved away from the Lord Howe Rise Plate (Liu 1989). Sediment, which accumulated in the valley bed during high sea level stands, was repeatedly eroded and flushed from the floor of Port Jackson valley during sea level lows. The present-day absence of sediment in depression in the Port Jackson channel is maintained by high water velocities and scouring by turbulent currents moving around headlands protruding into the estuary.

Quaternary period

Oscillations of sea level from 5 m above to 120 m below the present day position occurred every 100,000 to 150,000 years during the Quaternary due to global climate change and by glaciation. The penultimate glaciation ended about 135,000 years ago with the succeeding interglacial extending to about 80,000 years before the present. Sediments which accumulated in estuaries in this region during interglacials were eroded during intervening glacial periods. However, for the majority of the last 135,000 years, sea level was 20 to 70 m below the present and therefore erosion of estuaries was more pronounced than deposition during this period (Roy 1998).

Holocene epoch

The world started to come out of the grip of the last glacial period about 17,000 years ago and sea level started to rise quickly (Thom & Roy 1985). At this time the coast was about 25 to 30 km east of its present position, but, with a slope of considerably less than one degree, small increases in sea level advanced the coastline thousands of metres. By 10,000 years before the present, sea level had risen to 25 metres below today's sea level and only 3–5 km off the present coastline. The sea reached its present position about 6000 years ago (Roy et al 1997).

Since the Australian Aborigines have inhabited the continent for more than 40,000 years, they would have experienced this rapid change in climate and rapidly advancing coastline. It is hard to visualise how they coped with such a rapidly fluctuating coastline which would have been highly unstable even over decadal periods. As the sea advanced across the continental shelf, it probably 'swept' ahead of it large quantities of sand that had accumulated on the shelf from rivers which disgorged sediment as the rivers flattened out and lost their energy. This sand was pushed into embayments and now form the beautiful golden sands which occupy the many beaches along the east coast of Australia. Some of this sand was transported by wave energy into the mouth of Port Jackson as a tidal delta. Meanwhile, as the sea advanced into the now drowned river valley, sediment transported by rivers started to be deposited in the upper parts of the estuary as a fluvial delta. Fine-grained sediments, carried mostly in suspension after floods, are deposited in the middle of the estuary between the tidal and fluvial deltas.

The present-day estuary comprises five sedimentological units. Shallow off-channel embayments of the central harbour are covered in thick mud, as is the 30-metre deep basin in Middle Harbour. The main channel of the upper harbour is moderately deep, and also mantled in mainly muddy sand, but in the central harbour, the main channel is deeply scoured. The sand content of bottom sediment increases gradually downstream and the main part of the lower harbour seaward of the Sydney Harbour Bridge is mantled in sandy sediment.

Environmental history

Early European occupation 1788–1800

Although the Aborigines had occupied the Port Jackson estuary area for ten thousands of years, evidence of their presence is hard to find. However, after the arrival of the Europeans in 1788, the environment changed rapidly. Soon after settlement the Europeans embarked on extensive land clearing, but because of the poor soils around Port Jackson, cultivation soon moved westwards to the Nepean and Hawkesbury Rivers. Clearing and poor land practices promoted erosion, and sedimentation rates increased more than ten times pre-European levels in the estuary.

The First Fleet, which had departed Portsmouth on 13 May 1787, landed in Botany Bay under the command of Captain Arthur Phillip between 18 and 20 January 1788. Captain Phillip quickly realised that the land in the Botany Bay area was not fertile enough to support the 1000-strong party of the First Fleet and decided to move to Port Jackson – "the finest harbour in the world". On 26 January 1788 Captain Phillip laid anchor in a wonderful cove with "spring water" which he called Sydney Cove. The next day Captain Phillip established the colony and took possession of New South Wales, while the convicts began cutting down trees. The Second and Third Fleets arrived in June 1790 and July–August 1791 respectively and the colony spread rapidly. More fertile land to the west around Parramatta and further away in the Hawkesbury and Nepean Rivers was cultivated and settled (McLoughlin 2000).

Industrialisation and urbanization 1800–1854

Industries began to take shape on the banks of Darling Harbour in about 1800 and soon spread to nearby Cockle, Rozelle and Blackwattle Bays close to the present-day Sydney central business district (CBD). Metal foundries were the first to be established and the number of these industries increased from three to 14 between 1831 and 1851 (Taylor, Birch & Links 2004; Walsh 1963). Tanneries started operation in 1803 in the same area and were soon joined by other small industries. By 1828, metal foundries, coppersmiths and paint manufacturers were established adjacent to Blackwattle Bay due to readily available water supply and proximity to the city (MacDonnell 1975). The region south and west of the city grew rapidly during the 1820s and the Darling Harbour – Rozelle Bay area was by this time fully developed. By 1848 this environment had become so degraded that legislation was passed to remove all tanneries and polluting industries out of the city to Botany, Willoughby and Parramatta.

Period 1854–1889

Prior to 1870, effectively all industrial activity in the Sydney region was located close to the present-day CBD, but steam power led to considerable growth in Sydney after this time. Metal working, engineering, building materials, clothing and textiles became major industries between 1861 and 1890. The introduction of tramways, railways and major bridges in the late 1880s prompted rapid urban expansion. Industrial activity in the Iron Cove catchment in 1870 consisted of only one blacksmith shop, but by 1891 the number had increased to 10 (Links 1998; Taylor, Birch & Links 2004). Also at this time, chemical industries, metal working, boat building, dye use, electrical and glass manufacturing, as well as horse-drawn vehicle building had taken root in the Iron Cove catchment. Land adjacent to Homebush Bay has been used for industrial purposes, including a naval armament store and brickworks, since the 1880s (Homebush Bay Corporation 1994; Suh, Birch & Hughes 2004; Suh, Birch & Hughes 2004; Suh, Brown & Birch 2003; Taylor, Birch & Links 2004).

Period 1889–1922

Sydney spread rapidly westwards between 1889 and 1922 and Iron Cove, Hen and Chicken and Homebush Bays became urbanised and industrialised. Detailed land use mapping (Jolly 2005) shows Iron Cove catchment changed from a suburb supporting predominantly large estates (30–40% of the total area) to one of mainly small residential blocks (57% of land use) in the period 1905 to 1930. In 1916 major abattoirs were relocated from Rozelle Bay to Homebush Bay. A large base metal foundry and a smelter commenced operations on the shores of Hen and Chicken Bay during the early 1900s.

Industry replaced agriculture in the Parramatta River region (Powell 1987) and because the movement of imported goods and manufactured items required proximity to waterways, almost all waterfront on the shores of lower Parramatta River was occupied by industry by the end of the 19th century.

1922 to the present

Factories manufacturing heavy electrical equipment, large oil refineries and power supply stations were constructed close to the estuary between the First and Second World Wars. Many heavy industries situated in the inner, mixed residential/industrial areas of the city were relocated outside the Port Jackson catchment after the Second World War (Links 1998; Taylor, Birch & Links 2004). However, these industries were soon replaced with light industry, wholesalers and transport companies. Further decentralisation of industry occurred in Sydney after the Second World War due to a movement of people to the outer suburbs and a change in transportation, mainly toward trucking and containerisation (Webber & Daly 1971). Hen and Chicken Bay catchment remained predominantly agricultural until after the Second World War when it changed to medium-density housing.

Extensive parts of the Homebush Bay shoreline were reclaimed. The western shore was completely remodified prior to 1955, whereas the Rhodes Peninsula, on the eastern shore, was reclaimed later, between 1956 and 1975, creating opportunities for housing, industrial, commercial and recreational redevelopments. However, many of these industries have moved away from this region in recent times.

Foreshore development and reclamation in the harbour

Port Jackson has been extensively modified by reclamation over the last 200 years, especially in the upper and central estuary. Approximately 77 km of the 322 km of original shoreline has been lost due to reclamation and infilling of intertidal areas (Pitblado, 1978). Reclaimed areas are used mainly for industrial, recreational and residential uses and cover a total 11.35 km^2 of the total 50 km^2 or 23% of the estuary (Birch & Murray 2007; Murray 2003). Natural foreshores of mud flats and mangroves have given way to sea walls, wharves and buildings. The head of many embayments have been enclosed by sandstone walls and intertidal areas reclaimed by infilling. Reclamation has resulted in a loss of almost 9 million cubic metres of water on each tidal cycle, which has resulted in large changes in water movement, water quality, sedimentation and ecology of the upper harbour (Liu 1989). Sea walls have changed a ramp foreshore to a vertical shoreface altering the hydrology and ecology of the estuary. The following history of reclamation is mainly from the work of Murray (2003).

Period 1788–1854

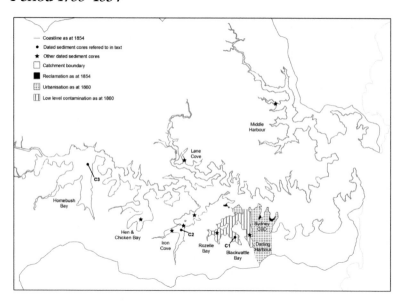

Figure 7.1 Only the central area of Sydney was urbanised by 1860 and foreshore reclamation was confined to Sydney and Farm Coves. The intensity of industrial activity can be judged by the number of ships in a photograph of Sydney Cove taken about this date (Figure 7.3). Sediment mantling Darling Harbour, Blackwattle Bay and Rozelle Bay began to show signs of heavy metal contamination by this time.

The first change in the foreshore occurred when large allotments were given out to the military, civilian administration, wealthy merchants and the clergy and by 1830 minor reclamation had started for wharfage and farming (Godden Mackay Pty Ltd 1991; Liu 1989). The first major reclamation project in the harbour occurred in the period 1835–1854 when the head of Sydney Cove was remodelled into a semi-circular sandstone quay with the Tank Stream channelled and buried. Mort and Walsh Bays were infilled and the opening of the Australian Gas Light Company transformed Darling Harbour (Godden Mackay Pty Ltd 1991, 1993).

Period 1854–1889

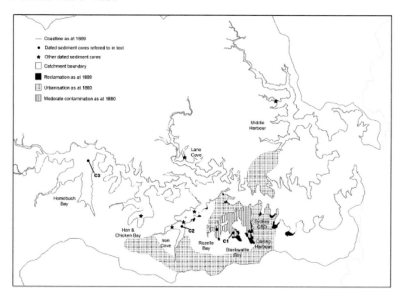

Figure 7.2 By 1880, urbanisation had spread to Iron Cove and most of the bay heads in the south, central part of the estuary had been reclaimed. At this time, sediments of Darling Harbour, Blackwattle Bay and Rozelle Bay had become moderately contaminated with heavy metals.

The introduction of trams and trains lead to a boom in development and an increased need for residential, industrial and recreational space. This resulted in reclamation of embayments close to central Sydney, that is Sydney Cove, Blackwattle Bay, Pyrmont Bay, Darling Harbour, Woolloomooloo Bay and Rushcutters Bay (Fitzgerald & Golder, 1994; Godden Mackay Pty Ltd 1991, 1993; Shore 1981; Stephensen, 1966). A photograph taken of Sydney Cove in the late 1850s shows numerous ships and intense industrial activity in this area during these times (Figure 7.3). In the second half of the 18th century, domestic waste, sewerage, offal and dead animals were discarded into foreshore areas considered dumping grounds for unwanted waste (Stringer 1984). It was believed that disease was communicated by noxious vapours emanating from damp areas where faecal waste accumulated, and odours and the fear of disease emitted from these wetlands contributed greatly to reclamation during this period (Solling & Reynolds 1977).

Figure 7.3 An early photograph of Sydney Cove taken in the late 1850s by an unknown photographer. The number of ships in the cove demonstrates the intensity of activity in this part of the harbour at this time. The period portrayed in this photograph correlates well with date of onset of contamination as indicated in a core taken from nearby Darling Harbour shown in Figure 7.6. The photograph is from the Macarthur Album titled "Sydney – The 1850s, the Lost Collections", by

Barry Groom and Warren Wickman from the Historic Photograph Collection, the University of Sydney.

Period 1889–1922

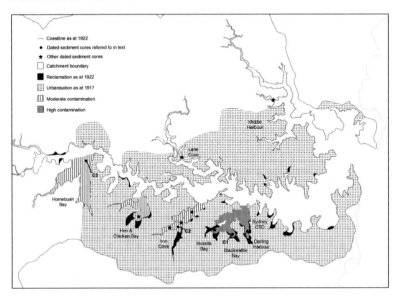

Figure 7.4 South of the harbour, urbanisation had spread from the estuary mouth to Homebush Bay by 1917, and the southern part of North Shore had become residential. Most of the upper ends of bays on the southern shores of the estuary had been reclaimed by 1922. Sediments in Darling Harbour, Blackwattle Bay and Rozelle Bay had become highly contaminated with heavy metals and Iron Cove, Hen and Chicken Bay and Homebush Bay sediments were moderately contaminated by 1917.

The continued widespread disposal of garbage in intertidal swamps (Coward 1988) to form industrial areas and parks (DEP 1986) was a major contributing factor to rat infestation and the outbreak of bubonic plague in 1898/99. The Sydney Harbour Trust (SHT) was formed under powers given by an Act of Parliament in 1900 to resume private enterprises and modernise dilapidated foreshores in Walsh Bay and Darling Harbour, which sheltered infestations of rats (Emery 1965; MSB 1974). Increased demand for accessible waterside land for port and industrial functions resulted in extensive reclamation in Canada Bay, Kings Bay, Hen and Chicken Bay, Iron Cove (Hawthorne Canal), White Bay, Rozelle Bay and Rose Bay.

Period 1922–2002

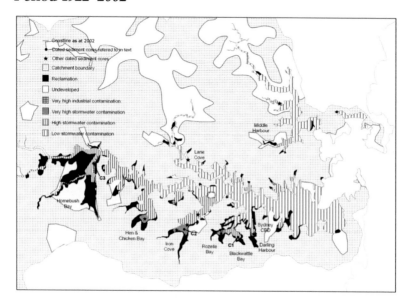

Figure 7.5 Urbanisation of the catchment is now almost complete, except for areas set aside for recreation and bush land reserves and foreshore reclamation has all but ceased. Sediments in the upper parts of bays, especially along the southern shores of the harbour, are highly contaminated with heavy metals and minor contamination is present in most sediment of the upper and central harbour, as well as in Middle Harbour and Lane Cove.

The most active period of reclamation took place in Port Jackson between 1922 and 1955 when about 5.7 km^2 of land was created adjacent to Parramatta River at Silverwater, Homebush Peninsula, Garden Island, Exile Bay, Kings Bay, Iron Cove, Glebe Island and Darling Harbour.

Between 1955 and 1978 reclamation was mainly by the use of landfill, including industrial wastes (Coward 1988) in low-lying areas adjacent to Middle Harbour, Parramatta River and Lane Cove River (McLoughlin, 1985). The last major reclamation period was from 1964 to 1981 when extensive foreshore areas were constructed to accommodate the new 'roll-on, roll-off' container shipping (Anglin & Associates 1990; Budin 1990; Fraser 1989; Proudfoot 1996).

Reclamation as a source of pollution

The total mass of material used to undertake 11.35 km^2 of reclamation in Port Jackson has been estimated at over 100 million tonnes (Mt) (McLoughlin 2000). The most common method used to undertake this reclamation was to construct a sea wall and infill behind the barrier using garbage, industrial waste and sediments removed from the floor of the adjacent estuary. The composition of material used as infill varied with location and date of reclamation and although few records were made, the composition of one site is well known. The nature and extent of waste in the Homebush Bay area is well documented due to clean-up operations associated with the Sydney 2000 Olympic Games.

Prior to European settlement, this area comprised extensive tidal wetlands and thick woodlands, which were cleared and reclaimed from the early 1800s for farming. The region was used as a racecourse, brickworks, armaments depot and an abattoir between the mid-1880s and 1969. Unauthorised filling was commonplace from the late 1960s to the late 1970s. During this period over nine million cubic metres of commercial, domestic and industrial waste was dumped in the area (Suh et al 2004). A 25 metre-high engineered landfill rose above the southern bank of Haslams Creek and only 30 per cent of the Homebush Bay site retained its natural top soil and remnant vegetation. By 1970 Wentworth Bay ceased to exist and most of the low-lying land had been filled by 1978. Final filling along the north and south banks of Haslams Creek took place between 1979 and 1988. The significant ecological damage had been recognized by 1975 when licensing of landfills became law, but a further five years lapsed before regulations became fully enforced. A total of $137 million was allocated for clean-up of the site in one of the largest remediation projects carried out in Australia (Suh, Birch & Hughes 2004; Suh, Birch, Matthai et al 2004). Waste comprised putrescible, building, chemical and garbage municipal waste, construction debris, household garbage, demolition waste, ash fill and dredged sediment containing heavy metals, asbestos, a range of hydrocarbons, including dioxins, benzene, toluene, ethylbenzene and xylene (BTEX) compounds and polycyclic aromatic hydrocarbons, as well as organochlorine pesticides. A total of 400 tonnes of hazardous waste comprising dioxins, furans and other organochlorine compounds was classified as Scheduled Chemical Waste which had to be destroyed by a thermal/catalytic treatment under NSW REPA license (Birch, et al, 2007). In one of the largest surveys of its kind, 4531 soil samples were collected by coring through the infill for chemical analysis (Suh, Birch & Hughes 2004; Suh, Birch, Matthai et al 2004). Areas infilled with estuarine sediment from the adjacent bay contained elevated concentrations of heavy metals and in some areas soil metal concentrations were considered high enough to pose a threat to groundwater. This soil was removed and consolidated into small manageable areas capped with impermeable clay and surrounded by leachate drains to protect surrounding aquifers. To date, monitoring of the leachate drains indicate contaminant concentrations are at acceptable levels.

In a project specially designed to test leachate production in reclaimed lands due to rainwater filtration and tidal action, Suh, Brown & Birch (2003a, 2003b) placed six boreholes through infill at Bicentennial Park adjacent to Rozelle Bay. The Park (1.01 ha) was reclaimed between 1972 and 1980 by removal of approximately 31,000 m^3 of material from the adjacent bay, primarily to attain navigation depths. In addition to the marine sediments, the fill comprised demolition waste, construction materials and industrial and domestic waste. Results of the experiment showed that during dry periods when water tables recede, oxygen ingress may lead to decreasing acidity (pH) and an associated increase in the concentrations of some heavy metals (copper, lead, zinc, arsenic and chrome). The results of the field study were tested under controlled conditions in the laboratory by percolating fresh and saline water through columns containing soil material from the park (Suh, Brown & Birch 2003a, 2003b). Although the parallel field studies had considerably higher concentrations of metals than that produced in the laboratory experiment, concentrations were orders of magnitude greater than natural sea water. It was concluded that elevated concentrations of heavy metals probably enter the estuary by tidal action and during periods of rainfall.

Although it has been demonstrated in the field and in controlled laboratory studies that the material used for infilling is a source of heavy metals to the estuary, the process has not yet been quantified. The juxtaposition of high contaminant concentrations in sediments at the heads of most estuary embayments and extensive reclamation in adjacent lands has obvious implications. However, stormwater canals also discharge to the estuary at these locations (Barry, Taylor & Birch 1999, 2001; Birch et al 1999) and differentiating the relative magnitude of each source is complex and has not yet been attempted. The extraordinary masses of materials dredged from the estuary floor for infilling and reclamation around Port Jackson gives an idea of the potential magnitude of this possible source. Almost a million tonnes of contaminated sediment from Iron Cove was used for reclamation at the mouths of Hawthorne and Iron Cove Creeks; 4.6 Mt in Homebush Bay and another 2.8 Mt on the banks of the Parramatta River (McLoughlin 2000).

Ecological effects of reclamation

It is not surprising that, with 23 per cent of the area of Port Jackson lost to reclamation, approximately 50 per cent of the shore is composed of retaining seawalls or other built habitats (Chapman & Bulleri 2003). Altered shorelines, particularly the construction of long stretches of seawalls, have major ecological impacts. The Centre for Research on Ecological Impacts of Coastal Cities at the University of Sydney is doing some excellent work on understanding the ecological role that seawalls and other intertidal structures have on urbanised estuaries (Blockley, Chapman in press; Chapman & Bulleri 2003;). Seawalls differ from natural rocky shores because they are usually steep and they have fewer crevices and overhangs than rocky shores and some habitats (e.g. rock pools) are absent. Also, vertical seawalls have a compressed intertidal area (1–2 m) in contrast to natural shores with lower gradients (10s of metres). These factors affect the distribution and abundance of intertidal organisms. At mid- and high-shore levels there are frequent differences between assemblages on natural shores and seawalls, but, at lower levels, differences between assemblages are considerably smaller.

The longest seawalls in Port Jackson have been constructed to support reclamation activities at the heads of embayments, for example Farm Cove, Woolloomooloo Bay and Iron Cove. These areas were once muddy, mangrove and saltmarsh wetlands with gentle slopes. The marked change in habitat in these areas has resulted in major alteration to ecological function, not to mention the reduction in biological productivity and changes in hydrology and physio-chemical attributes of the intertidal zone.

Historic effect of urbanisation and industrialisation on the Port Jackson estuary

The historic effect of increasing anthropogenic activity in the Port Jackson catchment on the adjacent estuarine environment has been established through an unusual collaboration by students and staff in urban geography and environmental chemistry in the Environmental Geology Group in the School of Geosciences at the University of Sydney (Birch & Murray 2007; Jolley 2005; Links 1998; Murray 2003; Taylor, Birch & Links 2004).

Studies of changing land use, development of industry and reclamation in Port Jackson, were undertaken by the School of Geosciences at the University of Sydney to determine potential adverse effects on the estuary by human activity in the adjacent catchment (Jolley 2005; Links 1998; Murray 2003; Taylor, Birch & Links 2004). Bottom sediments were used to determine possible effects on the estuary and to establish whether temporal changes in the catchment could be recorded in subsurface sediment in the estuary (Taylor, Birch & Links 2004). Sediment adsorbs contaminants from the overlying water column and thus has the ability to time integrate and to record the influx of contaminants into a water body. Because sediments are deposited layer-by-layer in a regular chronologic sequence, this sediment 'memory' can be used as an historic record of contaminant flux, which in turn reflects anthropogenic changes in the adjacent catchment (Taylor 2000). To test this concept in Port Jackson, 12 sedimentary cores where taken in nine highly contaminated embayments and down-hole samples were analysed for contaminants and dated using radioisotopes lead 210 and caesium 137 (Taylor 2000; Taylor, Birch & Links 2004).

Three of the 12 cores, one each from Blackwattle Bay (Core 1), Iron Cove (Core 2) and Homebush Bay (Core 3) are reproduced in Figure 7.6. These bays are all mantled in highly contaminated sediment and are located with increasing distance from central Sydney, that is, approximately 2, 5 and 12 km, respectively. All three cores show low concentration of heavy metals (copper, lead and zinc) at the bottom of the core and at some depth concentrations increase markedly. In some cases concentrations towards the top of the core remain constant, continue to increase, or begin to decrease. The depth at which concentrations begin to increase is the point, or time, where contaminants start to be discharged from the catchment, that is, the onset of contamination is faithfully recorded in the sediment. Contamination commenced in about 1860 in Blackwattle Bay (Core 1) and in approximately 1910 in Iron Cove (Core 2). Core 3 from Homebush Bay records adverse effects of human activity beginning at about 1925. The spread of urbanization and the development of industry outwards from central Sydney (Figures 1, 2, 4 and 5) are reflected in the expansion of contaminated sediment in the adjacent estuary.

The date of onset of contamination, as depicted in the cores, shows approximately the same timing as that of urbanisation and industrialisation in the adjacent catchments. Moreover, the severity of contamination in the sediment profile also decreases away from central Sydney with decreasing urban intensity. For example, zinc in sediment from the core taken closest to central Sydney (Core 1) in Blackwattle Bay is at a maximum of about 2000 μg/g and for the core taken in Iron Cove (Core 2) it is approximately 1500 μg/g, whereas in Homebush Bay the maximum zinc concentration in the sediment is approximately 1000 μg/g.

The data provided here are for heavy metals, but the same trend is evident for organic contaminants as well (Taylor, Birch & Links 2004). Organochlorine compounds are entirely artificial insecticides and herbicides and these chemicals came into use in Australia after the Second World War. The onset of these organic contaminants in the core profiles are dated at 1945, almost precisely when they were introduced into the catchment.

These results provide confidence in the methodology and the science of the current approach. Although similar results have been obtained for individual, site-specific studies, this is the only catchment-wide demonstration of this approach.

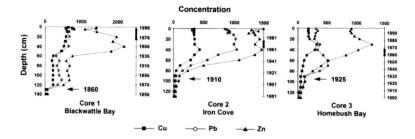

Figure 7.6 Cores from Blackwattle Bay, Iron Cove and Homebush Bay show the vertical distribution of heavy metal concentrations in the sediment. At the bottom of each core, the concentration of metals is uniformably low, but at some depth metal levels increase rapidly. This depth (marked with an arrow) is the date of onset of contamination. In Core 1, from Blackwattle Bay close to the city, onset of contamination was in about 1860, and onset dates are later for Cores 2 (Iron Cove) and 3 (Homebush Bay), which are located further from the city centre. This spread of contamination demonstrates how the estuary responded to encroaching urbanisation across the catchment.

Recent environmental history

More historic information can be gleaned from cores such as these. It is evident from Core 1 that zinc concentrations attained a maximum in the sediment in about 1955 and concentrations have been generally decreasing since that time. In fact, concentrations are almost half the maximum at present, whereas copper continues to increase in sediments at this location. There is evidence from the core profile that the concentration of lead has started to decline in recent times in Blackwattle Bay. There appears to have been two phases of contamination in this bay: a period of moderate contamination from 1875 to 1910, followed by a period of high contamination from 1910 to the present. In Iron Cove (Core 2), zinc concentrations reached a maximum in approximately 1960 and have remained high to the present day. Copper and lead also attained a maximum in Iron Cove at this time, but while lead appears to be decreasing slightly, copper concentrations have remained high and constant. Core 3 from Homebush Bay shows contamination reaching maximum concentrations in about 1970 for zinc and copper, but the maximum lead concentration occurred earlier in the 1940s, perhaps due to the introduction of industry manufacturing lead-based products on the shores of the bay. Increasing copper concentrations in recent times is commonly observed in sediments of Sydney Harbour, perhaps due to the continued use of copper-based antifouling boat paints, whereas declining lead over the last 15 years has been attributed to the introduction of unleaded petrol. The main source of zinc is vehicular emissions and component wear and is transported to the estuary by storm water.

Regional trends in contamination have been investigated by the Environmental Geology Group in the School of Geosciences at the University of Sydney using a considerably larger core database in conjunction with several vintages of surface sediment metal concentrations from about the mid-1970s to the present. Data from the cores and surficial sediments show that, in general, concentrations of metals in bottom sediment have been declining in the upper parts of the estuary, west of the Sydney Harbour Bridge, but have been increasing in the lower harbour, in Lane Cove and Middle Harbour over the last 25 years (Birch & Taylor 2004). The decrease in metal concentrations since the late 1970s is consistent with the introduction of the *Clean Waters Act* which required industry to discharge waste into the sewerage system and to reduce waste generation. A decision by industry to relocate out of the Sydney Harbour catchment over the last 25 years has also contributed to reduction of metal flux to the harbour. Relocating industry away from high-land value real estate on the water front with high-density housing has undoubtedly also reduced contaminant loads discharged directly to the estuary. The move has also changed appreciation of the harbour from former working class suburbs to high-value, middle class areas, for example Balmain and Woolwich.

Increased metals concentration over the same 25-year period in sediments of Lane Cove and Middle Harbour have been attributed to a rapid expansion of residential and commercial property, as well as increased transport services in the Chatswood and North Ryde areas (Taylor, Birch & Links 2004). High concentrations of metals in sediments of rivers and creeks draining these areas support this view (Birch & Taylor 2004).

Present status of Port Jackson

Sediment in some parts of Port Jackson is the most contaminated of any harbour worldwide. Sediments mantling the estuary contain high concentrations of a wide range of contaminants over extensive areas, including heavy metals, organochlorine pesticides, polycyclic aromatic hydrocarbons (PAHs), polychlorinated biphenyls (PCBs), polychlorinated dibenzo-*p*-dioxins and dibenzofurans (Birch & Taylor, 1999, 2000; Birch et al 2006; Irvine & Birch, 1998; McCready et al 2000). The origin of these substances can be broadly grouped as related to industrial activities, past and current stormwater discharge and leachates from reclaimed land. The industrial source is due largely to historical poor practices, whereas stormwater and leachate sources are past and contemporary. Early industry was located on the shoreline of the port for convenience and cheap delivery of raw materials, as well as for reducing haulage costs for coal to power stations. Export of heavy, bulky manufactured goods was also easy and inexpensive for shore-based industries. Contamination of adjacent sediment by waste associated with the movement of goods, and from cheap disposal of waste directly into the harbour, accounts for most of past industrially-sourced contamination.

Sampling of rivers and creeks discharging to Port Jackson has shown that stormwater continues to provide large quantities of contaminants, mainly heavy metals to the receiving basin. Although it is known that contaminants are being sourced from waste material contained within reclaimed lands surrounding the harbour, the magnitude of this supply remains unquantified, as with other diffuse sources, such as atmospheric deposition.

The majority of these contaminants are associated with the particulate phase, but the processes whereby these particle-bound contaminants are transported within the estuary and the effects of these materials on flora and fauna are poorly known and are the subject of current studies. Recent large ecotoxicological studies (McCready et al 2004; McCready et al 2005; McCready, Birch & Long 2006; McCready et al 2006a 2006b, 2006c) have shown that sediment in high impact areas of the harbour are toxic to some benthic animals, as was predicted by earlier investigations of sediment quality (Birch & Taylor, 2002a, 2002b, 2002c). To date little work has been done on the transfer of contaminants in the water column and bottom sediment to benthic and pelagic animals, termed 'bioaccumulation', or on the movement of these materials up the food chain, called 'biomagnification'.

Early studies detected high total PCB concentrations in mullet caught in Port Jackson (Woollard & Settle 1978), but mean values appear to have decreased since then (Richardson 1985). In a more recent study of chlorinated hydrocarbons in the tissue of seven fish types, concentrations exceeded National Food Authority Maximum Residue Limits for two species in Duck River, Homebush Bay and Iron Cove and one species in Parramatta River (Roach & Runcie 1998). High concentrations of polychlorinated dibenzo-*p*-dioxins and polychlorinated dibenzofurans in sediment in Homebush Bay have resulted in unacceptably high tissue concentration in fin fish. In 1989 fin fishing was banned in the bay and in the following year the ban was expanded to include the whole upper third of the harbour. More recent monitoring saw the NSW Food Authority posing a 3-month ban on commercial fin fishing in the whole harbour in December, 2005, which in January the following year was extended to include prawn trawling.

These bans were made permanent in February 2006. Blood tests of prawn fishermen showed one individual with four-times the average dioxin concentrations and his son with seven times average levels. One grandfather had concentrations 10 times average values. However, these levels were not deemed detrimental to human health. Studies continue to determine the extent of the problem and how best to reduce bottom sediment concentrations to levels where fish and prawn tissue levels decline to acceptable values.

The appropriate and successful governance of this estuary requires high-quality, science-based information. The current challenges for scientists are to identify and quantify sources, understand the mechanisms controlling the fate of contaminants, determine the effects of these substances on living resources and construct management tools based on robust science. Modelling the source, fate and effects of these contaminants in Port Jackson will enable managers and planners to make decisions on such issues as stormwater remediation options, relaxation times (natural cleanup), and the amount of dredging required to reduce tissue concentrations to acceptable limits and to set maximum daily loading for creeks entering the water way. In recent times, considerable effort has resulted in reduced industrial waste entering Port Jackson. Now is an appropriate time to initiate a new concerted environmental effort to install second generation remedial devices to reduce current stormwater contaminant inputs. It is also time to undertake appropriate remedial work in the catchment and in the estuary to restore the harbour to a condition in which it can support a complete and healthy ecological community.

Acknowledgements

Funding for ^{210}Pb and ^{137}Cs radioisotopic dating of sediment cores was provided by the Australian Institute of Nuclear Science and Technology. The authors thank Henk Heijnis and Andrew Jenkinson of the Environmental Radioisotope Laboratory at Australian Nuclear Science and Technology Organisation, Lucas Heights for their advice with radioisotopic dating. The author thanks Marco Olmos for drafting the figures to this manuscript and to Phil McManus for comments on an early draft of the manuscript.

References

Anglin and Associates, 1990. *Sydney Harbour: Maritime Services Board Heritage and Conservation Register: History, vol 1*, Anglin Associates, Sydney.

Barry S C, Taylor S E & Birch G F, 1999. 'Heavy metals in urban stormwater canals entering Port Jackson, Australia and their impact on the estuarine environment', Proceedings of the Eighth International Conference on Urban Storm Drainage, Sydney, Joliffe & Ball J E (eds.), August, vol. 4, pp. 1825-1832.

Barry S C, Taylor S E & Birch G F, 2001. 'Heavy metal supply to the Port Jackson Estuary, Australia by stormwater', *Australian Journal of Water Resources*, vol. 4, no. 2, pp. 147–154.

Birch G F, Scollen A, Snowden R & Suh J, 1999. 'Sources of heavy metals in stormwater draining into Port Jackson, Australia', Proceedings of the Eighth International Conference on Urban Storm Drainage, Sydney, Joliffe & Ball J E (eds.), August, vol. 4, pp. 2202–2209.

Birch G F & Taylor S E, 1999. 'Source of heavy metals in sediments of Port Jackson estuary, Australia', *The Science of the Total Environment*, vol. 227, pp. 123–138.

Birch G F, 2000. 'Marine pollution in Australia, with special emphasis on central New South Wales estuaries and adjacent continental margin', *International Journal of Environmental Pollution*, vol 13, pp. 1–6 & 411–423.

Birch G F & Taylor S E, 2000. 'The distribution and possible sources of organochlorine residues in sediments of a large urban estuary, Port Jackson, Sydney', *Australian Journal of Earth Sciences*, vol. 47, pp. 749–756.

Birch G F & Taylor S E, 2002a. 'Possible biological significance of contaminated sediments in Port Jackson, Sydney, Australia', *Environmental Monitoring and Assessment*, vol. 77, pp. 179–190.

Birch G F & Taylor S E, 2002b. 'Application of sediment quality guidelines in the assessment of contaminated surficial sediments in Port Jackson (Sydney Harbour), Australia', *Environmental Management*, vol. 29, no. 6, pp. 860–870.

Birch G F & Taylor S E, 2002c. 'Assessment of possible sediment toxicity of contaminated sediments in Port Jackson estuary, Sydney, Australia', *Hydrobiologia*, vol. 472, pp. 19–27.

Birch G F & Taylor S E, 2004. *Sydney Harbour and catchment: contaminant status of Sydney Harbour sediments: a handbook for the public and professionals*, Geological Society of Australia, Environmental, Engineering and Hydrogeology Specialist Group.

Birch G F, Harrington C, Symons R K & Hunt J W, 2006. 'The source and distribution of polychlorinated dibenzo-p-dioxin and polychlorinated dibenzofurans in sediments of Port Jackson, Australia', *Marine Pollution Bulletin*, no. 54, pp. 295–308.

Birch G F & Murray O A, 2007. Reclamation in Sydney Harbour, 1788–2002, *Australian Geographer*.

Blockley D J & Chapman M G, (in press). 'Exposure of seawalls to waves within an urban estuary: effects on intertidal assemblages', *Austral Ecology*.

Budin W H, 1990. Change in the use of portside lands in Sydney Harbour, MURP thesis, University of Sydney, Sydney.

Chapman M G & F Bulleri, 2003. 'Intertidal seawalls: new features of landscape in intertidal environments. landscape and urban planning', vol. 62, pp. 159–172.

Coward D, 1988. 'Out of Sight: Sydney's environmental history 1851–1981', Department of Economic History, Research School of Social Sciences, Australian National University, ACT.

DEP, 1986. Parramatta River Regional Environmental Study: open space and recreation: Heritage Study, Department of Environment and Planning, Sydney.

Emery J S, 1965. Port of Sydney, 1788–1945: a geographical study of development with particular emphasis on the influence of trade, MA thesis, University of Sydney, Sydney.

Fitzgerald S & Golder H, 1994. *Pyrmont and Ultimo*, Hale and Iremonger, Sydney.

Fraser D, 1989. *Sydney, from settlement to city: an engineering history of Sydney*. Engineers Australia Pty Ltd.

Godden Mackay Pty Ltd, 1991. *Sydney and Middle Harbours Heritage Study. Final report*. Report prepared for the NSW Department of Planning, Godden Mackay Pty Ltd, Sydney.

Godden Mackay Pty Ltd, Conybeare Morrison & Partners, 1993. *North Shore Heritage Study Review*, part 1, vol 1, main report.

Homebush Bay Corporation, 1994. *Briefing document on site contamination and environmental investigations at Homebush Bay*, Homebush Bay Corporation, NSW.

Irvine I & Birch G F, 1998. 'Distribution of heavy metals in surficial sediments of Port Jackson, Sydney, Australia' *Australian Journal of Earth Sciences*, vol. 45, no. 1, pp. 169–174.

Jolley R, 2005. Onset and flux of Cu, Pb and Zn loads in runoff in relation to historical changes in land-use, Iron Cove, Port Jackson, Australia 1885–1996.

Links F, 1998. Assessment of catchment control on the contaminant characteristics of receiving basin sediments. A study of Sydney Harbour, Australia, BSc Hons thesis, University of Sydney, Sydney.

Liu K, 1989. Evolution of the sedimentation in Sydney Harbour, MSc. Thesis, University of Sydney, Sydney.

MacDonnell, 1975. *The Glebe: Portraits and Places*, Ure Smith, Sydney.

Marine Services Board, 1974. *The Sydney Harbour Water-side Zoning Plan*, The Maritime Services Board of NSW, Sydney.

McCready S, Slee D, Birch G F & Taylor S E, 2000. 'The distribution of polycyclic aromatic hydrocarbons in surficial sediments of Sydney Harbour, Australia', *Marine Pollution Bulletin*, vol. 40, no. 11, pp. 999–1006.

McCready S, Spyrakis G, Greely C R, Birch G F & Long E R, 2004. 'Toxicity of surficial sediments from Sydney Harbour and vicinity', *Australia. Environmental Monitoring and Assessment*, no. 96, pp. 53–83.

McCready S, Greely C R, Hyne R V, Birch G F & Long E R, 2005. 'Sensitivity of an indigenous amphipod, *Corophium* sp. to chemical contaminants in laboratory toxicity tests conducted with field collected sediment from Sydney Harbour, Australia and vicinity', *Environmental Toxicology and Chemistry*, vol. 24, no. 10, pp. 2545–2552.

McCready, S., Birch, G. F. and Long, E. R., 2006a. Metallic and organic contaminants in sediments of Sydney Harbour and vicinity – A chemical dataset for evaluating sediment quality guidelines. Environment International, 32, 455–465

McCready S, Birch G F, Long E R, Spyrakis G & Greely C R, 2006b. 'Predictive abilities of numerical sediment quality guidelines for

Sydney Harbour, Australia and vicinity', *Environment International*, vol. 32, pp. 638–649.

McCready S, Birch G F, Long E R, Spyrakis G & Greely C R, 2006c. 'Relationships between toxicity and concentrations of chemical contaminants in sediments from Sydney Harbour, Australia, and vicinity', *Environmental Monitoring and Assessment*, vol. 120, pp. 187–220.

McDonald W S, Cocks L K, Wood N, Ive J R & Yapp G A, 1993. 'The future population of Australia's coastal lands' *Australian Geographic Studies*, vol. 31, no. 2, pp. 177–188.

McLoughlin L C, 1985. *The Middle Lane Cove River: a history and a future*, Centre for Environmental and Urban Studies, Macquarie University, NSW.

McLoughlin L C, 2000. 'Shaping Sydney Harbour: sedimentation, dredging and reclamation 1788–1990s', *Australian Geographer*, vol. 31, no.2, pp. 183–208.

Murray O A, 2003. *A history of reclamation in Sydney Harbour 1788–2002*. MApplSci thesis, University of Sydney, Sydney.

NLWRA, 2002. *National land and water resources audit (2002) Australian catchment, river and estuary assessment 2002, vol. 1*. National Land and Water Resources Audit, Canberra.

Phillips D J H, Richardson B J, Murray A P & Fabris J G, 1992. 'Trace metals, organochlorines and hydrocarbons in Port Philip Bay, Victoria, A historical review', *Marine Pollution Bulletin*, vol. 25, pp. 5–8 & 200–217.

Pitblado R M, 1978. Estuarine modelling; the development and validation of a 2-layer, real-time model for the Parramatta River estuary, PhD thesis, University of Sydney, Sydney.

Powell C, 1987. *A river revived: the Parramatta*. NSW University Press, Sydney.

Proudfoot P, 1996. *Seaport Sydney: the making of the city landscape*, University of Sydney, Sydney.

Richardson J, 1985. 'Polychlorinated biphenyls (PCBs) in Australian waters', in Chan M W H, Hoare R W M, Holmes P R, Law R J S & Reed S B (eds.), 'Pollution in the Urban Environment Palmet 85', pp. 652–658, Elsevier Applied Science Publishers, London.

Roach A C & Runchie J, 1998. 'Levels of selected chlorinated hydrocarbons in edible fish tissues from polluted areas in the

Georges/Cooks Rivers and Sydney Harbour, New South Wales, Australia' *Marine Pollution Bulletin*, vol. 36, pp. 323–344.

Roy P S, 1981. 'Quaternary Geology' in Herbert C, (ed.) *Geology of the Sydney*, 1:1000,000 sheet 9130, Geological Survey of New South Wales, Sydney, pp. 41–91.

Roy P S, Zhuang W, Birch G F, Cowell P J & Li C, 1997. *Quaternary geology of the Forster-Tuncurry coast and shelf, Southeast Australia*, Geological Survey of New South Wales, Department of Minerals Resources, Sydney.

Roy P S, 1998. 'Cainozoic geology of the coast and shelf', in Scheibner, E & Basden H (eds.), *Geology of New South Wales Synthesis. vol. 2 Geological Evolution*, Geological Survey of New South Wales, Memoir Geology, vol. 13, no. 2, pp. 361–385.

Shore H, 1981. *From the Quays*, NSW University Press, Sydney.

Snowdon R & Birch G F, 'The nature and distribution of copper, lead, and zinc in soils of a highly urbanised sub-catchment (Iron Cove) of Port Jackson, Sydney', *Australian Journal of Soil Research*, vol. 42, no. 3, pp. 329–338.

Stephensen P R, 1966. *History and Description of Sydney Harbour*, Rigby Limited, Sydney.

Solling M & Reynolds P, 1977. *Leichhardt: on the margins of the city: a social history of Leichhardt and the former Municipalities of Annandale, Balmain and Glebe*, Allen and Unwin, Sydney.

Stringer M, 1984. *Sydney Harbour: a pictorial history from the first settlers to the present day*, Rankin & Company, Sydney.

Suh J, Brown P & Birch G F, 2003a. 'Geochemical factors affecting leachate composition derived from soils in reclaimed land using laboratory freshwater and saline water column experiments', *Marine and Freshwater Research*, vol. 54, pp. 885–893.

Suh J, Brown P & Birch G F, 2003b. 'Hydrogeochemical characteristics and importance of natural and anthropogenic influences on soil and groundwater in a reclaimed land adjacent to Port Jackson, Sydney, Australia', *Marine and Freshwater Research*, vol. 54, pp. 767–779.

Suh J, Birch G F, Matthai C & Hughes K, 2004a. 'Spatial distribution and sources of heavy metals in reclaimed lands of Homebush Bay; the venue of the 2000 Olympic Games, Sydney, New South Wales', *Australian Journal of Earth Sciences*, vol. 51, pp. 53–66.

Suh J, Birch G F & Hughes K, 2004b. 'Hydrochemistry in reclaimed lands of the 2000 Olympic Games site, Sydney, Australia', *Journal of Coastal Research*, vol. 20, no. 3, pp. 709–721.

Taylor S E, 2000. The source and remobilisation of contaminated sediment in Port Jackson, Australia. PhD thesis, the University of Sydney, Sydney.

Taylor S E, Birch G F, & Links E, 2004. 'Historical catchment changes and temporal impact on sediment of the receiving basin, Port Jackson, New South Wales', *Australian Journal of Earth Sciences*, vol. 51, no. 2, pp. 233–246.

Thom B G & Roy P S, 1985. 'Relative sea levels and coastal sedimentation in southeast Australia in the Holocene', *Journal of Sedimentary Petrology*, vol. 55, pp. 257–264.

Walsh G P, 1963. 'The Geography of Manufacturing in Sydney 1788–1851', *Business Archives and History*, vol. 3, no. 1, pp. 20–52.

Webber & Daly, 1971. 'Location of manufacturing growth within cities: a predictive model for Sydney 1954–1966', *Royal Australian Planning Institute Journal*, vol. 9, pp. 130–136.

Woollard P & Settle H, 1978. 'PCB residues in mullet, *Mugil cephalus* fed to captive Eastern Australian water rats, *Hydromys chrysogaster*', *Bulletin of Environmental Contamination and Toxicology*, vol. 20, pp. 606–612.

Zann L P, 1996. 'The state of the marine environment report for Australia (SOMER). Process, findings and perspective', *Ocean and Coastal Management*, vol. 33, pp. 1–3 & 63–86.

8

Energy from offshore wind: an overview

Dong-Sheng Jeng and Yun Zheng

Abstract

Renewable energy has attracted a great deal of attention among governments, industries, academics and societies throughout the world in recent times. Offshore wind energy is a renewable energy source that has great potential in energy markets worldwide as our current knowledge of offshore engineering technology makes it ready for implementation immediately. In this chapter, offshore wind energy is compared with other renewable energy sources, and existing offshore wind energy projects throughout the world are reviewed. Current design codes of offshore wind energy are outlined and a set of criteria for the selection of appropriate sites for offshore wind energy is established for Australia. Finally, potential sites in Australia are evaluated and based on our analysis, the southern part of Western Australia (WA) is the most appropriate site for wind farms.

Introduction

Due to the world's rising energy consumption, limited existence of fossil energy sources and dramatic changes to the world's climate, the extension of renewable energy has drawn a great deal of attention from governments, industries and academics world-wide. Renewable energy has considerable potential and could theoretically provide a nearly unlimited supply of relatively clean and mostly local energy. Recently, global renewable energy supply has been growing strongly; the annual growth for wind energy, for example, has been around 30 per cent recently, from a very low base of 6.29 per cent of total renewable energy resources. In relative terms, however, the share of modern renewable energy, including large hydro-electricity, in the total primary energy supply will remain around 10 per cent by 2010 (WEC 2003). The cumulative global investment in renewable energy is expected to increase 23 per cent during 2005–2030 (Figure 8.1) (WEO 2006). As reported by World Energy Outlook (2006) fossil-fuel demand and trade flows and greenhouse gas emissions would follow their current unsustainable paths through to 2030 in the absence of new governmental action – the underlying premise of a 'reference scenario' (Figure 8.1). Furthermore, Figure 8.1 demonstrates, in an 'alternative policy scenario', that a package of policies and measures that countries around the world are considering would significantly reduce the rate of increase in demand and emissions. Importantly, the economic cost of these policies would be more than outweighed by the economic benefits that would come from using and producing energy more efficiently.

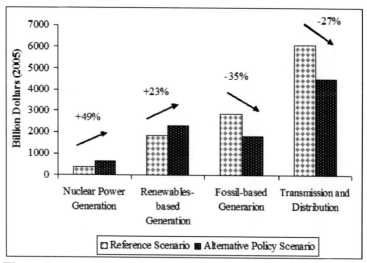

Figure 8.1 Cumulative global investment in electricity – supply infrastructure, 2005–2030 (WEO 2006).

The application of wind energy throughout the world is growing rapidly. Over the past two decades, onshore wind energy technology has been intensively studied and is now cost competitive with fossil and nuclear fuels for electric power generation in many areas worldwide (Owen 2003). According to World Energy Outlook (WEO 2006), the cost for onshore wind energy is around five US cents per kWh, which is competitive with nuclear power (5.5 cents per kWh) and coal stream (4.8 cents per kWh), as shown in Figure 8.2 (WEO 2006).

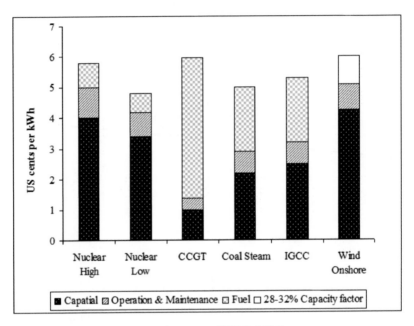

Figure 8.2 Electricity generating costs (WEO 2006)

IGCT = Integrated Gasification Combined Cycle. CCGT= combined cycle gas turbine

While onshore wind technology is maturing, offshore wind energy is in its initial stages. Offshore wind farms are different from onshore installations for several reasons. Despite the high costs compared with onshore wind farms, offshore applications allow increased energy efficiency, due to the higher average wind speeds and the reduction of the setting and environmental issues, particularly with regards to noise, visual constraints and space limitations, since offshore wind farms are commonly built several kilometres off the coast (Barthelmie et al 1996; Lavagnini, Sempreviva & Barthelmie 2003; Musial, Butterfield & Ram 2006).

In this chapter, we will focus on the development of offshore wind energy. Following a brief look at the nature of offshore wind energy, existing offshore wind energy projects will be reviewed. Then, design procedure of offshore wind farms will be outlined and, finally, the potential of offshore wind energy in Australia will be discussed.

Offshore Wind Energy

Renewable Energy

Energy resources removed from the ground, such as coal, gas and oil cannot be replaced in the short term, once they are used. Therefore, the development of social and economic activities will struggle once the supply of these energy resources becomes unavailable and, for this reason, renewable energy becomes an attractive energy resource to countries worldwide, especially the developed countries. The major differences between non-renewable energy and renewable energy are that the latter is less polluting and renewable.

To date, five major renewable energy resources – wind, flowing water, solar, biomass power and geothermal energy, have been widely used. The total power generation for various resources is given in Table 8.1 and a comparison of renewable energy resources is given in Table 8.2.

Cost of offshore wind energy

The cost of offshore wind energy varies widely depending on the project. However, it is reported that costs of offshore projects are significantly more than for those onshore. Most of the budget for offshore wind projects is attributed to higher costs for foundations, installation, operation and maintenance. A typical breakdown of total system costs for an offshore wind farm in shallow water is illustrated in Figure 8.3 (Owen 2003). This includes wind turbine, the onshore utility connection, the costs of operation and maintenance and decommissioning. As shown in the figure, the electrical and grid infrastructure, foundations and support structures, offshore construction, and operation and maintenance now represent the major fraction of the total project cost (Figure 8.3). To be successful, the offshore wind project must draw on the combined experiences and expertise of the cost-conscious wind industry, as well as the offshore oil and gas and marine industries (Musial, Butterfield & Ram 2006).

Table 8.1 Power generation of global renewable energy resources

Type of renewable energy	Production (gigawatts)	Percentage (%)
Hydro power	816 GW	86.94
Wind turbines	59 GW	6.29
Biomass power	44 GW	4.69
Geothermal power	9.3 GW	0.99
Solar power	5.5 GW	0.59
Other renewable energy	4.7 GW	0.5

Table 8.2 Comparison of various renewable energy resources

Type of energy	Cost	Technology	Production	Policy	Commercial use	Individual use
Hydro power	high		high		yes	
Wind power	low	mature	high	feasible	yes	
Biomass power	low		high		yes	
Geothermal power	high				yes	
Solar power	low		high		yes	yes

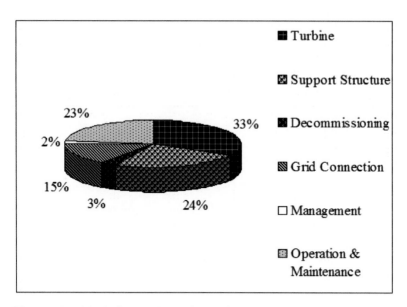

Figure 8.3 Typical cost breakdown for an offshore wind farm in shallow water (Owen 2003)

The wind energy market

Figure 8.4 shows an increasing world wind energy capacity from 1997 to 2006, and provides a prediction to 2010 (WWEA no date). The wind power capacity reached 73,904 Megawatts (MW) in 2006. In terms of economic value, it shows the strength of wind power in the world energy market.

The Global Wind Energy Council gives the total wind power capacity for countries to year 2006 (Table 8.3). Germany, Spain, the United States, India and Denmark are the top five countries that invested a large amount of capital on wind power. Germany leads the world wind energy market with 16,000 wind turbines, while the government of United States has set a target of supplying 10 per cent of total electricity by 2010.

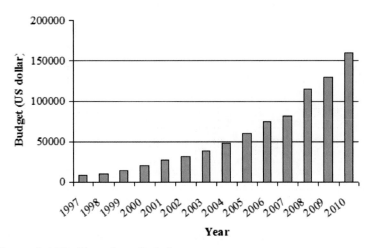

Figure 8.4 World market of wind energy

Table 8.3 Total installed wind power capacity in various countries

Rank	Nation	2005 (MW)	2006 (MW)
1	Germany	18,415	20,622
2	Spain	10,028	11,615
3	United States	9,149	11,603
4	India	4,430	6,270
5	Denmark	3,136	3,140
6	China	1,260	2,604
7	Italy	1,718	2,123
8	UK	1,332	1,963
9	Portugal	1,022	1,716
10	France	757	1,567
	World total	**59,091 MW**	**74,223 MW**

Environmental impact

Unlike the burning fossil fuel, wind energy does not produce carbon dioxide, mercury and other air pollutions. Furthermore, wind as a renewable energy source will provide a long-term energy supply while saving fossil fuels, which are limited. However, during the manufacture of the wind farm, large amounts of steel, concrete and other materials are needed and fossil and coal are also used to produce and transport these materials.

Another important type of pollution that has to be considered is noise pollution. Due to the mechanical motion of the turbines and transmission of electricity to the power station, noise will be a significant factor affecting the functioning of normal human life.

Offshore wind farms in the world

Comparison of onshore and offshore wind farms

Offshore wind farms are different from onshore installations for several reasons: (1) the wind turbine generators have, on average, larger diameters and rated power; (2) installation and maintenance are more expensive; (3) the submarine electrical connection to shore increases the investment costs (Pryor & Barthelmie 2001); and (4) offshore wind energy requires more advanced technology, especially in the coupling design of wind farms.

An important factor is the amount of energy production. Due to the large wind power generating capacity, energy production offshore wind farms may be significantly larger than from onshore installations. Moreover, the wind turbines used offshore are usually larger with higher production capacities than onshore facilities.

In addition, onshore wind farms block the sunshine and produce considerable noise to the annoyance of local residents, while offshore wind farms are more or less invisible. Most of the offshore sites are constructed about 10 to 20 kilometres offshore, eliminating both shadow and noise problems, and the influence upon onshore populations is minor.

Cost is a major disadvantage of offshore wind energy generation. The cost of an offshore wind farm is considerably greater than that for one onshore. Offshore wind farms normally are installed in shallow water with maximum water depths of up to 30 metres. This requires higher costs and more advanced technologies to build the foundations and the submerged parts of the monopile. Since offshore sites are far offshore, the power has to be transmitted from the wind turbines to the power stations on land through under-sea cables, which is more expensive, especially with the higher voltage required. Another extra cost for offshore wind farms is maintenance. As offshore wind farms are in a saltwater environment, and most of the wind turbines are designed and tested on land without considering saltwater corrosion, the repair and maintenance costs are generally much greater.

Table 8.4 provides a comparison of advantages and disadvantages of onshore and offshore wind farms.

Table 8.4 Comparison of offshore and onshore wind energy

	Advantages	Disadvantages
Onshore wind farm	Costs less Easy to install	Noise and shadow problems for residents Lower energy production Can only install limited number of small turbines
Offshore wind farm	Higher energy production (up to 90% higher wind power than onshore) Saves land Less noise for onshore residents Large wind turbines can be installed for higher quality electricity production	Costs more on both installation and transmission Navigation effect on shipping Extra cost of maintenance (e.g. saltwater corrosion) Higher technical expertise required (hydrodynamic action and submerged foundation) Influence on marine ecology during construction

Offshore wind energy in Europe

Offshore wind energy began in shallow water off the North Sea where the abundance of sites and higher wind resources are more favourable in comparison with Europe's land-based alternatives. The first installation was in Sweden with a single turbine in 1990. Currently, there are 21 operating projects, four projects under construction and 15 planned projects (Figure 8.5) (Offshore Wind Energy, 2006). Figure 8.5 shows the location of installed capacity as a percentage of the total capacity and by country (Musial, Butterfield & Ram 2006). The majority of the capacity is now located in Denmark and the United Kingdom (UK) (Figures 8.5 and 8.6). Most installations have been constructed in water depths less than 18 m and at a distance from shore of 1 km to 14 km. Several large-scale offshore wind energy projects are summarised below.

Arklow Bank

Arklow Bank Wind Park, which is located on the coast off Arklow in Ireland, is co-developed by Airtricity and GE Energy. It is not only the first offshore wind project in Ireland, but is also the world's first commercial offshore wind turbine of over 3 MW. The first phase of this project was operated by seven GE 3.6 MW turbines with a 25 MW capacity. The second phase of the project is planned to install a further 193 turbines, and the total capacity will increase to 520 MW at the end of the project.

London Array

London Array is proposed as an offshore wind farm in the UK with a capacity of 1 GW, and is expected to become the world's largest offshore wind farm. This wind park will consist of 271 wind turbines with 3100 GWh energy output amount per year and will supply over 750,000 homes when completed. When fully operational, it would make a substantial contribution to the UK Government's renewable energy target of providing 10 per cent of the UK's electricity by 2010. It would also prevent the emission of 1.9 million tonnes of carbon dioxide each year compared to the same amount of electricity produced by a fossil fuel power station.

London Array turbines will range between 3 MW and 7 MW in electrical capacity, depending on when they are installed. Hub heights will be between 85 m and 100 m above sea level, and the total turbine height will not be greater than 175 m. The wind turbines will typically begin generating electricity at a minimum wind speed of 3 m/s and shut down at wind speeds greater than 25 m/s with full power at a wind velocity of 13m/s.

Three different types of foundations will be considered to support the towers. They are: steel monopile driven into the seabed directly, which is used on most of the offshore wind sites; gravity base foundation, which is a large concrete structure sitting on the seabed and stabilised by weight; and a tripod foundation, which has multi-legs pinned on several steel piles and normally used in deep water. The type of foundation used is decided after geotechnical investigations.

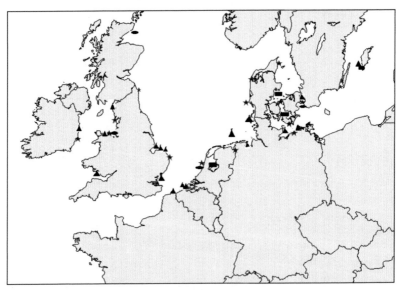

Figure 8.5 Map of existing and planned wind farms in North-West Europe. Notation: ★ = (built large wind turbines), ■ = (built small wind turbines), ● = (under construction), ▲ = (planned).

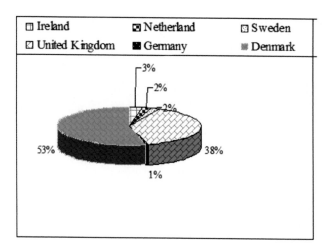

⊡ Ireland	⊠ Netherland	⊠ Sweden
⊡ United Kingdom	■ Germany	※ Denmark

3%
2%
2%
53%
38%
1%

Figure 8.6 Offshore wind project installation

Kentish Flats

The Kentish Flats offshore wind farm has 30 large wind turbines from Vestas V90-3.0 installed in the UK providing a total of 90 MW rated capacity. The offshore site is located about 6 to 10 miles off East Quay in Whitstable. The wind farm was erected by the leading Danish power company Elsam, which has more than 25 years of experience with wind energy projects. The Kentish Flats project alone will reduce emissions of carbon dioxide by over 4 million tonnes over its 20-year life time.

North Hoyle

The North Hoyle offshore wind farm was built in 2003 at North Hoyle, which was the first full-scale offshore wind farm in UK. North Hoyle is 8 km offshore from north Wales. Thirty V80-2.0 MW wind turbines were installed in shallow water depths of about 12 metres, and the unit displaces about 160,000 tonnes of carbon dioxide annually. The project was constructed by Vestas and Mayflower Energy and cost £81 million over all.

Offshore wind energy in other countries

The potential of offshore wind energy in other regions, such as North America and Japan, are currently under investigation (Henderson, Lentz & Fujii 2002; Tap-Johansen 2006). Due to the great water depths near shore in these regions, offshore wind energy facilities will have to be constructed in deep water. In these cases, the conventional offshore wind farms (e.g. monopiles, tripods and jackets) will be adapted to floating structures, as with the Cape Wind farm in the USA.

Cape Wind

Cape Wind is the first offshore wind farm in USA, and is located in shallow water towards the centre of Nantucket Sound at Horseshoe Shoal. The proposal is for installing 130 offshore wind turbines from GE 3.6, so that Cape Wind will produce up to 420 megawatts of wind power with 3.6 MW for each wind turbine. Average expected production will be 170 MW, which will be 75 per cent of the electricity demand for Cape Cod and the Islands of Martha's Vineyard and Nantucket. Steel monopiles are the preferred option for the wind farm foundations to support the towers. The monopiles will be driven 50–90 feet into the seabed depending on the character of the subsurface marine sediments.

A summary of the offshore wind energy projects described above is given in Table 8.5 (following page).

Design of offshore wind farms

Wind power

Wind energy is generated by moving air, so the amount of energy depends on wind speed and the density of the air. The wind power can be estimated by

$$P = 0.5C_p \rho A v^3 . \tag{1}$$

where P is power in watts (W), ρ is the air density in kg/m^3, A is the swept rotor area, C_p is the performance coefficient of the rotor, which has a maximum value of $16/27$, v is the wind speed (m/s).

Table 8.5 Summary of offshore wind energy projects

	Kentish Flats	Cape wind	North Hoyle	Arklow Bank	London Array
Location:	UK	USA	UK	Ireland	UK
Number of wind turbines	30	130	30	7 then 193	271
Wind turbine type	Vestas V90/3.0 MW	GE 3.6 MW	Vestas V80 2 MW	GE3.6 MW	3–7 MW
Total output	90 MW	420 MW	60 MW	25 MW then 520 MW	1,000 MW
Expected annual output (kWh)	280,000,000		200,000,000		3,100,000,000
Rotor diameter	90 m	104 m	80 m	104 m	
Hub height	70 m	75 m	67 m	73.5 m	85–100 m
Weight, blade	6.6 t	150-500t	6.5 tonne	150-500 t	
Weight, rotor	39.8 t				
Weight, tower	108 t		160 tonne	160 tonne	
Weight, foundation	247–292 t	250 & 350 t	280 t		
Full power output from	14 m/s	14 m/s		14 m/s	13m/s
Depth of water	5 m		7-11 m	3–30 m	0–23 m
Distance from shore	10 km	4–11 miles	7 km	10 km	20km
Wind farm site	10 km²		10 km2		232 km2
Project costs (GBP)	105 million	30 million so far, over 1 billion funds	£81m		
Foundation type	Steel monopile	Monopile	Monopile	Monopile	Steel monopile, Gravity base foundation, Tripod foundation
Company	Vattenfall	Cape wind	Vestas and Mayflower Energy	Airtricity & GE Energy	

As shown, wind speed can be considered in several velocity ranges:

- start-up wind speed – the wind speed which starts the rotor
- cut-in wind speed – the wind speed referring to a specific blade-tip velocity in the case of a specific turbine, at which the wind turbine starts supplying useful output power at the shaft
- full output wind speed – the wind speed at which the machine can reach the maximum capacity
- furling speed (i.e. cut-out wind velocity) – the wind velocity at which the protective device fitted to a wind turbine is actuated to prevent mechanical damage to the machine
- maximum design wind speed – the wind speed above which damage could occur to the machine.

Types of wind turbines

Six major wind turbines have been used mostly on offshore wind farms. They are: Repower, Vestas, Multibird, Enercon, Siemens, and GE Energy. Table 8.6 outlines the technical data for the turbine prototypes with over 3 MW power rate from these six companies.

Vestas

Vestas is the world's largest wind turbine supply company, since more than 30,000 wind turbines in over 60 countries are operating Vestas machines. Their products with capacities from V52–850 kW toV90–3.0 MW are used in both onshore and offshore wind farms. V80–2.0 MW was used on North Hoyle offshore wind farm and Horns Rev with expected annual output of 200,000,000 kWh and 600,000,000 kWh, respectively. A V90-3.0 MW unit was used on Kentish Flats with annual output of 280,000,000 kWh.

V120 is designed for large offshore projects. Carbon-fibre reinforced plastic turbine blades, which are of extremely light material, will reduce turbine weight. This will reduce foundation cost and improve the economy of offshore projects.

Table 8.6 Comparison of numerous wind turbines (WWEA 2006)

Prototype	Repower 5M	Vestas V120	Multibrid M5000	Enercon E-112	Siemens SWT-3.6	GE Energy 3.6s
Rotor diameter	126 m	120 m	116 m	114 m	107 m	104 m
Swept area	12.469 m²	11.310 m²	10.568 m²	10.207 m²	8.992 m²	8.495 m²
Rated capacity	5.0 MW	4.5 MW	5.0 MW	4.5 MW	3.6 MW	3.6 MW
Gearbox	3-step	3-step	1-step	–	3-step	3-step
Generator	df ASG	df ASG	pm SG	SG	ASG	df ASG
Rotor blade	17,8 t	12,3 t	16,5 t	21 t	16 t	k.A.
Rotor with hub	120 t	65 t	110 t	k.A.	90 t	85 t
Nacelle	290 t	145 t	200 t	k.A.	120 t	210 t
Nacelle + Rotor	410 t	210 t	310 t	500 t	210 t	295 t
Tower	750 t	220 t	1.138 t	2.500 t	250 t	250 t
Hub height	120 m	90 m	102 m	124 m	80 m	76.5 m
Operation since	Nov 2004	2007	Dec 2004	Aug 2002	Dec 2004	June 2004
Specific power	401 W/ m²	398 W/ m²	473 W/ m²	441 W/ m²	400 W/ m²	424 W/ m²
Specific mass	32.9 kg/m2	18.6 kg/m2	29.3 kg/m2	49.0 kg/m2	23.4 kg/m2	34.7 kg/m2

SG = synchronous generator, pm SG = permanent-magnet synchronous generator, ASG = asynchronous generator, df ASG = asynchronous generator (doubly fed)

Repower

Repower Systems AG is one of the leading turbine producers in Germany and was founded in 2001. This company focuses on the development, production and installation of multi-megawatt wind turbines with capacities from 1.5 to 5 MW and which are installed in water from 70 to 126 metres deep. The Repower 5M is one of the world's largest wind turbines for offshore wind projects with a rated output of 5 MW and is designed to satisfy the conditions of the sea environment with its effective corrosion protection and permanent monitoring.

Multibrid

Multibrid M5000 is designed for offshore wind farms with simple installation requirements. Since the converter system, transformer and switch gear are already installed on the tower, only the transmission step is needed to operate the turbine. Therefore, repairs are very difficult for such a design, especially at sea. The turbine blades are made of carbon fibre to provide low weight, and it is operated with independent electrical pitch systems to reduce risk of failure in high-speed wind conditions.

Enercon

To date, Enercon is one of the world's leading companies in wind power. In 2005, Enercon made the E-112 design with a rate of 4.5 MW and rotor diameter of 113 m, and was the largest wind turbine in the world at that time. Then at the end of 2005, the E-112 was upgraded to 6 MW. The E-112 failed in the offshore project at Wilhelmshaven when the bucket foundations, which were designed for this project, deformed. Due to considerable power of the E-112, it cannot be used in the shallow waters of Wilhelmshaven and new foundations will have to be designed for the device

Siemens

Siemens, as one of the world largest electrical engineering companies, leads the market in a wide range of business areas. Siemens produces wind turbines with a range between 1.3 MW (SW-1.3) and 3.6MW (SW-3.6). Different from other types of wind turbine, the blades from Siemens are made of fibreglass reinforced epoxy with no joints between spars and shells, so water cannot gain access, thereby reducing the risk of saltwater erosion.

GE Energy

GE Energy is one of the world's leading companies for power generation and energy delivery, which includes energies from water, wind, oil and gas. Over 7500 wind turbines were installed around the world from GE Energy with a range from 1.5 to 3.6 MW. The 3.6 MW turbines are specifically designed for offshore sites, with higher wind speeds, larger rates and 104 m diameter rotor blades.

Turbine design basis

Due to the rapid development of wind energy, the size of wind turbines has increased to satisfy market requirements. Since the turbine size is becoming larger, the design concepts are also developing in relation to the number of the blades, the position of the rotor, wind speed, power of the rotor and so on.

In this section, we will discuss the turbine concept and power control system.

Turbine Concept

Hansen and Hansen (2007) state four different concepts for turbine design: fixed speed wind turbine concept (Danish concept); variable speed wind turbine concept with variable rotor resistance (Optislip concept); variable speed wind turbine concept with partial-scale frequency converter (doubly fed induction generator concepts); and variable speed concept with full-scale frequency converter (pitch concept with a synchronous generator). These four concepts are outlined below.

Among all concepts, the Danish concept is the most standard and most used. This concept can be simply explained as a turbine operating at a fixed wind speed, and with an asynchronous generator.

The doubly fed induction generator concept (partial-scale frequency converter concept) entails a pitch-controlled turbine, which means the rotor runs at varied wind speeds. This design has an asynchronous generator and a partial-scale frequency converter, which operates only within a speed range of 30% of synchronous speed. The turbine blades turn off during strong winds. Since a partial-scale frequency converter is used in this design, it can reach 25–30% cent of output from the full-scale power converter. This concept can only be considered because of its economic impact of its smaller converter.

The pitch concept with a synchronous generator (full-scale frequency converter) is also pitch controlled. This is different from a partial-scale frequency converter; the wind speed can be controlled from 0 to 100% of synchronous speed, but at a higher cost. The variable speed wind turbine concept with variable rotor resistance is for a turbine operated under a limited range of wind speeds, and controlled by the pitch and rotor resistance. Therefore, the rotor resistance will cause a loss of energy due to the transferring process, this design is more costly and is less efficient.

Power control system

Power control is used on all turbines to avoid the damage in high wind speeds.

Stall control is the earliest and simplest method to control power output (Hansen & Hansen 2007). When wind speed exceeds a certain limit, the rotor blades are designed to stall to protect the rotor. This design may lose some energy, but the advantage is that the design is simple without the high mechanism complexity as pitch controlled turbines.

Pitch control turbines can generate power with fast turning blades at high wind speeds. The system is highly efficient, but the mechanism is much more complex, and the machine cannot adapt well to power fluctuations at high speed winds.

Table 8.7 gives design concepts and control abilities for wind turbines over 3.0 MW from the six largest wind companies.

Substructure of wind farms

In general, three different sub-structures have been used to support offshore wind mills. They are: gravity based caisson foundations, monopiles, and torpid foundations.

Gravity based caisson foundations

Offshore wind mills can be supported by a concrete caisson or a steel gravity foundation. The concrete caissons are used more frequently than gravity foundations (Houlsbey & Bryne 2000). Since the increase in turbine size and tower height, the size of the concrete caissons has been increased to satisfy the design criteria. The cost of the caissons is considerably greater than the monopile structures. Steel gravity foundations are much lighter than concrete caissons, so they are easier to transport and install. However, the cost of producing these enormous steel foundations is considerable.

Table 8.7 Design concept and power control system used by six offshore wind energy companies

Manufacturer	wind turbine	Concept	Power Control
Vestas	V120-4.5MW	Doubly fed induction generator concept	Pitch controlled
Repower	5 MW	Doubly fed induction generator concept	Pitch controlled
Multibrid	M 5000	Pitch concept with synchronous generator	Pitch controlled
Enercon	E112-4.5MW	Pitch concept with synchronous generator	Pitch controlled
Siemens	3.6 MW	Pitch concept with synchronous generator	Pitch controlled
GE Energy	GE3.6 MW	Doubly fed induction generator concept	Pitch controlled

Monopile foundations

Monopiles are used on most offshore projects. At present monopiles can reach up to 4.5 m in diameter. This type of foundation is suitable for most seabed conditions and requires a smaller area. Zaaijer (2002) compared the three foundation models, namely monopile, torpid and gravity based. He found the monopile has the longest lifetime, but the torpid and gravity based structures have considerably more lateral strength. The disadvantages of monopile foundations are that it requires more time and cost to construct and position them compared with gravity foundations, and they can only be used in shallow water of less than 30 metres deep.

Torpid foundation

The torpid foundation is designed for deep water. This structure is pinned by three- or four-legged steel jackets to small diameter steel piles or caissons. This design has a big future in the development of offshore wind farms.

Floating offshore wind farms, which can be installed in deep water, are another option for the future. However, the main disadvantage of this concept is the cost (Hansen & Hansen 2007), which could be double that of seabed-mounted structures. A possibility to reduce cost is to install the floating turbines on offshore rigs in oil or gas fields to run instead of using gas.

Analysis of offshore wind farms

In this section, we will outline a simplified model for an offshore wind farm using the monopile foundation concept. Figure 8.7 illustrates various loadings on a monopile, including wind, hydrodynamic and soil loadings.

Hydrodynamic loading

Hydrodynamic loading on an offshore monopile consists of two components: static and dynamic loading. The static water pressure varies only with one parameter, which is the water depth. It is easily expressed by Pascal's Law:

$$p = \rho g z \,, \tag{2}$$

where ρ is the density of the fluid; g is the acceleration due to the gravity (9.8 m/s2) and z is the water depth at some specific point in metres.

Dynamic wave loading on an offshore monopile

$$p = -\frac{i\rho g H_i}{4} \frac{\cosh k(z+d)}{\cosh kd} e^{-iwt} \times [i(1+\lambda) \sum_{m=0}^{\infty} \sum_{n=0}^{\infty} \varepsilon_m \varepsilon_n i^m Q_{mn}(r,\theta),$$

$$+ 2(1-\lambda) \sum_{m=0}^{\infty} \sum_{n=0}^{\infty} \varepsilon_m i^m Y_{mn}(r,\theta)] \tag{3}$$

where Q_{mn} and Y_m are Bessel function for the first-order velocity potential, which are available in Zhu (1993); H_i is incident wave amplitude; d is water depth; λ is reflection coefficient; k is wave number; θ is angle around cross-section of the cylinder; ε_m and ε_n are coefficients.

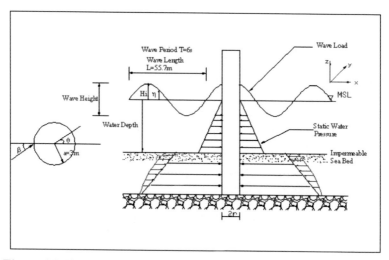

Figure 8.7 Sketch of loading on offshore mono-pile

Lateral earth pressure within a seabed

The soil at the foundation part of the pile gives a lateral pressure on the concrete cylinder. In the current study, only the static soil pressure is considered, which is obtained by using the equation of the soil weight pressure:

$$p_s = \gamma_s h, \tag{4}$$

where p_s is the pressure due to soil weight; γ_s is the unit weight of soil; h is the distance from the soil surface to a specific point in soil layers in metres.

Wind loading

The wind velocity on the top layer of the monopile can be affected by considering both the inverse of the annual probability of exceedance (R) and the height (z). The function of wind velocity for the structure with a height between 10 m and 100 m can be determined by (AS/NZS 1170.2:2002)

$$V(z)_{1170.2} = V_R M_d (M_{z,cat}(z) M_s M_t), \tag{5}$$

where M_d is wind direction multiplier; M_s is shielding multiplier; M_t is topographic multiplier; $M_{z,\ cat}(z)$ is height multiplier as a function of height (z)

$$M_{z,cat} = 0.15 \ln z + 0.0003z + 0.67, \tag{6}$$

where z is the reference height of the structure above the average local ground level in metres;
In (5), VR is regional 3 second gust wind speed in m/s at 10m height

$$V_R = 67 - 41R^{-0.1}, \tag{7}$$

where R is the inverse of the annual probability of exceedance of the wind speed.

The wind pressure (p) in Pascal, can be followed by the code AS/NZS1170.2:2002, as a function of height (z):

$$p(z) = (0.5\rho_{air})[V(z)]^2 C_{fig} C_{dyn},$$ (8)

where ρ_{air} is density of air, taken as 1.2 kg/m³; C_{dyn} is dynamic response factor, taken as 1.0; and C_{fig} is aerodynamic shape factor defined by

$$C_{fig} = C_{p.b}(\theta_b) = k_b C_{p1}(\theta_b),$$ (9)

where θ_b is the angle from the wind direction to a point on the wall of the monopile, in degrees, k_b is factor for a circular cylinder, given as:

$$k_b = 1.0 \text{ for } C_{p1} \geq -0.15$$

$$k_b = 1.0 - 0.55(C_{p1}(\theta_b) + 0.15)\log_{10}(c/b) \text{ for } C_{p1} < -0.15;$$ (10)

in which c/b is unit aspect ratio in a range 0.25 to 4.0; and $C_{p1}(\theta_b)$ is external pressure coefficients as a function of angle θ_b.

Overturning force from wind turbine

The overturning force due to the wind turbine is expressed as

$$T = 0.5 C_T \rho_{air} \pi R^2 U^2,$$ (11)

where C_T is thrust coefficient, taken as 8/9 for ideal case, ρ_{air} is the density of air, taken as 1.2 kg/m³, R is the radii of wind turbine, and U is free stream velocity.

Potential of offshore wind energy in Australia

Assessment of offshore wind farms sites

We have established a set of selection criteria to assess possible sites for offshore wind energy generation in Australia, (Tables 8.8–8.16). Based on existing offshore wind energy projects in Europe, the major criteria for the selection of sites for offshore wind farms are summarised below:

Water depth and distance to shoreline

Water depth and distance to shoreline are two extremely important criteria for the selection of offshore wind farms. All current offshore wind turbines are installed in shallow water with monopiles and gravity foundations. Current trends indicate that offshore wind turbines will become much larger even than the present largest structures (e.g. in the Irish Sea). It is well known that wind speed increases markedly with distance from shore with less visual impact and less competing use of the seabed. These criteria will gradually attract developers into deep water, that is substructures will change from current monopiles and gravity foundations in shallow water to floating structures in deep water. However, the costs of offshore wind farms will increase as water depth increases (Figure 8.8) (Dolan 2004).

Wind Speed

Wind Speed is another dominant criterion for the selection of sites, as it is the main resource for offshore wind energy. A comparison of potential power production at onshore and offshore sites was reported by Pryor and Barthelmie (2001). In their study, four sites in the Danish wind monitoring network were selected for case studies. Their observation indicated that offshore wind speed at Rødsand, located 9 km from the closest coastline, reached 17 m/sec. Their research also pointed out that the average power production in the offshore site (Rødsand) was a constant 900 kW/hour, which is double the peak value of the onshore site at Tystofte (Pryor & Barthelmie 2001).

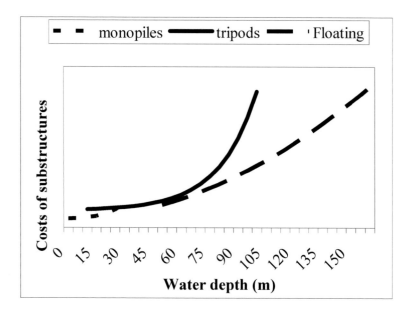

Figure 8.8 Cost of offshore wind turbine substructures with water depth (adapted from Dolan (2004))

Environmental and Biological aspects

The biological and environmental state of the proposed site needs to be thoroughly investigated as minor disturbances to the ecology may cause devastating effects. If there is not a full assessment and appropriate planning, environmental groups in Australia and the population living close to the proposed site would become extremely active. The surrounding environment should be assessed for possible parks, reserves and heritage protected areas and all levels of local, state and federal protected areas need be consulted.

Leisure

The level of boating and recreational activities may lead to complications for the construction of offshore wind farms. If the selected area has active boating and recreational use, public disapproval would result. Due to these difficulties, leisure is included as part of the criteria in selecting sites for offshore wind farming.

Land use (effects on population)

Types of land use on the adjacent coastline is important. If there is a large concentration of people, building a wind farm may obstruct water views, which would be extremely undesirable. Problems during and after construction can affect the local population, including job creation and social aspects.

Proposed development of sites

The size of the proposed development areas will affect the position of the offshore wind farms, as will the size and number of wind turbines. This will also affect operation and maintenance costs.

The aforementioned aspects are included in the general selection criteria listed in Table 8.8, and details of each item are listed in Tables 8.10–8.16. Note that the small number of selection criteria is favourable for offshore wind energy.

Table 8.8 General selection criteria

Locations	
Distance to shoreline (km)	<3
	4–9
	10–15
	>15
Land use	Industrial
	Settlement
	Rural
Proposed area development	Large
	Moderate
	Small

Table 8.8 General selection criteria (continued)

Locations	
Water depth (m)	<1
	2–5
	6–5
	6–9
	10–30
	>30
Leisure	Major
	Moderate
	Minor
Environmental	Heritage area
	Parks and reserves
	Shipping
Biological	Birds
	Fish school
	Mammals
Wind speed (m/s)	<4
	5–10
	11–15
	16–25
	>25
Total score	
Rank (1, 2, 3 etc.)	
Overall sensitivity (pref, med, high)	

Table 8.9 Scoring for distance to shoreline

Factor	Score	Description
<3 km	3	Too close to the shoreline
4–9 km	2	Close to the shoreline
10–15 km	1	Not close to the shoreline
>15 km	0.5	Far away from the shoreline

Table 8.10 Scoring for water depths

Factor	Score	Description
<1 m	3	Extremely large visual impact
2–5 m	2	Large visual impact
6–5 m	1	Moderate visual impact
6–9 m	0.5	Small visual impact
10–30 m	-1	Minor visual impact
>30 m	-2	No visual impact

Table 8.11 Scoring for land use factor

Factor	Score	Description
Industrial	0	Absent
	1	Small scale factories & fishery activities
	2	Medium to moderate scaled factories & shipping activities
	3	International shipping activities & large scaled factories
Settlement	0	Absent
	1	Country town
	2	Township
	3	Metropolitan
Rural	0	Absent
	1	Scarcely populated
	2	Small to moderately populated
	3	Large populated

Table 8.12 scoring for proposed development area

Factor	Score	Description
Small	1	< 20 turbines
Moderate	2	< 150 turbines
Large	3	>200 turbines

Table 8.13 Scoring for leisure factor

Factor	Score	Description
Major	3	Tourist destination, ferry & boating activities (>5000 hrs per yr)
Moderate	2	Leisure boating activities (< 5000 hrs per year)
Minor	1	Occasional boating activities (<500 hrs per year)
None	-2	Absent

Table 8.14 Scoring for environmental factor

Factor	Score	Description
Heritage Area	3	Federal protection area
	2	State protection area
	1	Local protection area
	-2	Absent
Parks	3	National reserves
	2	State reserves
	1	Local reserves
	-2	Absent
Shipping	3	High intensity (7500–20000 hrs per annual)
	2	Moderate intensity (2500–7500 hrs per annual)
	1	Low intensity (1 – 2500 hrs per annual)
	-2	Absent

Table 8.15 Scoring for wind speed factor

Factor	Score	Description
Wind speed	3	<4 m/sec
	2	5–10 m/sec
	1	11–15 m/sec
	0	16–25 m/sec
	-2	>25 m/sec

Table 8.16 Scoring for biological factor

Factor	Score	Description
Birds	3	Internationally designed migrating & protected area
	2	Nationally designed migrating & protected area
	-2	Absent
Fish schools	3	Spawning beneath sediment & benthic & demurral species
	2	Spawning beneath water & pelagic species
	-2	Absent
Mammals	3	Protected species
	2	Native species
	-1	Unprotected species
	-2	Absent

Evaluation of potential sites for offshore wind energy in Australia

Based on the selection criteria proposed in the last section, we chose five sites around Australia for evaluation: (1) southern part of Western Australia, (2) Darwin, (3) Adelaide, (4) Sydney and (5) Whitsunday Islands, Queensland (Figure 8.9). The ranking scores for all sites are given in Table 8.17. As mentioned previously, the smaller number of selection criteria favour offshore wind energy over other renewable energy sources. As shown in Table 8.17, the southern part of WA is the preferred site for offshore wind energy in Australia (Figure 8.9).

Table 8.17 Ranking for selected sites

Location	SWA	W	D	S	A
Distance to shoreline	2	3	1	1	0.5
Land use					
Industrial	-1			2	2
Settlement .	1	2	2	3	3
Rural	0	2	0		
Proposed area development	3	1	2	2	1
Water depth	0.5	2	-1	0.5	0.5
Leisure	1	-2	2	3	3
Environmental					
Heritage area	3	3	1	-2	-2
Parks and reserves	2	2	2	-2	-2
Shipping	-1	3	2	3	3
Biological					
Birds	-2	1	0	-2	-2
Fish schools	-2	3	3	2	2
Mammals	2	3	2	2	3
Wind speed	-2	-2	-2	3	3
Total score	6.5	21	14	15.5	15
Rank	1	5	2	4	3

Notes: WA = Southern part of WA; W = Whitsunday island; D = Darwin; S = Sydney; A = Adelaide

Regions off Queensland are not chosen due to the large protected world heritage areas, such as the Great Barrier Reef. The northern tip of Queensland and Northern Territory are not included in the list due to frequent cyclonic activity throughout the year, but especially during summer periods. The shorelines of New South Wales and Victoria are not favourable due to the high concentration of population which makes offshore wind farms unwelcome. Tasmania is a good location for offshore wind farms; however, it would attract excessive initial capital and operation and maintenance costs. This narrows potential areas down to regions of Southern Australia and the southern parts of Western Australia (Figure 8.9). The advantages of these two regions are the consistent wind supply and large areas of shallow water.

The above assessment is based on the assumption that offshore wind farms will be constructed in Australia as monopiles in shallow water. Perhaps this is the first option for energy companies in Australia at present. However, floating offshore wind farms in deep water will be another option for the development of offshore wind energy in Australia in the future.

Figure 8.9 Potential site of offshore wind energy in Australia

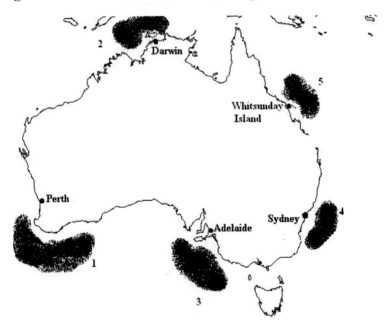

Conclusions

An overview of offshore wind energy was provided in this chapter. Based on the numerical examples and discussions, it can be concluded that, compared with other renewable energy resources, offshore wind energy has great potential in the future – even if it has some shortcomings and limitations.

A set of selection criteria for an appropriate site of offshore wind energy has been established. Based on these criteria, the southern part of Western Australia is suggested as having the most potential for generation of offshore wind energy in Australia.

Acknowledgement

The authors are grateful for support from a University of Sydney Sustainable Energy Research Grant (2007–2009).

References

Barthelmie R J, Courtney M S, Højstrup J & Larsen S E, 1996. 'Meteorological aspects of offshore wind energy: observations from the vindey wind farm', *Journal of Wind Engineering and Industrial Aerodynamics*, vol. 62, pp. 191–211.

Dolan D, 2004. Deepwater fixed bottom wind turbine platforms, Deepwater Wind Energy Workshop, Washington DC http://www.energytics.com/deepwater.html.

Hansen A D & Hansen L H, 2007. 'Wind turbine concept market penetration over 10 years (1995–2004)', *Wind Energy*, vol. 10, pp. 81–97.

Henderson A R, Leutz R & Fujii T, 2002. 'Potential for floating offshore wind energy in Japanese waters', Proceedings of the 12th International Offshore and Polar Engineering Conference (ISOPE2002), Kitakyushu, Japan, pp. 505–512.

Houlsby G T & Byrne B W, 2000. 'Suction caisson foundations for offshore wind turbines and anemometer masts' *Wind Engineering*, vol. 24, no. 4, pp. 249–255.

Lavagnini A, Sempreviva A M & Barthelmie R J, 2003. 'Estimating wind energy potential offshore in Mediterranean areas', *Wind Energy*, vol. 6, pp. 23–34.

Musial W,2006) Energy from offshore wind, Offshore Technology Conference (OTC2006), Houston, USA, OTC18355.

Offshore Wind Energy, http://www.offshorewindenergy.org/ last accessed November 1, 2006

Owen A D, 2003. 'Renewable energy: externally costs as market barriers', *Energy Policy*, vol. 34, pp. 632–642.

Pryor S C & Barthelmie R J, 2001. 'Comparison of potential power production at on- and offshore sites', *Wind Energy*, vol. 4, pp. 173–181.

Tap-Johansen N J, Sempreviva A M & Barthelmie R J, 2006. 'Application of design standards to the design of offshore wind turbines in the US', Offshore technology Conference, Houston, USA (2006), OTC18357.

World Energy Council (WEC), 2003. Renewable energy targets http://www.worldenergy.org.

World Energy Outlook, WEO2006. http://www.worldenergyoutlook. org/.

World Wind Energy Association, http://www.world-wind-energy.info/

Zaaijer M B, 2002. Foundation models for the dynamic response of offshore wind turbines. Marine Renewable Energy Conference, Newcastle, UK.

Zhu S P, 1993. 'Diffraction of short-crested waves around a circular cylinder', *Ocean Engineering*, vol. 20, no. 4, pp. 389–407.

9

Household environmental pressure from consumption: an Australian environmental atlas

Christopher Dey, Charles Berger, Barney Foran, Miles Foran, Rowena Joske, Manfred Lenzen and Richard Wood

Abstract

Modern living means consuming, and consuming causes resource depletion and environmental degradation. Environmental education and action plans for households typically focus on the environmental pressures associated directly with household requirements, such as electricity generation, the direct combustion of fuels and direct water use. Though important, such direct environmental pressures are generally smaller than the indirect pressures associated with the consumption of goods and services by households. These indirect 'requirements' occur in the numerous producing industries of the Australian as well as overseas economies. However, in accordance with Adam Smith's classic statement that 'consumption is the sole end and purpose of all production', these requirements are ultimately being demanded by households. Total household environmental pressure is then the combination of direct and indirect requirements.

By combining detailed census, household expenditure and environmental data with an economy-wide model, we have calculated the total household environmental pressure for over 1300 Australian statistical local areas (SLAs). These estimates of the wider environmental pressure of average households at a fine spatial scale, represent a new resource for environmental education. We have produced maps of these results, for the indicators of greenhouse gas emissions, water use and ecological footprint, to reveal the sources of environmental pressures in terms of average per capita impacts. Results show that impacts are highly correlated with household expenditure, but that within clear general trends there can be large differences between the average households in different SLAs. The results were transformed into an interactive web-based tool, the Australian Consumption Atlas, which allows users to see maps of environmental performance by SLA, as well as find the typical performance by postcode, coupled with explanations and suggestions for action. The launch of the Atlas was supported by a national media and outreach campaign. The public's and media's response to the Atlas were considerable: interest was both widespread and sustained over many weeks. There was particularly strong interest in the magnitude of indirect impacts as well as the variations between SLAs. It appears that this response is indicative of the public becoming more sophisticated in its understanding of the sources of environmental pressures.

Introduction

There is extensive academic literature on the links between household consumption and environmental impacts (Chen 2007; Christoffersen et al 2005; Munksgaard et al 2005; Turner et al 2007; Wiedmann et al 2007; Wier, McDonald & Forgie 2006;). Most of these studies correctly point out the importance of off-site impacts, which are in addition to direct or on-site environmental impacts which are the normal focus of environmental education campaigns (Lenzen, Dey & Foran 2004; Munksgaard, Pedersen & Wier 2000). Indirect impacts in most developing countries are typically two to three times higher than the direct impacts (Lenzen 2001c). Resource requirements of cities has long been of interest, but on a per capita basis, similar resource requirements are involved in most lifestyles in developed countries (Moll & Norman 2002). Furthermore, indirect impacts are highly related to affluence; so, as the general affluence of households increases, so do the indirect environmental impacts of those households (Lenzen 1998). This is despite the commonly held notion that, as affluence increases, there is more opportunity for households to reduce (direct) impacts by increasing energy and water use efficiency. This may occur, but in general any reduction in direct environmental impacts are more than countered by an increase in the wider, indirect impacts associated with increased spending. This is particularly the case if trade effects are included: the embodiment of environmental impacts in the products purchased by developed countries (Ghertner & Fripp 2007). In short, there is increasing evidence to suggest that globally the Environmental Kuznets[1] curve does not hold, particularly for greenhouse gas emissions (Ghertner & Fripp 2007).

Public knowledge of off-site impacts of consumption has been stimulated by the relatively fast acceptance of the ecological footprint concept, which attempts to measure the total land requirements for supporting a lifestyle (Lenzen & Murray 2001; Wackernagel & Rees 1995). The ecological footprint is fundamentally a communication metric describing the notion that the impacts of lifestyles' spread well beyond their immediate vicinity. Although only about 15 years old as a concept, the word 'footprint' is now in general public usage, though it has been diluted and broadened from the original meaning of the ecological footprint. The analogous term 'carbon footprint' is now also in common usage, and is part of the growing interest in carbon neutrality and the related practice of carbon offsetting.[2] *Environmental footprint* is being used increasingly as a general phrase to mean environmental pressures as measured by a range of indicators, such as water use, pollution, air travel and food miles.

Despite the increasing public awareness of the wider drivers of environmental pressure, there is a need for further education and outreach tools that will stimulate real action (Lenzen, Dey & Murray 2002; Lenzen & Murray 2001a; Lenzen & Smith 2000). Success in this area depends upon a number of factors. Firstly, tools, results and their meaning must be accessible to the general public, make connections with their current understanding and not be loaded with jargon. Secondly,

---

[1] The Environmental Kuznets curve is the general hypothesis that, as populations develop, they pass over a pollution 'hump' after which further development, in terms of rising income, leads to reductions in environmental impacts.
[2] See ISA report, *Carbon Neutrality – sense and sensibility*, http://www.isa.org.usyd.edu.au/publications/CarbonNeutral.pdf.

education material must still be sufficiently quantitative, independent and reliable to secure the public's trust. Thirdly, sheer volume of information – for example, many individual indicators addressing multiple issues – will not be as effective as a selection of key indicators covering major concerns. Fourthly, communication of results and meanings will be enhanced if there can be personal relevance, such as results related to particular demographic groups, lifestyle factors or locations. Finally, to be ultimately successful, any education campaign should stimulate significant action or behaviour change.

This chapter is not only concerned with the calculation of household impacts, largely an academic exercise for which there is a general convergence of methods and an understanding of the importance of the wider impacts of households.[3] Rather, this work also examines the effectiveness of communication of these issues to the general public, and the response of the public and the media to such issues. The work is the outcome of a partnership between researchers from the Centre of Integrated Sustainability Analysis at the University of Sydney and educators from the Australian Conservation Foundation, a non-governmental organisation with a long history of environmental education and advocacy.

In this chapter we outline the methodology behind the calculation of average environmental pressures across Australia and present a sample of results to illustrate the web-based tool known as the *Consumption Atlas*. We then discuss the responses to the launch and education campaign of the Consumption Atlas, before concluding and discussing briefly ideas for future work in this area.

Methodology

The principle methodology behind this work is well developed and is described elsewhere (Lenzen 1998; Lenzen, Dey & Foran. 2004). The objective of the project was to estimate the total environmental impacts, meaning the direct plus indirect impacts, for typical households down to

---

[3] However, there is still not yet complete agreement on metrics and scopes of analyses; see, for example, discussions and references in Turner et al (2007) and Wiedmann et al, (2007).

a fine spatial level covering all of Australia. In summary, the work here combines an input–output analysis approach for calculating indirect requirements for households, with household expenditure data for a sample of Australian households, with comprehensive population census data for the whole nation. The work therefore relies on the extensive, publicly-available datasets collected and provided by the Australian Bureau of Statistics (ABS). The methodology is outlined in the following sections.

Input–output analysis

Input–output analysis is a macroeconomic technique that uses data on inter-industrial monetary transactions to account for the complex interdependencies of industries in modern economies. Since its introduction by Leontief (Leontief 1936; 1941), it has been applied to numerous economic and environmental issues, and input–output tables are now compiled on a regular basis for most industrialised, and also many developing countries. To obtain regional results we combine the national Australian input–output tables and national data on resource use and pollution (modified by regionalising some important state-specific impacts such as those from electricity provision and meat production) with regional household expenditure data. The assumption inherent in this approach is that products purchased by regional households are produced regionally and nationally using a similar production recipe. Hence it is a study of national impacts that result from regional consumption. In contrast, regional input–output tables are required for the analysis of regional impacts and inter-regional flows (Tiebout 1960). The technique of combining input–output and household expenditure data has been used previously by a number of authors (see comprehensive reference list in Lenzen, Dey & Foran 2004).

The environmental impact of households is determined via

$$\mathbf{F} = \left(\mathbf{Q}^{emb} + \mathbf{Q}^{hh}\right) \times \mathbf{Y}$$
(1)

The variables in Equation 1 are in turn:

F Matrix of *household factor requirements.* Its elements $\{F_{ij}\}_{i=1,\ldots,f\,;\,j=1,\ldots,g}$ describe the total amount of factor i required by household group j. The term *factor* represents resource and environmental quantities (such as land disturbance, fuel consumption, water use, greenhouse gas emissions and the aggregated quantity ecological footprint). **F** comprises both factors $\mathbf{Q}^{hh} \times \mathbf{Y}$ used directly by the household (in the house or by using private vehicles), and also factors $\mathbf{Q}^{emb} \times \mathbf{Y}$ used by Australian and foreign industries, that are required indirectly to provide goods and services purchased by the household. The latter are also called *embodied factor requirements.* **F** has dimensions $f \times g$, where f is the number of factors (only results for three will be presented here: greenhouse gas emissions, water use and ecological footprint) and g is the number of household groups. For this study an average household was established for each of the 1346 Statistical Local Areas (SLA) defined by the Australian Bureau of Statistics (ABS). This procedure is discussed further below.

$\mathbf{Q}^{hh}$ Matrix of *household factor multipliers.* Its elements $\{Q_{ij}^{hh}\}_{i=1,\ldots,f\,;\,j=1,\ldots,s}$ describe the usage by private households of factor i per A\$ value of final consumption of commodities from industry j. $\mathbf{Q}^{hh}$ has dimensions $f \times s$, where s is the number of classified industries. The Centre for Integrated Sustainability Analysis at the University of Sydney (ISA) has expanded the more aggregated Australian *input–output tables* compiled by the ABS to distinguish $s = 344$ industry sectors. These range from primary industries such as agriculture and mining, via secondary industries such as manufacturing and electricity, gas and water utilities, to tertiary industries such as commercial services, health, education, defence and government administration. This expanded input–output framework applies to the year 1998–99.

$\mathbf{Q}^{emb}$ Matrix of *embodied factor multipliers.* Its elements $\{Q_{ij}^{emb}\}_{i=1,\ldots,f\,;\,j=1,\ldots,s}$ describe the usage of factor i per A\$ value of final consumption of commodity j, (1) by the industry sectors producing commodity j, (2) by all upstream industry sectors supplying industry sectors producing commodity j, (3) by all upstream industry sectors supplying industry sectors that supply industry sectors producing commodity j, and (4) so on, infinitely. $\mathbf{Q}^{emb}$ thus captures the *total factor requirements* of industries in the entire economy that are needed to produce commodities consumed by households. $\mathbf{Q}^{emb}$ has dimensions $f \times s$.

$\mathbf{Y}$ Matrix of *household expenditure*. Its elements $\{Y_{ij}\}_{i=1,\dots,s;\,j=1,\dots,h}$ describe the amount of A\$ spent on commodity i by household group j during the reference year. $\mathbf{Y}$ has dimensions $s \times h$.

$\mathbf{Q}^{emb}$ can be calculated according to the *basic input–output relationship*

$$\mathbf{Q}^{emb} = \mathbf{Q}^{ind}\left(\mathbf{I} - \mathbf{A}\right)^{-1}. \tag{2}$$

The variables in Equation 2 are:

$\mathbf{Q}^{ind}$ Matrix of *industrial factor multipliers*. Its elements $\{Q_{ij}^{ind}\}_{i=1,\dots,f;\,j=1,\dots,s}$ describe the usage of factor i by industry sector j per A\$ value of total output by industry sector j. In contrast to $\mathbf{Q}^{emb}$, $\mathbf{Q}^{ind}$ represents only factors used directly in each industry, but not in upstream supplying industries. $\mathbf{Q}^{ind}$ has dimensions $f \times s$.

$\mathbf{I}$ The *unity matrix*. Its elements $\{I_{ij}\}_{i=1,\dots,s;\,j=1,\dots,s}$ are $I_{ij}=1$ if $i=j$, and $I_{ij}=0$ if $i \neq j$. $\mathbf{I}$ has dimensions $s \times s$.

$\mathbf{A}$ Matrix of *direct requirements*. Its elements $\{A_{ij}\}_{i=1,\dots,s;\,j=1,\dots,s}$ describe the amount of input in Australian Dollars (A\$) of industry sector i into industry sector j, per A\$ value of total output of industry sector j. $\mathbf{A}$ has dimensions $s \times s$. It comprises imports from foreign industries and transactions for capital replacement and growth. $\mathbf{A}$ captures the interdependence of industries in the Australian economy and their dependence on foreign industries, and – assuming that imports are produced using Australian technology – thus enables the translation of industrial factor multipliers $\mathbf{Q}^{ind}$ into embodied factor multipliers $\mathbf{Q}^{emb}$.

Furthermore, factor requirements for Australian industries producing exports are removed from $\mathbf{Q}^{ind}$, since responsibility for these impacts are borne by the purchasers of the exported commodities (see Gallego & Lenzen 2005; Lenzen et al 2007)). In Australia there is a strong trade surplus of environmental impacts, associated mainly with impacts relating to the export of primary commodities. For a comprehensive description of the Australian input–output framework, see papers by Lenzen (Lenzen 2001b; 2001a; Lenzen & Foran 2001).

Data sources, regression and results breakdowns

A traditional problem in undertaking generalised input–output analysis is the alignment of different data sources which may vary in industry sector classification and reference year. Approaches to these problems are described elsewhere (e.g. Gallego & Lenzen 2006; Lenzen, Gallego & Wood 2007). The Household Expenditure Survey (Australian Bureau of Statistics 2000) commodity classification and the Input–output Tables (Australian Bureau of Statistics 2004a, 2004b) refer to the year 1998–99 but Australian population census data from 2001 were used. The industrial energy and greenhouse multipliers were obtained by consulting a range of sources such as fuel statistics (Australian Bureau of Agricultural and Resource Economics 1999, 2001), the Australian National Greenhouse Gas Inventory (National Greenhouse Gas Inventory Committee 1998) and motor vehicle and transport surveys (Australian Bureau of Statistics 1996, 1997). These industry multipliers are used to calculate energy embodied in consumer items. Producers making up the supply chains of these establishments are likely to be distributed across the whole of Australia, so that we apply state adjusted energy multipliers for the first and second layer of suppliers, and national averages further upstream. Household energy multipliers $\mathbf{Q}^{hh}_{energy}$ are generally specific to a state, and were therefore sourced separately. Examples of regionally adjusted figures are those for electricity (NSW Department of Energy and Utilities 2000), petrol (Australian Automobile Association 2000) and local transport data (Lenzen 1999). Other sources include data for water (Lenzen & Foran 2001; Vardon et al 2007) and land use, weighted by degree of disturbance (Barson, Randall & Bordas 2000; Graetz, Wilson & Campbell 1995; Lenzen & Murray 2001). In order to match the

Household Expenditure Survey data, all factor multipliers were extrapolated to 1998–99 values, considering trends in industrial factor use, changes in product taxation, and developments in the Consumer Price Index (CPI) to account for inflation (Bureau of Labor Statistics 2002). While this procedure introduces additional uncertainty into the estimates of factor requirements, this uncertainty is well below the variability of these requirements across different household groups in a typical sample.

The average household expenditure matrix (**Y**) by SLA was derived from the 1998–99 Household Expenditure Survey (HES) aggregated to statistical sub division (SSD) level and then regressed against the census data. The range of the explanatory variables used in this derivation was as follows: weekly per capita income, average number of persons in the household, average age from HES structure, educational qualification, population density (km^{-2}), and household type (renting, purchasing, owners, average number of employed persons in household, car ownership, state, and dwelling type). The multivariate regression technique used is similar to that employed for the ISA study on Sydney households (Lenzen, Dey & Foran 2004).

Previously employed techniques known as production layer decomposition, sectoral breakdowns, and structural path analysis may be used to provide breakdowns of aggregated results (Lenzen & Treloar 2003; Treloar 1997).

Results and discussion

This section presents a selection of the results of the analysis, including a sample of the typical Consumption Atlas maps. Key findings and responses to them in terms of environmental policy and action are also discussed. Average Australian, and by state, greenhouse gas emissions, water use and ecological footprint results are given in Table 9.1. These are calculated from the SLA data, weighted by population. To support the average Australian lifestyle, 18.9 t CO_2-e (tonnes of carbon dioxide equivalent) of greenhouse gases are emitted, 720 000 litres of water are used, and an ecological footprint of 6.45 ha is required.

The principle reason for differences between states is different levels of affluence, as indicated by the annual per capita income figures. One exception to this is due to the predominant electricity generation infrastructure in each state. Tasmania, being largely powered by hydroelectricity, is lower than average, whereas Victoria, largely powered by brown coal generated electricity, is higher. Note that despite Tasmania's own electricity being mostly low-emission hydropower, the average Tasmanian still has significant emissions because their consumption draws on power consumed by industries in the higher emitting mainland states. The other major instance for state differences not following per capita income is in the ecological footprint and is due to different stocking rates for grazing, particularly for Western Australia.

The high water use and greenhouse emissions in the ACT are predominantly an affluence effect, as indicated by the ACT's high average per capita income. Differences in household water use reflect these income differences, but also variations in climate. Where water is relatively plentiful, as in Tasmania and parts of the Northern Territory and Queensland, less water extraction is required for gardening and other uses.

Table 9.1 Average per capita national results, and for each state, for the indicators greenhouse gas emissions, water use and ecological footprint.

	Annual income	Greenhouse gas emissions	Water use	Ecological footprint
	$ / capita	t CO_2-e / capita	ML / capita	ha / capita
ACT	25,016	22.5	0.86	6.96
NSW	20,092	19.3	0.74	6.33
NT	19,274	19.0	0.65	6.73
QLD	18,201	18.4	0.68	6.51
SA	18,166	17.2	0.68	6.67
TAS	16,529	14.3	0.65	5.50
VIC	19,504	19.7	0.75	6.18
WA	18,949	18.0	0.72	7.32
Australia	19,309	18.9	0.72	6.45

Breakdown of average Australian household impact

Profiles of the environmental impacts of consumption for the three cross-cutting indicators (greenhouse gas emissions, water use, and ecological footprint) are given in Figures 9.1–9.3. For each indicator a breakdown of the direct and indirect contributions to these environmental impacts for the average Australian household is given. A key overall finding, and that which is consistent with earlier work, is that indirect impacts of consumption outweigh direct household use of energy, water and land. That is, the major environmental impacts occurring in the production and distribution of goods and services that households consume far outweigh the direct household impacts.

Certainly, the direct use of petrol, electricity and water might be the most visible and most discussed areas of personal impact on the environment, and these typically are some of the largest single components of household impacts. However while many Australians are increasingly aware of the need to conserve water and reduce energy use, information about the hidden environmental costs of many products and services is much harder to acquire. Direct household and personal activities account on average for only 30 per cent of a household's total greenhouse gas emissions, 23 per cent of total water use, and just 10 per cent of the total ecological footprint.

The profiles in Figures 9.1–9.3 are challenging, for individuals as well as governments and organisations seeking environmental change. They suggest that even drastic measures to reduce direct personal water and energy use may not have the desired effects, unless they are complemented by strong action to reduce the environmental impacts associated with such activities as food and clothing provision, and goods and services purchased in general.

Burning fossil fuels for the provision of energy, mostly electricity, accounts for approximately 70 per cent of total greenhouse gas emissions in Australia (Australian Greenhouse Office 2007). This energy is used mainly in the production and distribution of goods, with household electricity and personal transport being important secondary components. The direct use of energy and the indirect use of energy embodied in goods and services consumed by an average Australian in one year result in the generation of about 19 t CO_2-e greenhouse gas emissions. Agriculture, largely emissions from livestock, is a significant source of non-energy emissions embodied in household consumption. Areas where a household has relatively direct control – such as their own electricity, natural gas, and transport use – on average account for less than a third of total emissions (Figure 9.1). In fact, if every Australian household switched to renewable energy and stopped driving their cars tomorrow, total household emissions would decline by only about 18%. The emissions generated from producing the food we eat and the goods we purchase are together more than four times the emissions from our own personal use of electricity. This suggests that for households to make a serious reduction in greenhouse gas emissions, they must go well beyond merely reducing household energy and petrol use.

Figure 9.1 Breakdown of the total greenhouse gas emissions for the average Australian (18.9 t CO_2-e)

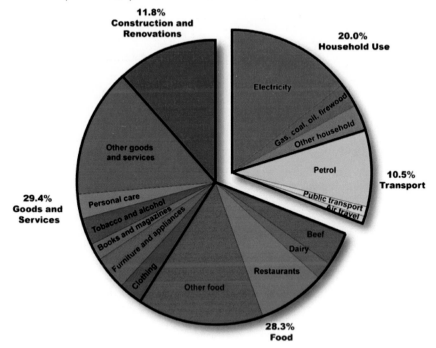

Figure 9.2 Breakdown of the total water use for the average Australian (720 kL)

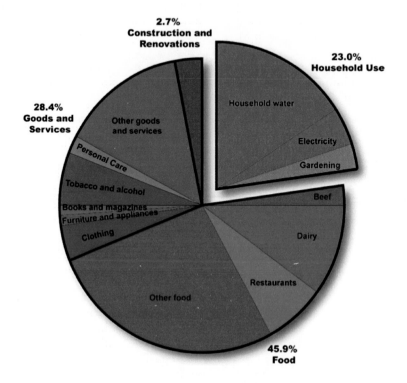

The total water use by the average Australian amounts to 720 kL (kilo litres) per person, per year, including water embodied in all food, goods and services (Figure 9.2). This amount of water is comparable to the volume of an Olympic-sized swimming pool. Direct water use in the household only accounts for just over 16 per cent of total water use. The water used to produce all goods and services consumed is more than six times greater than direct household water use. Production of dairy and beef products is particularly water-intensive; the dairy sector alone accounts for one out of every ten litres of total household water use. Traditional electricity generation, which uses water for cooling, is a large user of water, amounting to nearly 4 per cent of the total water used by households.

The ecological footprint is a measure of the total amount of land required to supply all the resources a person's lifestyle demands. This includes land disturbance related to agriculture and other activities, as well as a component to account for greenhouse gas emissions. At an average of 6.45 ha (hectares) per person, Australians have one of the highest ecological footprints in the world (World Wide Fund for Nature 2006).

Figure9. 3 Breakdown of the ecological footprint for the average Australian (6.45 ha)

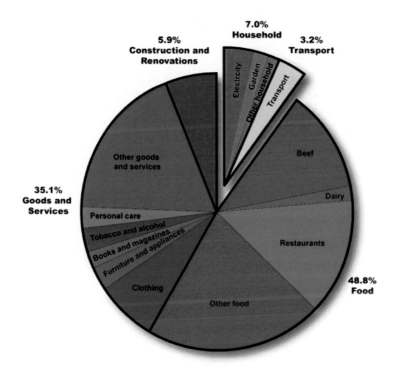

As Figure 9.3 shows, nearly half of the average person's ecological footprint is attributable to the land disturbed by food production. Cattle grazing in particular requires vast amounts of land in Australia. However, stocking rates and land use characteristics in the Australian rangelands are quite different from more intensively stocked and developed grazing land in other countries, closer to being in a natural state. Nevertheless, because direct household and transport contributions to land disturbance are relatively small, the most practical way for individual households to reduce their impact in terms of land disturbance is to alter their patterns of consumption of food, clothing, and other goods heavily reliant on agriculture.

General trends in total impacts from consumption

The per capita average greenhouse emissions for all SLAs are plotted against average per capita income in Figure 9.4. Despite the scatter of many different SLAs, there is a clear trend towards increasing emissions for higher incomes, as observed many times previously (e.g. Munksgaard, Pedersen & Wier 2000). Groups of symbols reflecting the state SLAs can be observed, with the Tasmanian SLAs particularly noticeable toward the bottom of Figure 9.4, due to their own electricity being mainly hydropower, as mentioned above. The shape of the curve shows no evidence for decreasing emissions for higher incomes, as would be expected if a Kuznets relationship did hold. The significant scatter of the data is indicative of the vastly differing lifestyles of Australian households, where it is quite feasible for emissions to range over a factor of two for the same per capita income. This is not surprising perhaps, since consumer preferences and activities vary enormously. Note that a central assumption of the methodology used here is that impacts are linearly related to expenditure. In reality, higher quality goods (and services) and therefore generally higher priced, will have higher impacts, but not necessarily as high as their premium price suggests. However, in the absence of extremely detailed goods and services information, both in terms of what households buy and the profiles of different quality goods in the economy, the linearity assumption is reasonable, since it is unlikely that all consumption of a household is of above-average goods and services, meaning overall uncertainties are acceptable (Lenzen 2001a). Expenditure is in general a better proxy for environmental impact, but the income data by SLA is more reliable here and for the purposes of showing important relationships, income is shown in Figures 9.4–9.6.

Closer examination of the HES shows that, while high income households spend more on high–cost, low–impact activities such as entertainment and other services, they also spend more on electricity and most other categories of goods. Furthermore, some activities with high greenhouse impacts, such as air travel and construction and renovation, tend to be concentrated in high income groups.

Figure 9.4 Greenhouse gas emissions (t CO_2-e) for each SLA as a function of annual per capita income, with states indicated

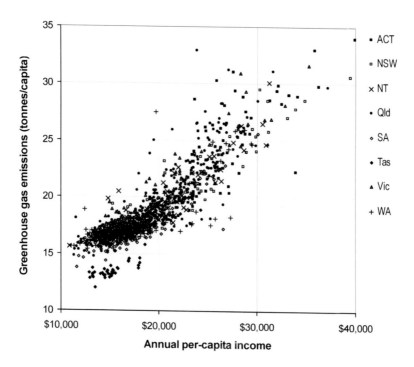

In contrast to the greenhouse gas relationship shown in Figure 9.4, there is less of an income dependence of water use and ecological footprint, as shown in Figures 9.5 and 9.6 respectively. This is readily explained since the production of food tends to be water- and land-intensive, and above a certain level of affluence average expenditure on food starts to plateau.

Figure 9.5 Total water use for each SLA as a function of annual per capita income, with states indicated

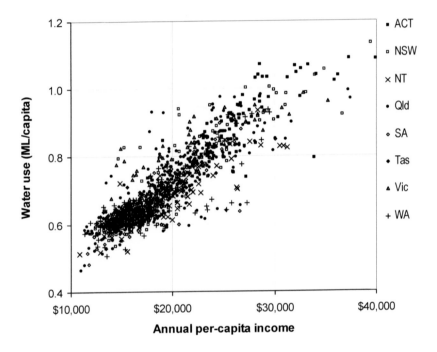

From the results shown in Figures 9.4–9.6 it can be concluded that increased wealth is leading to higher expenditure, or higher consumption of goods, services and fuels, and ultimately higher environmental impacts. It is often assumed that affluent societies and individuals will have the means to be environmentally responsible and to be able to afford to purchase better technologies with lower impacts. In theory, increased wealth could enable individuals to purchase higher quality, more environmentally sound products, and consume greater levels of services. To the extent that well-off people also have high levels of education, one might expect an increased awareness of the environment and capacity to seek out a sustainable lifestyle. However, far from enabling a sustainable lifestyle, increases in wealth appear to go hand-in-hand with greater environmental pressures. Aside from the sheer increase in expenditure, it may be that well-off individuals are 'time poor' and thus more likely to take consumption short-cuts rather than pursuing sustainable lifestyle options. For instance, households with higher incomes tend to waste more food than those on lower incomes (Hamilton, Denniss & Baker 2005).

Figure 9.6 Ecological footprint for each SLA as a function of annual per capita income, with states indicated

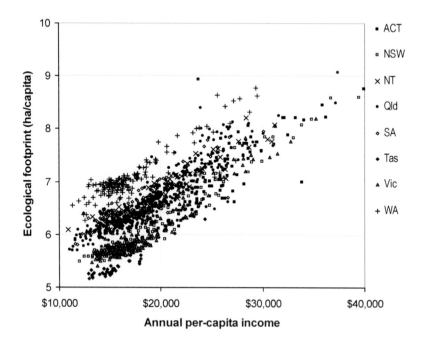

Wealth does not have to have an environmental penalty: the impact depends more importantly on how wealth is used. It is not how much is earned, but how it is spent, and on what, that determines the environmental impact. In Australia, and indeed in many other developed countries, wealth could be utilised in a more environmentally sound way. More of our individual and national wealth could be used to enable us to lead fulfilling, sustainable lives rather than just consuming more, and to invest in environmental protection and a more sustainable economy.

Environmental impact vis-à-vis household size is another interesting relationship that arises from this study, shown in Figure 9.7 for greenhouse gas emissions. The general trend towards decreasing per-capita impact as more resources are shared in larger households is clear and has been well-observed before (Lenzen 1998; Lenzen, Dey & Foran 2004). On average, single-person and small households have greater environmental impacts than larger households. As Figure 9.7 shows, areas with higher than average household size tend to have markedly lower levels of greenhouse gas emissions per capita. However there is large scatter in emissions for different households of the same (smaller) size, primarily reflecting the income effect. Large households are relatively rare in Australia, and this is reflected in the small number of large households in the HES sample. The comparatively small scatter in the results for large households probably reflects the fact that, by necessity, large households are much more similar to each other in profile (age, education, house type, etc) than are smaller households, which are more diverse.

There are several plausible explanations for this correlation. In larger households, people tend to share common living areas, which will lower the per-person heating and electricity bills. In addition, larger households can share items such as furniture and appliances, whereas a person living alone generally owns a full suite of such items. It is also reasonable to think that larger households are more likely to cook together, resulting in more efficient purchasing patterns and lower levels of food waste. In short, communal living is, in many respects, more efficient than single-person living or small households. In Australia, though, the general trend for household size is moving in the other direction: numbers of people per household are decreasing, and at the same time, the physical size of the average house is increasing in terms of floor area and number of bedrooms (Australian Bureau of Statistics 2007).

Figure 9.7 Dependence of greenhouse gas emissions on household size for all SLAs

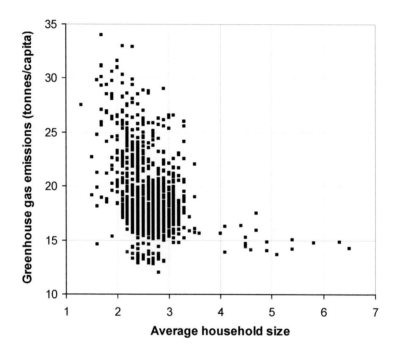

The Consumption Atlas – regional differences in environmental impacts

The detailed statistical local area data presented above may be plotted on maps using the Consumption Atlas to show patterns of consumption and environmental impact across Australia.[4] The Atlas directly illustrates

---

[4] The Consumption Atlas is accessible at: www.acfonline.org.au/consumptionatlas (Fig. 9.8)

how much water and land is needed, and how much greenhouse pollution is created, to support the average household consumption in each SLA in Australia. Designed and hosted by the Australian Conservation Foundation (ACF) as an interactive web-page, the Atlas is publicly accessible and supported by considerable explanations and educational material. The Atlas is a central part of environmental campaigning by the ACF, in particular their 'Green Home' initiative which is aimed at engaging Australian households through seminars, incentives and comprehensive online materials to reduce their environmental impacts. SLAs can be browsed by individual states, capital cities, and some high population areas to show environmental impact in terms of the three indicators. Impacts by SLA are shown in a colour-scale which is the same for all of Australia, allowing consistent comparisons to be made. Users can also enter postcodes and the site returns the most appropriate SLA. In the following, several examples are presented to demonstrate the Atlas.

Figure 9.8 Main page of the Consumption Atlas website

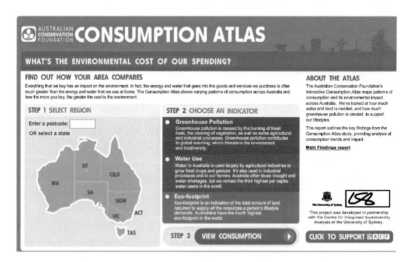

The first example is the greenhouse emissions by Queensland SLAs, showing the whole state (Fig. 9.9), zoomed to the populous south east areas (Fig. 9.10), and then zoomed into the capital of Brisbane (Fig. 9.11). Per capita emissions over the Queensland SLAs vary from 15-17 t CO_2-e in the poorer rural areas, to around an average of 20-22 t CO_2-e in metropolitan areas, to 28-32 t CO_2-e in the most affluent inner Brisbane SLAs.

Figure 9.9 Greenhouse gas emissions map for Queensland

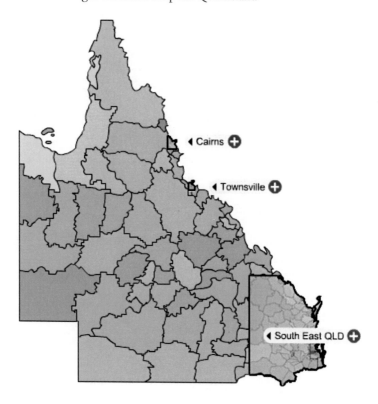

Figure 9.10 Greenhouse gas emissions map for South East Queensland

The dark areas near Brisbane indicate where the majority of the high emissions SLAs are located.

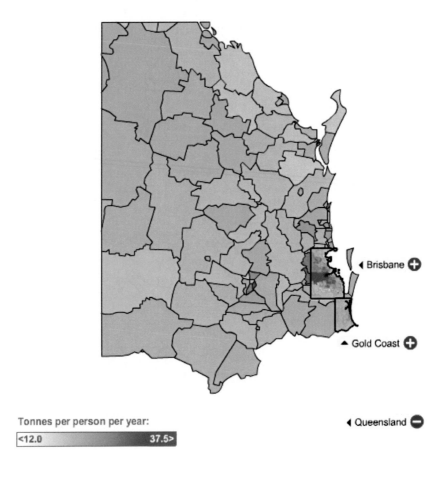

Tonnes per person per year:

<12.0   37.5>

◀ Brisbane ➕

▲ Gold Coast ➕

◀ Queensland ➖

Figure 9.11 Greenhouse gas emissions map for Brisbane

The dark areas around the centre of Brisbane represent the more affluent
SLAs with corresponding high per capita emissions. A pop-up window
reveals the actual results for a sample SLA and shows the postcode.

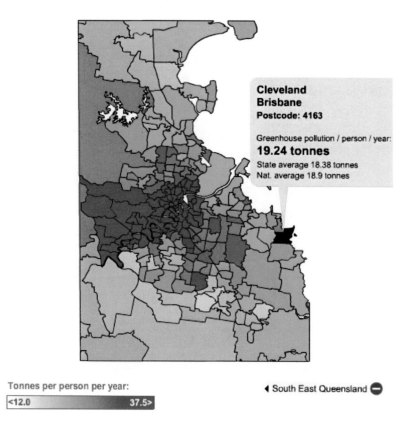

**Cleveland
Brisbane
Postcode: 4163**

Greenhouse pollution / person / year:
19.24 tonnes
State average 18.38 tonnes
Nat. average 18.9 tonnes

Tonnes per person per year:
◀ South East Queensland ⬤
|<12.0|　　　　　37.5>|

A water example is shown in Figure 9.12 for Melbourne, again clearly
showing that the affluent inner–city suburbs have considerably higher
water 'footprints' than the rest of Victoria. The area on the right shows a
typical consumption breakdown and some further information.
Those households with the highest water use (up to nearly one

million litres per capita) are indicated on the map by the darkest shade (blue in the original Atlas). These households appear predominantly in central Melbourne and throughout the wealthy coastal suburbs bordering Port Philip Bay. The highest water use occurs in Prahran South Bank and Docklands. On average, Melbourne's water use is about 5 per cent higher than the state average and 9 per cent higher than the national average.

Figure 9.12 Water use map for Melbourne

The highest SLAs have water uses of up to 950,000 litres per capita.

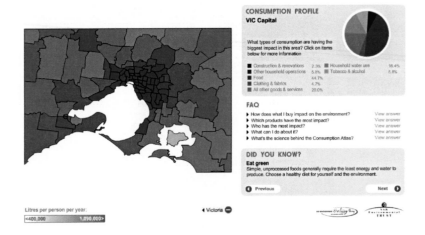

The third example of the Consumption Atlas is for the ecological footprint indicator for Sydney SLAs (Figure 9.13). As with the other capitals, the highest footprints (up 8.2 ha per capita) are in the most affluent suburbs located around Sydney Harbour.

Figure 9.13 Ecological footprint map for Sydney

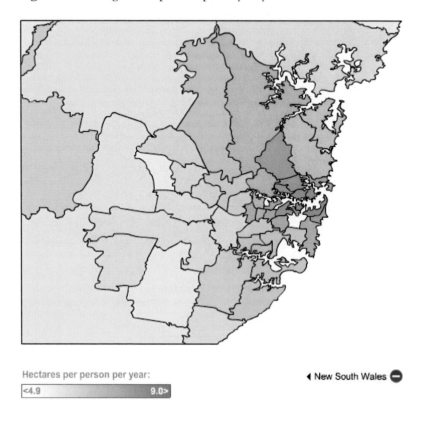

Hectares per person per year:

| <4.9 | 9.0> |

◀ New South Wales ⬤

Discussion of results in environmental policy and action terms

Four main points can be made about the Atlas results. Firstly, any benefits from urbanisation, such as higher population densities in the inner cities leading to increased use of public transport, are completely over–ridden by the negative impacts of the additional consumption of the (affluent) inner-city areas. In each state and territory, the centre of the capital city is the area with the highest environmental impacts, followed by the inner suburban areas. Rural and regional areas tend to have noticeably lower levels of impact. Affluence is the dominant effect, even though urban living patterns offer many opportunities for efficiency and reduced environmental impacts, compared to more dispersed populations.

The second point is that there is 'under' consumption in some remote areas, indicative of significant social and economic disadvantage. These low levels of consumption in remote areas may be offset to some degree by non-monetary or traditional economic activities, which are not reflected in the results. Nevertheless, the results are also consistent with a range of studies finding conditions of severe hardship in many remote communities.

The third point is that 'smarter consumption' is a valid response to reduce the environmental impact of consumption. Household environmental initiatives such as reduced waste, and lower water and energy consumption, though important, may offer much smaller environmental improvements than those achievable through smarter consumption. In terms of personal action for smarter consumption, households have many options such as: reducing their expenditure on non-essential goods; engaging in activities and choosing to consume services rather than goods; sharing goods amongst friends, neighbours and family; choosing goods which are recycled, recyclable, of high quality and high efficiency; and finally, reducing waste, particularly food waste. Smarter consumption is not necessarily incompatible with a vibrant and growing economy, but it does represent a substantial shift away from the current high consumption economies which are the norm in most developed countries.

The final point is that there is a role for governments to educate and encourage populations to consume sensibly. Viable initiatives include: education on sustainable consumption (the importance of the indirect components of the environmental impacts of households); regulation on improved product labelling; higher performance standards for equipment; and investments in infrastructure which will improve the choices available to households.

Public and media response

The Consumption Atlas was launched in July 2007 by the Australian Conservation Foundation (ACF), with state-specific media releases made possible by the detailed national data broken down by SLA. The Atlas received very strong media attention throughout Australia, with significant articles continuing to appear in major newspapers for two months after the launch. It appears that, through this coverage, the Consumption Atlas has contributed constructively to generating a national dialogue on the impacts of household consumption on sustainability in Australia. It is rare in Australia that an interactive environmental website and associated messages be so widely viewed. A summary of the main media exposures include:

- six segments on televised news and current affairs programs, reaching an estimated 2 million viewers
- strong national and state newspaper coverage, encompassing at least 25 articles mentioning the Atlas. Of particular note were a front-page story in the *Sydney Morning Herald*, a front-page story and a strong associated editorial in the *Canberra Times*, detailed pieces in the Melbourne *Herald-Sun* on two Sundays, and good coverage in the Adelaide *Advertiser* over two weekdays
- very substantial interest over several weeks by radio, including at least 47 segments covering all capital cities and numerous regional areas
- significant coverage in about 20 local newspapers across Australia, relating the information about the relevant suburbs to local readerships
- a growing list of links and articles on the internet, with mentions on prominent websites and blogs such as the *New Scientist* environment blog, *Choice* news online, *domain.com.au*, *treehugger.com*, and others.

The ability to compare the environmental performance of individual suburbs was unquestionably the major attraction for much of the mainstream media coverage. It seems that, without this geographic specificity, there would not have been any local media interest, and state and national coverage would have been much less prominent. Having attracted the attention of the media in this way afforded an opportunity to discuss messages around the environmental impacts of consumption that are otherwise difficult to raise in the mainstream media. The media responded strongly to the 'league-table' nature of the website and detailed breakdown of SLAs. The affluent suburbs are a popular target for journalists and the general public alike.

There were also challenges in dealing with the differences between the consumption issues and the traditional environmental messages around waste reduction, efficiency, and direct household action. The main top-line message for mainstream media articles tended to be "New study finds rich are the biggest polluters", whereas more empowering and sophisticated messages around the opportunities for reductions in consumer environmental impact, and the differences between different expenditure patterns, tended to appear later in the articles or, in some cases, not at all. The ACF worked hard on media strategies to ensure that the media did not stray from reasonable interpretation and that they communicated good action messages.

The duration of media interest in the story is noteworthy. Major media pieces occurred well after the launch and initial media flurry, such as a front-page story in Sydney that appeared six weeks after the launch. An explanation for this extraordinary interest is a combination of the novelty and depth of the data and analysis itself, but also the differentiated messages for each state and individual localities. In other words, the fact that a Victorian Sunday paper did a major story did not preclude a major story some weeks later by a rival Sydney paper, because the Sydney story was different enough from the Melbourne story in its particulars.

The geographical specificity of the Atlas has made it an ideal tool to supplement other community outreach strategies the ACF is pursuing as well. For instance, in GreenHome workshops, rather than simply presenting national aggregate statistics on per capita emissions, average results for the specific area in which the workshop is being held can be shown, and consumption patterns in that area discussed. This makes the message much more 'real' for audiences, and thus more effective at driving behavioural changes.

There were, however, some misconceptions and lost messages in some of the media activity that warrants discussion. Several letters to the editor in the days following major stories about the Consumption Atlas challenged the results and argued that inner city suburbs had lower impacts, meaning direct-only impacts. This response demonstrates that, despite the clear media messages, and in fact the good representations of most of the articles, the public can still choose to rely on their traditional thinking and understanding. It is clear from some of the reactions that the results were an affront to members of the public who consider themselves good environmental citizens. Furthermore, this highlights that some people have difficulty with the concept of the performance of the average person in SLA.

Even some environmentally-aware commentators missed the premise of the study and the meaning of the results. In a newspaper story, which was printed more than two months after the launch, a local environmental commentator responded to the result of above average local greenhouse gas emissions by describing direct-only effects contributing to emissions, such as air conditioning use and lack of renewable energy sources. Similarly, an Australian academic prominent in the field of sustainability challenged the findings using direct-only arguments when questioned by a journalist. Despite the main point of the actual stories, and the basis of the Consumption Atlas, even environmental experts had difficulty recognising the fundamental message here. Whilst some of these reactions may be due to their being unfamiliar with the Consumption Atlas, or because they were asked leading questions, it appears that the issue of indirect aspects of consumption is not universally recognised.

Public attitudes to and understanding of environmental issues have been surveyed in NSW every three years since 1994 (*Who cares about the environment?*). A general result from the most recent survey (2006) is that there is a growing awareness of the complexities and linkages between environmental issues, and more generally about the concept of sustainability (Department of Environment and Conservation NSW 2007). However, none of the survey questions were aimed at examining attitudes and understanding of environmental effects of the general purchase of goods and services by households. For example, reductions in energy, water and plastic bag consumption were consistent activities in the responses, but these responses (and indeed their questions) were almost universally about direct effects, not about wider impacts from general consumption of households. In fact the only mention of consumption concerns the category of responses called 'green purchasing' where 're-using things' is noted as a response. Water consumption is particularly closely linked to direct household behaviour, although an increasing number of people recognise that the majority of water use in NSW is for agriculture. This commentary is not a criticism of the *Who cares...?* survey, which is a very valuable gauge of public knowledge and action on the environment over the last 13 years. Rather, the lack of attention in the survey to the wider impacts of consumption (e.g. the water and greenhouse footprints of consumers) is indicative of the lack of awareness of these issues even among environmental professionals.

Conclusion

This chapter described the rationale, methodology, results, interactive website, and the public response to a detailed set of environmental performance data for Australian households. The data fundamentally includes upstream or indirect contributions to environmental pressures from households and is therefore substantially different from most environmental education material. The website and results in general provided a wider scope for environmental action and campaigning. An extensive but carefully managed outreach program by the Australian Conservation Foundation achieved substantial public and media interest, covering a relatively new area of environmental message.

The success of the project can be attributed to the 'personalisation' of environmental performance that the good spatial breakdown afforded: despite the use of average figures, the public still considered themselves to have a personal connection with the results. The results of the project are a significant benchmark of national environmental performance by households for three important indicators. Web-based delivery and good media and communications have enabled very successful outreach of research to be achieved. This represents a good partnership between researchers and committed media and education specialists.

Although difficult to assess, some of the success of the project may be attributable to the current high public environmental awareness in Australia, due to a combination of the protracted drought, recent major natural disasters and their links, even without good evidence, to climate change. Relatively recently there has been acceptance in the mainstream that climate change is a significant issue. All these factors are likely to have had an important bearing on the media and public's receptivity to the Consumption Atlas.

Acknowledgements

This project was supported by the NSW Government through the NSW Environmental Trust.

References

Australian Automobile Association, 2000. 'Yearly average retail petrol prices 1983–1999'.

ABARE, 1999. *Australian energy consumption and production*, Australian Bureau of Agricultural and Resource Economics Canberra, Australia.

ABARE, 2001. *Australian farm surveys report 2001: financial performance of Australian farms 1998–99 to 2000–01*, Australian Bureau of Agricultural and Resource Economics, Canberra.

Australian Bureau of Statistics, 1996. *Survey of motor vehicle use, Australia, preliminary*, Australian Bureau of Statistics, Canberra.

Australian Bureau of Statistics, 1997. *Motor vehicles in Australia*, Australian Bureau of Statistics, Canberra.

Australian Bureau of Statistics, 2000. '1998–99 Household Expenditure Survey – Detailed Expenditure Items, Confidentialised Unit Record File', Australian Bureau of Statistics, Canberra.

Australian Bureau of Statistics, 2004a. *Australian National Accounts, Input–output Tables, 1998–99*, Australian Bureau of Statistics, Canberra.

Australian Bureau of Statistics, 2004b. '*Australian National Accounts, Input–output Tables, 1998–99*, IOPC 8-digit Commodity Cards', Australian Bureau of Statistics, Canberra.

Australian Bureau of Statistics, 2007. *Australian Social Trends*, Australian Bureau of Statistics, Canberra.

Australian Greenhouse Office, 2007. *National greenhouse gas inventory 2005*, Australian Greenhouse Office, Canberra.

Barson M, L Randall & V Bordas, 2000. Land cover change in Australia. Bureau of Rural Sciences, Kingston, ACT.

Bureau of Labor Statistics, 2002. 'Consumer Price Index, All Urban Consumers – (CPI-U), U.S. city average, All items', Bureau of Labor Statistics.

Chen B, Chen C Q, Yang Z F & Jiang M M, 2007. 'Ecological footprint accounting for energy and resource in China', *Energy Policy*, vol. 35, no. 3, pp. 1599–1609.

Department of Environment and Conservation NSW, 2007. *Who cares about the environment in 2006?*, NSW Government.

Gallego B & Lenzen M, 2005. 'A consistent input–output formulation of shared consumer and producer responsibility'. *Economic Systems Research*, vol. 17, no. 4, pp. 365–391.

Gallego B & Lenzen M, 2006. 'Estimating regional input–output systems: a case study of Australia', in Ruth M & Davidsdottir B, *Dynamics of Industrial Ecosystems.*

Ghertner D A & Fripp M, 2007. 'Trading away damage: Quantifying environmental leakage through consumption-based, life-cycle analysis', *Ecological Economics*, vol. 63, no's 2–3, pp. 563–577.

Graetz R D, Wilson M A & Campbell S K, 1995. *Landcover disturbance over the Australian continent*, Department of the Environment, Sport and Territories Biodiversity Unit, Canberra.

Hamilton C R, Denniss & Baker D, 2005. Wasteful consumption in Australia, The Australia Institute.

Lenzen M, 1998. 'The energy and greenhouse gas cost of living for Australia during 1993–94', *Energy*, vol. 23, no. 6, pp. 497–516.

Lenzen M, 1999. 'Total energy and greenhouse gas requirements for Australian transport', *Transportation Research Part D*, vol. 4, pp. 265–290.

Lenzen M, 2001a. 'Errors in conventional and input–output-based life-cycle inventories', *Journal of Industrial Ecology*, vol. 4, no. 4, pp. 127–148.

Lenzen M, 2001b. 'A generalised input–output multiplier calculus for Australia', *Economic Systems Research*, vol. 13, no. 1, pp. 65–92.

Lenzen M, 2001c. 'The importance of goods and services consumption in household greenhouse gas emissions calculators', *Ambio*, vol. 30, no. 7, pp. 439–442.

Lenzen M, Dey C & Foran B, 2004. 'Energy requirements of Sydney households', *Ecological Economics*, vol. 49, no. 3, pp. 375-399.

Lenzen M, Dey C & Murray J, 2002. 'A personal approach to teaching about climate change', *Australian Journal of Environmental Education*, vol. 18, pp. 35–45.

Lenzen M & Foran B, 2001. 'An input–output analysis of Australian water usage', *Water Policy*, vol. 3, no. 4, pp. 321–340.

Lenzen M, Gallego B & Wood R, 2007. 'A flexible approach to matrix balancing under partial information', *Journal of Applied Input-Output Analysis*, in press.

Lenzen M & Murray J, 2001. 'The role of equity and lifestyles in education about climate change: experiences from a large-scale teacher development program', *Canadian Journal of Environmental Education*, vol. 6, pp. 32–51.

Lenzen M, Murray J, Sack F & Wiedmann T, 2007. 'Shared producer and consumer responsibility - theory and practice', *Ecological Economics*, vol. 61, no. 1, pp. 27-42.

Lenzen M & Murray S A, 2001. 'A modified ecological footprint method and its application to Australia', *Ecological Economics*, vol. 37, no. 2, pp. 229–255.

Lenzen M & Smith S, 2000. 'Teaching responsibility for climate change: three neglected issues', *Australian Journal of Environmental Education*, vol. 15/16, pp. 69–78.

Lenzen M & Treloar G, 2002. 'Differential convergence of life-cycle inventories towards upstream production layers', *Journal of Industrial Ecology*, accepted for publication.

Leontief W, 1936. 'Quantitative input and output relations in the economic system of the United States', *Review of Economics and Statistics*, vol. 18, no. 3, pp. 105–125.

Leontief W, 1941. *The Structure of the American Economy, 1919–1939*, Oxford University Press, Oxford, UK.

McDonald G W, Forgie V E & MacGregor C, 2006. 'Treading lightly: ecofootprints of New Zealand's ageing population', *Ecological Economics*, vol. 56, no. 3, pp. 424-439.

Moll H C & Norman K J, 2002. *Towards sustainable development at city level: evaluating and changing the household metabolism in five European cities*, Lifecycle Approaches to Sustainable Consumption, Laxenburg, Austria, International Institute for Applied Systems Analysis (IIASA), National Institute for Advanced Industrial Science and Technology (AIST), and Sustainable Consumption and Production Unit of the United Nations Environment Programme (UNEP).

Munksgaard J, Pedersen K A & Wier M, 2000. 'Impact of household consumption on CO_2 emissions', *Energy Economics*, vol. 22, pp. 423-440.

Munksgaard J, Wier M, Lenzen M & Dey C, 2005. 'Using input-output analysis to measure the environmental pressure of consumption at different spatial levels', *Journal of Industrial Ecology*, vol. 9, no's 1–2, pp. 169–186.

National Greenhouse Gas Inventory Committee, 1998. *Australian methodology for the estimation of greenhouse gas emissions and sinks*, Australian Greenhouse Office, Canberra.

NSW Department of Energy and Utilities, 2000. *Energy at a glance*, NSW Department of Energy, St Leonards, NSW.

Tiebout C M, 1960. 'Regional and interregional input–output models: an appraisal', in Pfouts R W, *The techniques of urban economic analysis*, Chandler-Davis Publishing Co, West Trenton, New Jersey, pp. 395–407.

Treloar G, 1997. 'Extracting embodied energy paths from input–output tables: towards an input–output-based hybrid energy analysis method', *Economic Systems Research*, vol. 9, no. 4, pp. 375–391.

Turner K, Lenzen M, Wiedmann T & Barrett J, 2007. 'Examining the global environmental impact of regional consumption activities – Part 1: A technical note on combining input-output and ecological footprint analysis', *Ecological Economics*, vol. 62, no. 1, pp. 37–44.

Vardon M, Lenzen M, Peevor S & Creaser M, 2007. 'Water accounting in Australia', *Ecological Economics*, vol. 61, no. 4, pp. 650–659.

Wackernagel M & Rees W, 1995. *Our Ecological Footprint: Reducing Human Impact on the Earth*, New Society Publishers, Philadelphia.

Wiedmann T, Lenzen M, Turner K & Barrett J, 2007. 'Examining the global environmental impact of regional consumption activities – Part 2: review of input-output models for the assessment of environmental impacts embodied in trade', *Ecological Economics*, vol. 61, no. 1, pp. 15-26.

Wier M, Christoffersen L B, Jensen T S, Pedersen O G, Keiding H & Munksgaard J, 2005. 'Evaluating sustainability of household consumption – using DEA to assess environmental performance', *Economic Systems Research*, vol. 17, no. 4, pp. 425–447.

World Wide Fund for Nature (WWF), 2006. *The living planet report*, from http://www.panda.org/news_facts/publications/living_planet_repor/footprint/index.cfm.

Part 3
Community issues

10

Civilising nature: museums and the environment

Jennifer Barrett and Phil McManus

Abstract

Interpreting the natural environment in the cultural context of a museum is common practice in the early 21st century. It was also quite common in the 19th century. This chapter considers some of the key discourses in natural history and science museums to reveal a rich legacy of engagement with the environment. It begins with a review of a contemporary film that portrays the wonders of the museum at night when its history and politics come alive. Museum history demonstrates that, far from being a mausoleum, museums are crucial sites for environmental education and research. This paper argues that museums shape and reflect environmental attitudes. Using Australia's oldest museum, the Australian Museum located in Sydney, the chapter demonstrates the complex connections between museum cultures of collection and display, and research and environmental issues.

Introduction

In a popular comedy movie released in 2006, a natural history museum in a large American city mysteriously comes to life at night when there are no visitors. The corollary, and the trope that contributes to the film's success, is that the museum is dead during the day. The museum is a mausoleum – a dead boring place. It is a challenge experienced by many people associated with museums. While museum curators and educators promote the concept of the museum as being alive in the minds of visitors, whether by responding to social changes or technological changes in the form of interactive displays that engage new audiences, the idea of museums as being places of old, decrepit and dead things is a difficult stereotype to overturn. Yet it is this very stereotypical characteristic that the new night watchman in the film *Night at the museum*, soon realises is indeed untrue: the natural history museum is in fact abundant with history, discoveries, unresolved problems and questions. Unable to be contained by the museum, the exhibits escape and are seen on the streets of Manhattan. This generates a news item that in turn brings in the curious tens of thousands, in the film and in reality. Such is the mythical status of the museum and its work.

One sector of museum activity burdened by the 'museum as a mausoleum stereotype' is that of relationships between museums and 'the environment'. The stereotype of large generalist museums and natural history museums filled with skeletons and the labour of taxidermists does not do justice to the complex relationships between museums and the environment, nor does it reflect the controversies inherent in knowledge creation and dissemination. As we demonstrate in this chapter, far from being mausoleums, or even focused on the past, museums are playing important roles in shaping, documenting, cataloguing and reflecting our relationship with nature.

There are three aims of this chapter. The first is to identify how museums are positioned in relation to the environment. The second is to analyse how this positioning has changed over time due to changing environmental conditions and discourses, and changes in museum practice and context. The third is to identify how museums can engage with environmental issues in the 21st century.

The chapter begins with an overview of museum history, particularly in relation to the development of environmental thought and concern. It then looks at how three Australian museums have constructed the environment, or mediated the environment and presented it to audiences, through examples of temporary and permanent exhibitions. It is important to remember that these examples reflect thinking in specific places at particular points in time. The chapter then looks in more detail at the Australian Museum in Sydney, and demonstrates how it engages with environmental thought and concerns, and how this engagement has changed over time. The chapter concludes that museums have important roles to play in engaging with nature in ways that are educational, participatory, scientific, ethical and sometimes controversial.

Museums and the evolution of environmental thought

The development of museums and natural history museums

The word 'museum' is a Latin word from the Greek word 'mouseoin' (Alexander 1979). The term initially meant "the abode of the muses; these abodes were groves on Mounts Parnassus and Helicon" (Dixson 1919, p. 3). They later became temples, then universities with many colleges. Some of the earliest museums were located in cities such as Alexandria, Athens and Rome. They were associated with knowledge creation and dissemination similar to the role of modern universities, or were devoted to displaying captured treasures. With the destruction of the city of Alexandria, the term "museum" was virtually unheard, "and was only revived with the arts and sciences about the middle of the 17th century" (Dixson 1919, p. 3). While the art collections of royalty and wealthy buyers were the forerunners of public art galleries, and the royal menageries became the ancestors of modern zoological gardens, the museum emerged from the private 'cabinet of curiosities' to become the public collection of history, anthropology, geography and technology. The first university museum opened in Basel in 1671, with the Ashmolean Museum in Oxford being established as the first public natural history museum in 1683 (Alexander 1979).

By the middle of the 19th century, museums were vital in the industrialisation and colonial processes. Museums catalogued and presented socio-economic and technological change in particular ways to their audiences. The major imperial museums displayed the wealth and curiosities of the dominions to the imperial core of the various European empires. Museums displayed the 'riches' of the colonies to citizens in the important cities of empire – London, Paris, Berlin – and in doing so had various and often profound environmental and cultural impacts in the colonies and territories.

The emergence of natural history museums in London, New York and other major cities during the 19th century was related to notions of civilisation and the perceived separation of humans from nature. The growth of the cities often led to nostalgia for rural and non-urban environments, partly because of the squalid character of many parts of the industrial cities. Nature was generally perceived as those areas outside the city. In the USA, a frontier mentality reinforced this construct of urban-civilisation versus nature-wilderness (Luke 2002). Natural history museums, in particular, were conduits for both places and time. The natural history museums connected the urban dweller with nature that existed beyond the frontier of civilisation, in much the same way as exotic displays of tribal art, clothing and weaponry connected urban Australians with inland communities. The natural history museums also connected the urban dweller with the former character of their now-urban region. In the USA this selective recalling of the past was important in the nineteenth century because of the rate of change in population, landscape modification and technological and cultural development.

There was a rapid and unprecedented growth in the number of museums during the nineteenth century. Focusing only on natural history museums, by 1900 there were 150 museums of natural history in Germany, 250 in Britain, 300 in France and 250 in the United States (Sheets-Pyenson 1988). Speaking at the Australian Museum in 1919, Thomas Storie Dixson noted that in 1903 there were 31 natural history museums in New York state (population 7 million), 10 such museums in California (population 1.5 million) and only one such museum in New South Wales in 1919, despite the state having a population of 2 million people (Dixson 1919). Dixson qualified this last remark by noting the existence of the Macleay Museum at the University of Sydney, "which the public can hardly be said to know of" (Dixson 1919, p. 8).

The growth in the number of museums throughout the world resulted from the confluence of technological progress and ideas about civilised societies. The technological progress of the 18th and 19th centuries enabled various countries in western Europe to explore and colonise distant lands. The display of objects from these colonies in the largest cities of the imperial power not only showed the citizens of the imperial country what they possessed, how they were changing it, but was also following the earlier ideas of leading scientists, such as Francis Bacon, to broaden knowledge and challenge the intellect. According to Bacon, "... we should no longer dance around within small Circles (as if we were enchanted by a Spell) but should equalize the Circumference of the World in our Circuits" (Bacon 1670, p. 4; also cited in Parrish 2006, p. 71). The orderly display of objects, perusal and the resultant education of the viewer, was intended to engender a fascination with the world, and a respect for authority, particularly from the working classes.

The museums, along with various organisations, such as the Royal Society in London, were responsible for promoting scientific and cultural advancement, and were influential in the promulgation of ideas about nature. Museum curators taught at universities, and museums were involved in research activity to elucidate knowledge about the world (Yanni 1999). The 19th century witnessed profound changes in our understanding of the world. The natural history museums generally built on the new knowledge of this period, particularly the work of Charles Darwin on evolutionary theory and the development of the new science of geology (Asma 2001; Sheets-Pyenson 1988). The knowledge was developed through the principles of scientific inquiry – systematic observation, experimentation, development of laws, the ability to replicate. Over time, scientific inquiry came to replace gentlemen naturalists, with profound impacts on the relationships between science, religion and various concepts of nature.

The intellectual foundations of natural history museums

The 19th century was also important for the changes in museum culture and display practices with regard to, amongst other things, nature. The idea of collecting and displaying natural history is a humanist concept that is much older – "Natural history was invented in the Renaissance" in western Europe in the 16th century (Ogilvie 2006, p. 1). The natural historians were often young men who could travel, initially within Europe, but increasingly by the eighteenth century to more remote places and for longer periods. This idea of constant motion, as Ogilvie (2006, p. 141) wrote of the sixteenth century naturalist – "motion between the library, the cabinet, the salon (or dinner table and printers' shop), the garden, the wharf, and the countryside" highlights the relationships between the texts about nature (the library), the museum (the cabinet of curiosities) and the collecting practices. Another crucial change in the eighteenth century is the classification of objects. The earlier forms of classification included alphabetisation, but this became impractical as curiosity cabinets expanded. Various scientific systems of classification were developed as disciplines, such as biology and geology produced new knowledge and re-ordered existing knowledge.

There was also a major change in the way displays were arranged, and for whom they were arranged. In the cabinet of curiosities, displays were comprehensive in the sense that virtually everything collected was displayed. The criteria for collection and display of material were often based on qualities of uniqueness, distance between the location of its collection and display, and the individual or sometimes the aesthetic properties of the object. In the 19th century, displays in many major museums became selective. Sir William Flower, Director of the Natural History Museum in London, was an advocate of displaying fewer objects in the public exhibition so that the lay visitor could gain a general understanding and appreciation of nature (Flower 1898; Sheets-Pyenson 1988). The increasing quantity of objects held by the major museums could be kept in storage drawers and cabinets for specialist research purposes. Despite this separation of the research and exhibition functions of museums, natural history museums may still be perceived as "eccentric treasure chests of weirdness [which] with their displays of the exotic and the rare, have always existed at the frontier of credulity and wonder" (Asma 2007, p. 27).

The notion of ecosystems was not available to 19th century museum curators, so the individual objects were displayed like stamp collections (as in the Pitt Rivers Museum in Oxford), or in easily observable habitats and relationships, as in many dioramas of predator-prey relationships. From inception there was a division between zoos and natural history museums. In zoos, the animals were alive and often placed in unsympathetic settings to experience social isolation from the herd (although this critique has led to improvements in zoological practice over the years). In natural history museums, the dead animals were made life-like by skilled taxidermists and placed in contrived settings to highlight the natural environment and particular traits of the animals. In the museum, the fox's jaws remain open forever – the fox never catches the rabbit and the frightened rabbit is never safe from the predator.

Nature, science and religion

The will of Sir Hans Sloane, who died in 1753 and whose massive private collection became the basis for the establishment of the British Museum, provides an interesting insight into the relationships between nature, science and religion. The will stated that Sloane had made the collection for "the manifestation of the glory of God, the confutation of atheism and its consequences, the use and improvement of physic and other arts and sciences, and benefit of mankind" (Alexander 1979, p. 45).

In the 19th century, the growth in the number of natural history museums, and expansion of individual museums, both reflected and shaped a concern with nature and questions about human existence. The rise of scientific inquiry led to new understandings of nature, but these understandings were, generally, intended to demonstrate through science the greatness of God. It was in the latter half of the 19th century, and particularly through the work of T H Huxley in promoting Charles Darwin's version of evolution, that the potential for conflict between religious and scientific explanations of the world was realised (Yanni 1999). This was important not just in ascribing credit for creation or evolution, but also in situating humans in the world in relation to other species. Collections were no longer amassed primarily to show the manifestation of the glory of God and to confute atheism, but increasingly to further scientific understandings of nature. The exploration and collecting were "galvanized by Darwin's theories of evolution, and the world's naturalists were busily reconstructing the tree of life" (Hennes 2007, p. 90). According to Griffin (1992 p. 3), "natural history collections provided a three dimensional map on which the course of evolution could be charted". The 19th century natural history museum was a "cathedral of science" (Sheets-Pyenson 1988). Central to this cathedral was the concept of evolution, which was heretical to many devout religious people, because it challenged the position of God as the Creator of the universe and all that was in it.

This conflict between science and religion was addressed by Sir William Flower, Director of the Natural History Museum in London, in a paper read at the Church Congress in Reading on 2 October 1883. Flower (1898 p. 134) noted that while science was increasingly discovering "the processes or methods by which the world in which we dwell has been brought into its present condition", this did not take away the mystery of Creation. Science, according to Flower, was discovering explanations for "the succession of small miracles, formerly supposed to regulate the operations of nature", but it could not explain the origin of the world and that it was inconceivable that the world "could have originated without the intervention of some power external to itself" (Flower 1898, p. 134).

It is apparent that since the late 19th century, natural history museums have evolved to incorporate new scientific understandings in areas such as biodiversity and climate change (Griffin 1996). Concepts, such as ecosystem, have been incorporated into research and exhibitions in these museums. Evolutionary thought, and the classification systems that were developed in the 19th century, are now so normal in contemporary natural history museums that they are almost invisible. One of the significant challenges today is how natural history museums show or re-present the significant research and development they continue to undertake (Krishtalka & Humphrey 2000; Suarez & Tsutsui 2004; Worts 2006). However, the role of scientific evidence in informing the display of objects, and in the process of creating new knowledge through museum-based research, has recently been called into question by the opening of a new museum in Petersburg, Kentucky, that challenges the 19th century scientific basis of natural history museums.

The Creation Museum is a 'rebuttal museum' to these natural history museums, with its critique that "almost all natural history museums proclaim an evolutionary, humanistic world view. For example, they will typically place dinosaurs on an evolutionary timeline millions of years before man" (Asma 2007, p. 26). The Creation Museum is designed to "proclaim the accuracy of the Bible from genesis to Revelation, ... show that there is a creator, and that this creator is Jesus Christ ..." (Asma 2007, p. 26). This museum highlights the diversity of thought about nature/environment/ecology/Creation. While it is only one Christian perspective on the environment (see Gatta 2004; Leal 2006; Rue 2006) it calls into question the roles of science and faith in knowledge creation and dissemination. It shows that museums are engaged in the politics of knowledge, whether this be natural history museums, anthropologically oriented museums or art museums. It also shows that what is at stake is which knowledge is valid and which is invalid.

Australian museums and environmental thought

Contemporary museum displays about the environment are informed by different environmental knowledge from that in the 19th century. This does not mean that contemporary museums focus on similar environmental themes, or have a common understanding of how to present environmental issues. While not exhaustive of all possibilities, the following three snapshots highlight the diversity of environmental constructions and representations in contemporary museum practice in Australia.

The Australian Museum - Biodiversity

Until very recently the exhibition *Biodiversity* at the Australian Museum in Sydney integrated science and popular environmental concerns. The theme of the exhibition would not have been possible in the 19th century. It was not until the environment was repackaged as biodiversity, and biodiversity was valued in some form, that this theme could exist and attract visitors.

This display (Image 10.1) was not simply a collection of biodiversity to show as a curiosity, it also embodied four of the dominant discourses in contemporary environmental thought: the sense of loss, the sense of ongoing vulnerability, and the urgency of a race against time to both slow the rate of loss and to repair damaged environments. Visitors to the biodiversity display had generally seen other environmental displays in the museum – including dinosaurs, skeletons and the collections of stuffed birds, pinned butterflies and dead insects that represent earlier understandings of 'the environment' before they encountered *Biodiversity*, which included live baby crocodiles. This display was a departure from the other displays because it was based on the principles of scientific ecology (rather than biology) and incorporated concern about the importance of biodiversity, the vulnerability of biodiversity and the loss of biodiversity in various parts of the world.

(c) C. Bento Australian Museum

Figure 10.1 Biodiversity Gallery: specimens. Photo by Carl Bento, copyright Australian Museum, no date

With the current forty million dollar renewal and refurbishment project of the Australian Museum and its galleries, the associated collections and program on biodiversity will be dispersed throughout the museum and the concepts of biodiversity will be addressed in the new Surviving Australia Gallery, opening in 2008. This gallery will focus on the diversity of Australia's habitat, its unique species and their evolution. On a practical level, the subject of biodiversity is also explored in Search and Discover, the 'hands on' education centre of the museum (see Image 10.2). Kidspace (formerly Kid's Island) is also a place in the museum where children can explore the themes of biodiversity.

Figure 10.2 Search and Discover (education centre). Photo by Carl Bento, copyright Australian Museum, no date

The Powerhouse Museum – *EcoLogic*: creating a sustainable future

The exhibition, *EcoLogic* at the Powerhouse Museum in Sydney includes, among other things, displays and information about sustainable living. It recreates a 'sustainable house' and presents "new ideas and technologies that can reduce our individual and collective impact on the planet" (www.powerhousemuseum.com/exhibitions/ecologic.asp). The exhibition is concerned with "the way we use the world" (see Image 10.3). The environment is presented not as surroundings, or as a collection of curiosities from a distant place, but as something that is part of the daily lives of people in their domestic space.

Figure 10.3 Visitors to *EcoLogic* can calculate the cost of different hot water systems, both in dollars and CO_2 emissions. Photo: Jean-Francois Lanzarone, Powerhouse Museum, Sydney, 2001

EcoLogic also highlights the importance of consumption (see Image 10.4) – whether this is at the stage of purchasing decisions, the environmental performance of fittings and appliances in dwellings, or the disposal of packaging and unwanted items as waste. In this exhibition, people are connected to nature through their lifestyles, and the interactive displays on issues such as hot water provision in the dwelling are clearly advocacy-oriented in informing people of more sustainable options. The exhibition also includes a population counter, reflecting the concerns of many people that the biggest threat to the environment is the growth in world population (currently at approximately 6.7 billion people).

Figure 10.4 A crushed car at the entrance to *EcoLogic* surprises viewers and raises awareness of our material consumption. The population clock nearby ticks over at an alarming rate. Photo: Jean-Francois Lanzarone, Powerhouse Museum, Sydney, 2001

The web presence of the exhibition is important and is linked to relevant resources. It includes teacher's exhibition notes and, in this sense, the exhibition and associated research is made available for the public to view and use, potentially for further research.

The National Museum of Australia

The environmental displays at the National Museum of Australia in Canberra are less advocacy oriented, but are important in emphasising the concept of the environment as being connected with people. The rotating audio-visual display *Circa* has the theme of "land, nation, people" and, as indicated by the title, changes over time. Key themes in this display include the variation in Australian environments, the diversity of environmental ideas and beliefs and the heterogeneity of the Australian population. Other crucial themes include human reliance on the environment, the belief that the actions of environmentalists are preserving the environment for future generations, and that by showing respect for animals people are respecting themselves. Amongst other important displays is the *Biological avalanche* in the Old New Land Gallery (previously Tangled Destinies) (see Images 10.5 & 10.6). It comprises an electronic shape of Australia, where red lights highlight the spread of the red fox, European wild rabbit, starling, cattle tick and the European Carp at different times. The display shows the dynamic and spatial aspects of invasion. Other displays include photographs, objects, text, visual and audio recordings of various engagements with the land by men, women, Indigenous people, newly arrived settlers, and so on. Different forms of environmental knowledge are highlighted, including Indigenous knowledge, scientific knowledge, popular culture and various lived experiences.

These displays are notable for their relative impartiality towards ideas, activities and people who could easily be praised or condemned depending on how they are viewed by adherents of different environmental philosophies. There is no blaming of environmental vandals. This appearance of impartiality may be expected in such a museum, but from the perspective of radical environmentalists of various persuasions, the impartiality could be interpreted as political pandering to the vested interests of those who are, in many cases, continuing the activities that are questioned in the displays. If the environment is of such importance, displays that fail to highlight the causes of environmental damage and, where necessary, blame the catalysts of such damage, may be perceived as doing a disservice to environmental concerns. Alternatively, learning from the past and using this to guide future practice may be interpreted as a responsible action by a national museum. For example, there are warnings in the displays that extinctions have occurred, both high profile extinctions (such as the thylacine) and extinctions that have gone virtually unnoticed (birds in the wheatbelt regions of Australia), and that extinction is still possible. The idea of learning from the past, to avoid repeating mistakes, to contain rather than being able to eliminate certain environmental threats, and to be cautious about the introduction of non-endemic species, are all important points made at the National Museum of Australia in relation to the environment.

Figure 10.5 *Biological avalanche.* Photo: National Museum of Australia (c. 2002)

Figure 10.6 Old New Land Gallery. Photo: Dean Golja, National Museum of Australia (c.2002)

Complexities of museum–nature interactions

The above three snapshots of the changing relationship between museums and nature over time, and the differing approaches of contemporary museums in Australia, highlight the complexities of museum-nature interactions. As a number of natural history museum directors in the United States noted in a special issue of *Museum News* in

1997, there is no single correct answer as to the form of this engagement (various, 1997). More recently Hennes (2007) revisits the question: What is the role and character of natural history museums in the 21st century? He identifies that museums are no longer part of an "ontologically-driven study representing an ordered natural world we sought to master" but are part of a "more interdisciplinary study of a disordered, self organizing natural world in which our species is but one of many co-dependent actors" (Hennes 2007, p.91).

The opportunities, and the obligations, to address environmental issues are not restricted to natural history museums. Davis (1996) discusses the opportunities for all museums to become "environmentally friendly", emphasising the importance of environmental audits and highlighting the need for museums to sell products that minimise environmental impacts, to reduce energy consumption and to place environmental policy in a central position in the organisation. The relationships between museums and the environment are negotiated processes and outcomes that are influenced by ideas, individuals, the mandate of the museum, perceptions of audience desires, museum culture, politics and other factors that vary between institutions and through time.

Part of this negotiation involves the museums engaging with museum educators and others in the annual Museums Australia conference, the theme of which in 2007 was sustainable development. This theme alone highlights the changing character of museum-environment engagements, as the term 'sustainable development' was not coined until 1980 and was not popularised until the World Commission on Environment and Development (WCED) report in 1987 (WCED, 1987). How does such a global discourse, which emerged out of the United Nations' organisation, translate into museum culture in Australia and into the practices of individual museums on a day-to-day basis? As part of this quest, in the next section of this chapter we explore in more detail the changes in museum–environment relationships in one particular august institution, the Australian Museum.

Figure 10.7 Bird Gallery, first floor, west wing, about 1950. Copyright Australian Museum Archives

Changes in environmental understandings at the Australian Museum

The Australian Museum was founded in 1827, following the demise of the short-lived museum established by the Philosophical Society in 1821 (van Leeuwin 1995). According to van Leeuwin, "the achievements of the Philosophical Society and its Museum, while modest, do demonstrate the awakening of colonial science in New South Wales" (1995 p. 45). By 1827, the idea of a new natural history museum had "resulted in a collection of objects, apparently chiefly of birds" (Dixson 1919, p. 4) which formed the foundation collection for the museum (see Image 10.7 for a 1950s version.) The Australian Museum was established through the auspices of various people, but the role of the Colonial Secretary, Alexander Macleay, was crucial. Macleay was a Fellow of the Linnean Society (from 1794 and its Secretary from 1798) and a Fellow of the Royal Society as of 1808 (van Leeuwin 1995). He was keen to promote scientific endeavours in the colony, and intended to keep the best local specimens in this new museum and to export duplicates to England (to go to a hierarchy of institutions – the Linnean Society Museum, then the British Museum, followed by the College of Surgeons, and fourthly the English, Scottish and Irish universities) (van Leeuwin 1995).

The early role of the museum was the scientific understanding of nature and the promotion of interest in nature. This was achieved through display practices, but also through public lectures. The South Wing of the museum, for which construction started in the late 19th century but was not completed until 1910, had attached to it:

> a lecture hall, which had proved itself a necessity because of the large numbers of the public desirous of attending the lecturettes or lecture demonstrations given by the Scientific Staff. These had been begun in 1905, but relatively few persons could be admitted to them because of the scanty space available between the cases of exhibits amidst which these lecturettes were delivered. (Dixson 1919, p. 7)

The printed lecture delivered by Dixson in 1919 is also important in highlighting the perceived progress of the Australian Museum at that time in relation to other national and international museums. Dixon was impressed by some museums in the United States, particularly in "their methods of adapting their museums to the education of children" (Dixson 1919, p. 17). The Washington National Museum was cited for its child-friendly displays, while the Field Museum in Chicago was praised for its extension to schools: although only commenced in 1914, by 1916 it was servicing 250 000 children and included "476 cases of specimens being specially prepared for public schools" (Dixson 1919, p. 18). Dixson's first recommendation for the future of the Australian Museum was to "expand our work in connection with schools ... as regards loan collections, more extensive lecturing, and a children's science library, all modified to suit local requirements and possibilities" (Dixson 1919, p. 24).

Given this early vision, it is perhaps not surprising that, when we explore changes in the values and practice of the Australian Museum through an analysis of its annual report at ten year intervals, we see that one notable activity of the museum over many years has been to bring nature alive in the hearts and minds of children. The purpose and practice of annual reporting needs to be considered when employing this research method, which does highlight particular aims of the museum, changing environmental thought, the centrality of science in environmental discourse and engagement, and the continuities and changes in community relationships with the museum.

The 1962–3 report of the Trustees of the Australian Museum highlights the importance of quantification in terms of visitor numbers, the size of various collections, the number of new acquisitions of various items, and so on. It also emphasises the scientific research activity of museum staff, and the school service that involved 19,021 children attending museum classes for the year 1963, 803 people attending school vacation films and a children's room that was open during three school vacations and included special exhibits for children around themes such as 'Animals in your garden' and 'Australian minerals' (Trustees of the Australian Museum 1963).

By 1972–3 there was a strong emphasis on the Australian Museum and its community, including discussion on the formation of the Australian Museum Society in 1972. Talbot (1973 p. 11) noted that "there is agitation overseas that museums are not getting out to the people, that they need to develop travelling museums, neighbourhood museums, and temporary displays away from the city". In NSW, the links between the Australian Museum and other organisations, such as the National Parks and Wildlife Service and the Royal Botanical Gardens, were highlighted, as was the pioneering work in undertaking ecological surveys of Lord Howe Island for the Lord Howe Island Board (Talbot 1973, p. 11). These efforts "yield new species to the Museum's collections, solve specific problems for instrumentalities, and add further information to our understanding of our flora and fauna" (Talbot 1973, p. 11). The ongoing engagement with school children now saw 26,503 children attending museum classes, with approximately 62,000 children in 1,550 classes attending the museum without an appointment.

In 1982–83 the annual report included the "Aims of the Australian Museums", which were:

- to increase and disseminate knowledge of our natural environment and cultural heritage; and
- to increase our understanding and appreciation of these things.

It was also noted that, "in achieving these aims the Museum gives special emphasis to the Australian region" (Australian Museum 1983, p. 5). There were four functions of the Museum: a scientific function, an interpretive function, a service function and one of a public responsibility (which involved good public relations and promotional activities). The Australian Museum, responding to concerns about the need for travelling museums, and so on, had initiated a Museum Train, which in the previous five years had stopped at 111 country centres, had been visited by 336,000 people (including 159,000 students in school classes) and generated an average attendance of 42.4 per cent of a town's population. Along with existing activities, such as school loan cases, school holiday activities, and so on, it is evident that the Australian Museum was both engaging different communities and performing an important educational role for children.

The 1992–93 annual report shows a more corporatised museum, with a mission statement to "increase understanding of our natural environment and cultural heritage and to be a catalyst in changing public attitudes and actions. Research and the maintenance and improvement of collections are central to the achievement of the mission" (Australian Museum 1993, p. 13). The focus is still on the Australian region and, despite the importance given to engaging in public debates about the natural environment and cultural heritage, the final paragraph of the statement resonates nicely with the film, *Night at the Museum*: "we want the Museum to be an exciting and rewarding place to visit and work in … and it should be fun" (ibid. p. 13). There is recognition, in the section on scientific achievements, of growing concern about environmental issues: "There is a sense of urgency developing about the scientific work of institutions like the Australian Museum. Each year, the natural world faces increasing threats from the technologies and spread of the human population." (Ibid. p. 19). This was seen as leading to a shift in "the public image of natural history museums and their perceived role. More and more, they are being seen as informed representatives of community attitudes and welcomed as pivotal players in environmental debate." (Ibid. p. 19).

The Australian Museum is constructed as a natural history and cultural heritage museum for the Australasian region maintaining extensive collections for research purposes, but is also important in educating people about environmental matters. It does this through the application of scientific research to environmental issues, but also increasingly through its role as a respected institution cast as an informed representative of community attitudes. This is a challenging and important role because, as understandings of nature change and are continuously contested, being a representative of community attitudes, while maintaining scientific standards involves the balance of tensions within daily practice. As such, the Australian Museum continues to evolve as part of museum practice generally; evolving from 19th century cabinets of curiosities to public displays of exotic objects through to recent conservation practices that are commensurate with a vision of nature as relatively fragile and threatened by more powerful forces of technology (Australian Museum 2007). In the 21st century the cultural context of the museum's work is being used to enhance the museum's engagement with the public. Engagements with contemporary environmental issues, such as the loss of biodiversity (itself a fraught construct given that science has not classified and described about 90 per cent of the world's species) and climate change, highlight the need for visionary practice that builds on tradition, but departs from antiquated ideas and practices where appropriate.

Conclusion

Museums do not come alive only at night when all the visitors have gone home. Museums are not mausoleums for dead nature. They perform important roles in engaging with nature in ways that are educational, participatory, scientific, ethical and, possibly, controversial. These engagements are about representing and examining the past, and sometimes challenging stereotypes about history, but they are also about connecting people to the world today and facilitating thought and action that is oriented towards developing a better future. Whilst we have focussed on the institutional history and cited some recent exhibitions, vital work is being undertaken with the cultural aspect of collections that concern our understanding of the environment.

The challenge it seems, as museums in Australia become increasingly pressured by government to communicate to the public in new ways, is how to make the everyday significance of their research and ongoing programs more visible. Governments, and the public more generally, need to see that museums are pivotal sites of engagement for understanding and communicating about our changing environment in urban and rural Australia. If museums are accepted as sites of mediation with substantial collections that contain vital information about our environment and ways of understanding it, then the relevant identifiable communities need also to be involved in the process of sustaining the work of the museum.

Constructing museums as mausoleums makes invisible the diverse work being undertaken by many museums in relation to the environment. Even more importantly, it limits the potential for museums to engage in vital work in the future. It limits people's imagination about the potential partnerships. People who care about the environment and about museums will appreciate the importance of representing current work accurately to acknowledge the work being done now, and to enable appropriate environmental engagements to thrive in the future.

Acknowledgements

We'd like to thank the following people for their assistance: Janet Carding, Sophie Masters and Michelle Britton at the Australian Museum; Denis French and Kylie King at the National Museum of Australia, Des Griffin and Gavin Birch.

References

Alexander E P, 1979. *Museums in motion: An introduction to the history and functions of museums*, American Association for State and Local History, Nashville.

Asma S, 2001. *Stuffed animals and pickled heads: the culture and evolution of natural history museums*, Oxford University Press, Oxford.

Asma S, 2007. 'Natural history Spun with a young-earth doctrine', Higher Education Supplement, *The Australian*, 18 July, pp. 26–7.

Australian Museum, 1983. *Annual Report of the Australian Museum*, The Australian Museum, Sydney.

Australian Museum, 1993. *Corporate Report of The Australian Museum*, The Australian Museum, Sydney.

Australian Museum, 2007. *Australian Museum science research strategy 2007–2012*, The Australian Museum, Sydney.

Bacon F, 1670. *A Preparatory to the history natural and experimental*. Printed by Sarah Griffing and Ben Griffing, for William Lee, London.

Davis P, 1996. *Museums and the natural environment: the role of natural history museums in biological conservation*, Leicester University Press, New York.

Dixson T S, 1919. *Australian Museum, Sydney: lecture on its origin, growth and work*, printed copy of a lecture delivered on 10 June 1919, The Australian Museum, Sydney.

Flower W, 1898 (reprinted 1972). *Essays on museums (and other subjects connected with natural history)*, Books for Libraries Press, Freeport, New York.

Gatta J, 2004. *Making nature sacred: literature, religion and environment in America from the puritans to the present*, Oxford University Press, New York.

Griffin D, 1992. 'Natural History Museums, the Natural Environment and the 21st Century: Planning for the 21st Century and Preparing for the Next 5000 years'. Paper presented to the International Symposium and First World Congress on the Preservation and Conservation of Natural History Collections, Madrid Spain, May 1992. Available at: http://desgriffin.com/publications-list/environment21, accessed 30 July 2007.

Griffin D, 1996: 'Natural History Collections: A Resource for the Future', Paper presented to the Second World Congress on the Conservation and Preservation of Natural History Collections, Cambridge, England, August 1996. Available at: http://desgriffin.com/publications-list/nhc-future/, accessed 30 July 2007.

Hennes T, 2007. 'Hyperconnection: natural history museums, knowledge and the evolving ecology of community', *Curator: The Museum Journal*, vol. 50, no. 1, January, pp. 87–108.

Krishtalka L & Humphrey P S, 2000. 'Can natural history museums capture the future?', *BioScience*, vol.50, no. 7, pp. 611–617.

Leal R B, 2006. *Through ecological eyes: reflections on christianity's environmental credentials*, St. Pauls Publication, Sydney.

Luke T, 2002. *Museum politics: power plays at the exhibition*, University of Minnesota Press, Minneapolis.

Ogilvie B, 2006. *The science of describing: natural history in renaissance Europe*, The University of Chicago Press, Chicago.

Parrish S, 2006. *American curiosity: cultures of natural history in the colonial British Atlantic world*, University of North Carolina Press, Chapel Hill.

Rue C, 2006. *Catholics and nature: two hundred years of environmental attitudes in Australia*, Australian Catholic Social Justice Council, Sydney.

Sheets-Pyenson S, 1988. *Cathedrals of science: the development of colonial natural history museums during the late nineteenth century*, McGill-Queens University Press, Kingston and Montreal.

Suarez A V, and Tsutsui N D, 2004. 'The Value of Museum Collections for Research and Society', *BioScience*, January 2004, vol. 54, no. 1, pp. 66–74.

Talbot F H, 1973. 'The museum and the community', Trustees of The Australian Museum, 1973, *Report of the Trustees of The Australian Museum for the year ended 30th June, 1973*. The Australian Museum, Sydney, pp. 11–12.

Trustees of the Australian Museum, 1963. *Report of the Trustees of The Australian Museum for the year ended 30th June, 1963*, The Australian Museum, Sydney.

Trustees of the Australian Museum, 1973. *Report of the Trustees of The Australian Museum for the year ended 30th June, 1973*, The Australian Museum, Sydney.

van Leeuwin M, 1995. *the origin and growth of New South Wales museums 1821–1880*. MA (Hons) thesis, School of History, Philosophy and Politics, Macquarie University, Sydney.

Various, 1997. 'Toward a natural history museum for 21st century', *Museum News*, vol. 76, no. 6, pp. 38–49.

World Commission on Environment and Development (WCED), 1987. *Our Common Future*, Oxford University Press, New York.

Worts D, 2006: 'Fostering a Culture of Sustainability', *Museums and Social Issues*, vol. 1, no. 2, Fall, pp. 151–172.

Yanni C, 1999. *Nature's museums: Victorian science and the architecture of display*, The John Hopkins University Press, Baltimore.

11

Not just a pretty picture: art as ecological communication

Catriona Moore

Abstract

Indigenous art and the western landscape tradition form ongoing influences on Australian eco-art. A majority of Australians now acknowledge that reconciliation and environmental sustainability are related issues. At the same time, western conventions of the sublime and the picturesque landscape have remained effective campaign materials. While historical tensions between Indigenous stewardship and a culturally abject, sublime 'wildness' still sporadically reappear in the economic and political arenas, on the whole, these two powerful visions of the landscape have jogged along together for thirty or so years of environmental struggle. This paper traces a brief history of how the western landscape tradition has been modified by Indigenous concepts of country. It then opens the discussion to current projects that combine traditional and inter-disciplinary knowledge within a speculative framework of ecological aesthetics.

Introduction

In 1963, Yolngu elders petitioned the Menzies government against the alienation of traditional lands for bauxite mining at Yirrkala in the Northern Territory. The bi-lingual petition was bordered by a painted summation of Indigenous law: landscape features and clan designs specifying ownership and responsibilities for country, one Yirritja and the other Dhuwa, on two pieces of stretched stringy-bark.[1] This now famous 'bark petition' offered non-Indigenous people a rare opportunity to understand the creation and maintenance of the region, with its complex relations of Indigenous ownership, custodianship and obligation. Tragically, we ignored this opportunity to understand a comprehensive, deep knowledge of the environment that had kept it in a productive balance for millennia.

A decade later, equally traditional, picturesque views of Lake Pedder in Tasmania's south west were reproduced as campaign materials to save the lake from being flooded for hydro-electricity. They illustrated a pristine wilderness, by definition a veritable 'terra nullius' in danger of being irretrievably lost through unwanted state development.

These visual 'petitions' were politically unsuccessful in the short term, and differed on questions of ownership, habitation and wilderness. Nonetheless, Indigenous art and the western landscape tradition form ongoing influences on Australian eco-art. Indigenous art has helped to win hearts, minds and a fair share of battles for Native Title and environmental justice. A majority of Australians now acknowledge that reconciliation and environmental sustainability are related issues. At the same time, western conventions of the sublime and the picturesque landscape have remained effective campaign materials. Hardly an election goes by without sighting comparisons made between lush, dripping rainforest and blackened clear-fell.[2] Moreover, the historical tensions between Indigenous stewardship and western ideas of a culturally abject, sublime 'wildness' still sporadically reappear in economic and political arenas, as in the 2007 tussle between Cape York greenies, traditional owners and the local Indigenous cattle industry.[3] On the whole, however, these two powerful visions of the landscape have jogged along together for around thirty years of environmental struggle.

---

[1] See Attwood B, *Rights for Aborigines*, Allen & Unwin, 2003, pp. 215–236; and Mundine D, 'Saltwater', *Saltwater: Yirrkala bark paintings of sea country*, exhibition catalogue, Buku-Larrngay Mulka Centre & Jennifer Isaacs Publishing, 1999, pp. 20–27.

[2] As commented by Felicity Wade, 'Who's going to save me?', *Photofile* no. 76, Summer 2006, p. 62.

[3] 'Australian Story', Australian Broadcasting Corporation, 28 May 2007. See also Pearson N, 'The Ideal Equilibrium', *The Weekend Australian* 9–10th June, 2007, p. 21.

As a critical term, 'eco-art' only gained currency from the 1990s to highlight the environmental awareness or activist base of diverse projects that prioritised process and concept and combined social and environmental engagement. Critical categories, like ceremonial art, environmental art, conceptual art, feminist art, site-specific installation, performance and community arts have designated art working in conjunction with postmodern cultural theories, Indigenous law, our colonial history, environmental science and grass-roots politics. This interdisciplinary approach has brought about a move to looser, associationist modes of working in galleries, public art projects and political actions to make art 'make a difference'.

The western landscape tradition

From the late 1960s, feminist and conceptual artists embraced the natural environment through humbling gestures of reconciliation with the planet. They challenged the modernist belief in the dominance of humans as rational beings, along with its correlate, the environmental and social degradation of industrial capital. As they watched capitalism lurch towards an unsustainable First World post-industrialism, Second World implosion, Third World decolonisation and industrialisation, and continued Fourth World protest, the avant-garde once again sought to reconcile radical aesthetics and radical politics.

It is not surprising that the land looms larger when the order of the world changes. Writers observe how the recent call of the wild paradoxically echoed the late-18th century investment in the landscape as a privileged locus for thinking about universal human values, such as individual freedom, equality, fraternity – the moral bedrock of modern subjectivity.[4] The Romantic reaction against corrupt absolutist or theocratic regimes sought an Edenic, primordial space in which to reinvent humanity. Theirs was an image of nature as an active, divine force. The idea of *natura naturans*, nature as wild and majestic, was fuelled by the remote, New World landscapes of the imperial adventure.

---

[4] See for instance Ian McLean's quote from Slavoj Zizek in 'Sublime futures: eco-art and the return of the real in Peter Dombrovskis, John Wolseley and Andy Goldsworthy', *Transformations*, No 5, December 2002, p. 6.

Australian colonial landscapes followed those of the outlying regions of the British Isles, the Americas, Africa and other Pacific regions in hosting aesthetic and spiritual renewal, the reconciliation between humankind and nature, subject and object.[5]

By the end of the 19th century, Australian landscapes had also taken on board the British romanticism of John Ruskin and his fellow artist-artisan. They argued that the destruction of the natural environment and the social problems of urbanism were too high a price to pay for industrial development.[6] Already a highly urbanised population, Australian colonials sought their defining moral qualities in a mythic bush setting. Australian landscapes answered Ruskin's call for scientific accuracy and a profound reverence for nature. The intense, empirical scrutiny of the landscape could reveal higher moral truths, if the artist could link the understanding of natural phenomena with an imaginative response, akin to love.[7] From colonial photographer Nicholas Caire's alpine peaks to Jessie Traill's intimate, inter-war etchings of moonlit gullies and Dorothy Wall's ecologically-minded *Blinky Bill*, western pictorial bush-lore has been both empirical and expressive, feeding images of pastoralism, mining, tourism and conservation in varied measure.

Far horizons

Artist and art historian Ian Burn observed that the longstanding popularity of 'Gum Tree School' landscape painting was partly due to the confidence in which painters attacked their subject, a confidence

---

[5] See Bernard Smith's seminal study *European vision in the South Pacific*, Yale University Press, New Haven and London, 1985 (second edition), Bernard Smith, *Imagining the Pacific: In the wake of the Cook voyages*, Melbourne University Press at the Miegunyah Press, 1992; Bonyhardy T, *Images in opposition: Australian painting 1801–1890*, Oxford University Press, Melbourne, 1985, and *The colonial earth*, The Miegunyah Press, University of Melbourne, 2000; *New worlds from old: 19th century Australian & American landscapes*, exhibition catalogue, National Gallery of Australia, Canberra and Wadsworth Atheneum, Hartford, Connecticut, 1998.
[6] See Barringer T, *The Pre-Raphaelites*, Everyman Library, 1988, pp. 57–83.
[7] Ruskin J, 'That the truth of nature is not to be discerned by the uneducated senses', *Modern Painters*, Vol 1, Andre Deutsch, 1987 (1st pub 1843), p. 29.

grounded on close, empirical study of regional landscapes.[8] Ruskin had encouraged young artists to develop this heightened visual perception of nature, but reminded them that the expressive truths of the landscape could only be revealed through a union of the senses and the spirit. Burn argued that paintings, such as Arthur Streeton's *Land of the golden fleece* (1926) overlaid sense and sensibility in this manner, combining the spatial distance of the panoramic view with the idea of a national space (Figure 11.1). A horizontal composition and a balanced, blue-gold palette invited the viewer to take in foreground, middle ground and far horizon with a contemplative, proprietal gaze suggesting a seemingly natural and objective optical order.[9] We metaphorically associate the panoramic landscape with freedom, possibility and future, Avenel Mitchell observes, for it presents an incongruous "synthesis of nearness and remoteness".[10] The visitor's vantage-point is quasi-objective, disinterested and autonomous.[11] This combination of emotional attachment and detached moral viewpoint convincingly conveyed a national story of white progress, later animated in the elevated, cinematic panning shots of countless bush melodramas, from Franklin Barrett's *The breaking of the drought* (1920) to Baz Luhrmann's *Australia*_(2007).

---

[8] Burn I, 'Popular Melbourne landscape painting between the wars', Bendigo Art Gallery, 1982, reprinted in Burn I, *Dialogue: writings in art history*, Allen & Unwin, Sydney, 1991; and Burn I, *National life and landscapes*, Bay Books, Sydney 1992.

[9] Burn's critical review of the bush panorama paralleled the analyses within film theory of a similarly privileged, "3-dimensional, rationalised space" within cinematic realism, with its fixed viewpoint derived from Renaissance principles of perspective and Cartesian ideas of subjective rationality. See for instance The British Film Institute's *Screen* project of the later 1970s and early 1980s; also Martin Jay, 'Scopic regimes of modernity', *Modernity and identity*, ed Scott Lash and Jonathon Friedman, Oxford, 1992, p.184; Bryson N, 'The gaze and the glance', *Vision and painting. the logic of the gaze*, London, 1983, pp. 89–94.

[10] In her discussion of the Australian inter-war panorama and intimate landscape, Avenel Mitchell cites Yi-Fu Tuan's suggestion that "space lies open; it suggests the future and invites action". Tuan Y, *Space and place: the perspective of experience*, London, 1977, p.54, cited Mitchell A, 'The harvest of a quiet eye : the intimate expression of nature in Australian landscape painting from the late nineteenth century to c.1940', MPhil thesis, Department of Art History and Film Studies, University of Sydney, 1997, p. 101.

[11] Ibid, p. 103. See also Bauman Z, 'Strangers: The social construction of universality and particularity', *Telos*, 78. Winter 1988–89, pp. 17–18.

Figure 11.1 Arthur Streeton, *Land of the Golden Fleece* (1926)

Oil on canvas mounted on composition board 50.7 x 75.5, 69.0 x 96.0 frame. Bequest of Henriette von Dallwitz and of Richard Paul in honour of his father Dr Oscar Paul 1965. National Gallery of Australia, Canberra

The intimate landscape

Eco-artists have also been drawn to the familiar 'corner of nature.' Mitchell argues that traditional images of the country garden, orchard and bush clearing offered the sensual experience of belonging within a known place, a comforting image of humanised nature as the mechanisation of agriculture accelerated through intensive clearing of land for cropping and wool production from Federation to the 1930s. She also notes that the popularity of this sub-genre dovetailed with the promotion of native flora in suburban gardens, the emergence of bushwalking and conservation movements and the professionalisation of botany and ecology.[12]

---

[12] Mitchell, op. cit. 1997.

Clara Southern's *An old bee farm* (c1900) presents the bush beyond the fenced paddock (Figure 11.2). A constricted, Heidelberg-style composition and informal viewpoint holds the viewer's eye within a shallow visual field and emphasises a tacit knowledge of family farming and local environs through the sensory experience of 'bush enchantment'. This is also the space of the gardener, field naturalist, Gould League member and humanist geographer, whose valued empirical knowledge is grounded in the lived-world of immediate experience. The sensory attributes of the bush were valued, Mitchell attests, because they were distinctively, privately, almost secretly known.[13]

Figure 11.2 Clara Southern, *An Old Bee Farm* (c1900)
Oil on canvas 66.0 x 111.7cm, Felton Bequest, 1942 National Gallery of Victoria

The intimate landscape also connected with the national story, through close, empirical (including scientific) study, bush fantasy and human anecdote. The popular image of rural life and harmonious human settlement was honed to cozy perfection through paintings like Elioth Gruner's *Spring frost, Emu Plains* (1919) and Hilda Rix Nicholas' *Knockalong garden* (1941), and continue in the weekly televised dramas of

---

[13] ibid., pp. 44–45.

McLeod's Daughters. Its mythic base in peasant culture promotes a continuum between past and present. The image of the homestead at ease in the landscape is brought to life through loving attention to the intimate routines of everyday life, romantic interest on the verandah or at the home paddock gate and family members engaged in familiar chores, all welcoming scenes to the visitor. These enduring images of productive stewardship transformed earlier figures of the explorer, bush larrikin and pioneer into a more modern image of the primary producer.

The modernist desert

The emotional ties binding city-dwellers to the pastoralist landscape were loosened in the 1940s dryland images of Russell Drysdale, Albert Tucker and Sidney Nolan. This generation of artists reconceived 'our colonial pastoral myths' in the existential terms of modernist alienation of nature and culture, subject and object, individual and society. More generally, modernism's formal preoccupations placed the work of art centre-stage, sidelining or excluding nature and natural beauty. Art historically, the dominant drive of modernism was driven by a "turning away from, rejection or repression of nature", in tandem with the path taken by modern science. [14]

The alienated Australian bush became witness to histories of outcasts, colonial violence and environmental mismanagement. It was peopled by marginalised folk who appeared to be of the earth itself, dwarfed by trees and rock formations that seemed all too human. Drysdale's *The rabbiters* (1947) gives the bush a will of its own. Tree stumps and galvanized iron twist and turn in a grotesque echo of Antipodean space, host to a presumed timeless (Aboriginal, unknowable) essence or universal (European) existential truths. [15]

---

[14] Roberts D, 'Aura and aesthetics of nature', *Thesis Eleven*, no. 36, 1993, Massachusetts Institute of Technology, pp. 127–137.
[15] See Catalano G, *An intimate Australia: The landscape & recent Australian art*, Hale & Ironmonger, Sydney, 1985; Drew P, 'Things Becoming', *Verandah: Embracing Space*, Angus and Robertson, Sydney, 1992, pp. 180–198.

Behind this recurrent image of nature as mute witness lurked left-liberal guilt and anger for a displaced Aboriginal presence. Artists were starting to use landscape painting to express the violence of colonial settlement more directly (Drysdale's *Station blacks, Cape York*, 1953; Arthur Boyd's *Half-caste* series of 1959). At the same time, the western desert landscapes of Albert Namatjira were becoming increasingly popular, and for the first time, bark paintings from the Top End were finding their way from the natural history museums to the aesthetic realm of the art gallery.

The postmodern bush

From the early 1970s, the modernist reduction of aesthetics to a theory of art was reversed. Conceptual art and feminist aesthetics sought to understand the relationship between cognition and sensate perception. Artists returned the body to the bush, and physical immersion in nature was again valued as a basis for self-consciousness. Many open-form sculptures from this period resembled small-scaled, ecological systems, or enacted some change (installation, excavation, mark-making) in the immediate environment, as a means heightening our perception of place. The human body performed in the bush environment as just one element among others.

Australian environmental art was more modest than its US counterparts, with the exception of Christo and Jeanne-Claude's influential *Wrapped coast, Little Bay, one million square feet, Sydney, Australia* (1969) (Figure 11.3). A volunteer army of young artists and interested locals wrapped the rocky shoreline in sheets of erosion control mesh (a synthetic woven fibre usually manufactured for agricultural purposes). The project received broad public interest, and influenced many younger artists developing environmentally sensitive, site-specific work at the Mildura Sculpture Triennials from the early 1970s.

More radical projects embraced the local environment as active, sculptural material through site-specific work influenced by minimalism, post-object art and arte povera. In 1973 the Triennial extended to incorporate dry scrubland along the Murray River, and the event became known as Mildura Sculpturescape, under the direction of Tom

McCullough. John Davis wrapped trees with various materials along an informal pathway through the scrub (*Tree Piece*). Kevin Mortensen drew upon memories of dumped mining waste around Blinman in South Australia in fashioning four *Objects in a landscape* from coiled rope and bitumen, which also resembled gigantic hives, termite mounds or wombat scats set among the saltbush.

Figure 11.3 Christo and Jeanne Claude, *Wrapped Coast, Little Bay, One Million Square Feet, Sydney, Australia,1968–69*
Gelatin silver photograph 101.5 h x 127.0 w Gift of John Kaldor, 1982. Photo: Harry Shunk

Collection: National Gallery of Australia, Canberra

Ross Grounds' *Ecological well* created a space for reorienting oneself quite literally within nature. The *Well* was a simple, excavated bunker, which also resembled a nest, cave, mine-shaft, or a womb. This habitat hosted a variety of inhabitants, matter and meanings. Frogs, mosquito larvae, fish, lizards and pigeons all moved in at various levels, taking the Emersonian ideal of a 'home in the wilderness' a step further. Like other sculptural projects at Mildura, *Ecological well* embedded human visitors as just another life-form amongst other, equally opportunistic visitors. For the 1975 Sculpturescape, Alecs Danko scattered scraps of drawings, letters and other debris in a four square metre space demarcated by string, in partial reference to the sculpture park's previous life as the local town tip, while Alison Cousland and Margaret Bell used their sculptural allotment to plant a garden.

The idea of planting or marking objects in the landscape, or subtly modifying natural features was a gentle means of reorienting oneself in space and time, installing ephemeral systems of order upon the apparent indifference of the bush. These projects paralleled the conceptual art 'rambles' of British artists Richard Long, Hamish Fulton and Andy Goldsworthy, treading as lightly on the earth as their 19th century Romantic forebears.[16]

The natural materials used in these projects referred obdurately to themselves. The earth ceased being an inert material awaiting the artist's transformation, and instead became – at least partially – both subject and object of the creative process. Rocks, trees, soil, wind, water, fire and other environmental forces took creative centre-stage to illustrate the rationality of natural systems. This recognition brought humans down to scale as one of many generative elements in a dynamic ecology.

The urge to bunker down with the lizards extended the potential of the mimetic tradition through a sympathetic openness to nature, "experienced as something which speaks to us, affects and engages us".[17] The artist joins the conversation through ritual gestures that mime natural forces. John Wolseley's later drawings extended this early desire "to copy, imitate, make models, explore difference, yield into and become other".[18] Wolseley lays down his paper and canvas to allow the landscape to itself leave traces of scratching, rubbings and the brushing of burnt foliage across the page, recording the passage of the artist through the bush. He sees himself as a "facilitator for the landscape to

---

[16] Culminating in Hamish Fulton's 1979 Biennale of Sydney visit and accompanying project *Tasmania: A Slow Journey.*
[17] Boeme G, in Roberts D, op. cit., 1993, p. 129.
[18] Taussig M, *Mimesis and alterity: a particular history of the senses*, Routledge: New York 1993, p. xiii.

depict itself", as Sasha Grishin observes, rather than as someone who depicts the landscape.[19]

Gaia

These early performances and conceptual art projects often gendered nature as feminine. Performance artist Jill Orr described her 1981 exhibition, *Relics and rituals* in these terms:

> I am always aware of a connection with the earth; things born of the earth, return to the earth, life needing the earth, but also its femaleness, mother-earth, upon which we establish rituals of living and coping: surviving.[20]

Nature as Mother Earth or Gaia is a connection shared by many cultures. Ceramicist and teacher Thancoupie (Thainakuith) has developed a feminine imagery for her pots, tiles and tile-based murals from 1971. These are derived from the sand stories and sand pictures the women draw for children on the beach at Napranum, a small community near Weipa in west Cape York Peninsula. The motif of the circle was particularly important, as she noted in 2003:

> The circle symbolically (in) traditional tribal painting, that was on ground in areas here around Weipa, when on sand, the circle was a strong symbol and... the symbol of fire, the symbol of the world, the symbol of unity, the symbol of love, the symbol of mother. The circle is a very significant symbol in Aboriginal drawing, painting.[21]

Non-Indigenous artists have also conflated nature and the feminine. Dawne Douglas and Michael Liddle used Lovelock's Gaia theory of the earth as a super-organism, along with Lorenz's chaos theory of an inter-

---

[19] Grishin S. 'Sacred ecology', *Australian Art Review*, November 2005–Feb 2006, p. 55.

[20] Orr J, artist's statement, quoted Anne Marsh, *Body and self: performance art in Australia*, Oxford University Press, Sydney, 1993 p. 143.

[21] Thancoupie, 'Stories and tradition in clay', *Story Place*, Queensland Art Gallery, Brisbane, 2003, p. 73. The artist has described her symbolism in similar terms for a 1986 exhibition in Houston, cited in Grace Cochrane, *The crafts movement in Australia: a history*. New South Wales University Press, Sydney, 1992, p. 244.

connected world, as a literal design template for a walk-through park sculpture (*Vitae–Morte*, Gladstone, 1995).[22] A mounded spiral of stones was punctuated with vertical timbers of varying heights. These were recycled from an old wharf that once serviced Gladstone's meat packing industry, a reminder of past industry, sustainability and lost forests.

For many artists, however, the gendered view of nature as feminine posed philosophical and political problems. Heated debates through the 1980s had sought to clarify a less reductive formulation of nature and female agency. In western Cartesian thought, nature has been to culture what body or matter has been to the mind, the feminine to the masculine. Many North American feminists found this gendering of nature empowering, and used it to articulate the costs of presumptuously separating human action from the natural world. Australians were less inclined to privilege women in an eco-aware practice. Nonetheless, as writer and curator Julie Ewington noted in 1994, a predominance of women artists used natural materials and forces. "This agency is important", she argued, for "it is in direct contradiction to the influential western notion, at least as old as the philosophy of Aristotle, that women and the earth alike are passive, receptive, nurturing vessels, properly dominated by men."[23] Yet the artworks Ewington championed – such as Joan Grounds' open-air fire sculptures, installations and experimental film *We should call this a living room* (1972, with Alecs Danko), Joan Brassil's investigations of immaterial, electro-magnetic fields and Bonita Ely's longstanding research on the Murray River – shied away from retrogressive assumptions about femininity, masculinity, nature and creativity. Ely's 1980 *Murray River punch,* for instance, parodied both nature and kitchen goddesses in a cooking demonstration in Adelaide's Rundle Mall, concocting a mixed drink for passing shoppers (Figure 11.4). As the blenders whizzed, the artist cheerfully explained the punch's recipe ingredients: phosphate compound

---

[22] This artist-scientist team founded The ArtScience Interface (art accelerating cultural change by visualising philosophical concepts/scientific awareness of environment). See Lucy Grace, 'Vitae-morte: environmental art in Queensland', *Art Monthly Australia*, October 1995, pp. 15–17.

[23] Ewington J, 'In the wild: nature, culture, gender in installation art', *Dissonance: feminism and the arts 1970–90*, (ed. Catriona Moore) Allen & Unwin, 1994, pp. 228–9.

fertilizers, human faeces and agricultural chemicals were added to the mix, served up with a sprinkle of rabbit dung as garnish.

Figure 11.4 Bonita Ely, *Murray River Punch* (1981)
Performance at Rundle Mall, Adelaide, 1980. Photograph from the artist's collection, reproduced from Ann Marsh, *Body and Self: performance art in Australia, op. cit.*.

Art Activism

In the 1970s and early 1980s, eco-art was commonly aligned with the Trades Union Green Bans and campaigns for land and sea rights, anti-nuke and anti-uranium mining. Even the die-hard 'twigs and string' sculpture hippies at Mildura framed their work in political terms when calling for an artists' boycott of French sponsorship and participation in the 1973 Mildura Sculpturescape, in protest against French nuclear testing in the Pacific.[24]

---

[24] John Davis, Clive Murray-White and Ti Parks initiated the artists' protest, which prompted heated debate amongst participating Australian (and French) artists, and which postponed the show (but not the nuclear testing). See Sturgeon G, *The Story of the Mildura Sculpture Triennial, 1961–1982*, Mildura City Council, Mildura, 1985.

Tasmanian writers Peter Grant and Jonathon Holmes recall how romantic landscape imagery was an essential component of early conservation battles, which were fought over the meaning of wild places (Lake Peddar, 1972; the Franklin River, 1983). Olga Trucheras and Peter Dombrovskis' photographs, reproduced on posters and calendars, "showed scenes most urban dwellers would never visit in person, [but] they communicated an idea and an ideal of wilderness that worked more powerfully on the imagination than any number of arguments could have".[25] They were used in full colour newspaper advertisements in the lead-up to the 1983 election ('Would you vote for a party that would destroy this?'). The iconic power of Dombrovkis' *Rock Island bend*, Ian MacLean later added, partly rests on the fact that "The sublime is an aesthetic of both catastrophe and hope".[26]

Despite its popularity during the Franklin campaign, Dombrovskis' style of 'fine print and singular image' landscape photography soon came under criticism for an essentialist rendition of Mother Nature, the evasion of ongoing Indigenous habitation and its easy co-option by the advertising and tourism industries. Sculptor Julie Gough (Trawlwoolway) later reminded audiences that the Tasmanian wilderness has never been terra incognita or terra nullius. Her installations suggest stories in the landscape which pre-date the old-growth forests.[27] *The whispering sands (ebb tide)* (1998) locates colonial conflict as a part of the evolving Tasmanian landscape (Figure 11.5). Cut-out figures of named individuals associated with the scientific colonial project stand revealed then submerged by water as the tide ebbs and flows along the shores of Eaglehawk Neck.

---

[25] Grant P, 'Wild art at the world's end', *Artlink*, vol. 21, no. 1, March 2001, p. 14.

[26] McLean I, 'Sublime futures: eco-art and the return of the real in Peter Dombrovskis, John Wolseley and Andy Goldsworthy', *Transformations*, no. 5, December 2002, p. 6.

[27] Grant P, 'Wild art at the world's end', *Artlink* 21 no. 1, 2001, p. 17. See also Langton M, 'What do we mean by wilderness? Wilderness and terra nullius in Australian Art' *The Sydney Papers*. vol. 8, no. 1, 1996, pp. 11–31.

Figure 11. 5 Julie Gough, *The whispering sands (ebb tide)* (detail) (1998)

16 life-size poker worked ply figures installed at Eaglehawk Neck

From an Indigenous point of view, humans are fully imbricated in the natural world. The idea of an abjected space of utter wildness or 'wilderness' makes no sense here. The colonial conception of Tasmania as Ultima Thule was also taken up in Bea Maddock's *Terra Spiritus...* *with a darker shade of pale* (1993–98), an ambitious, delicately traced circumscription of the island. This 51-sheet uber-panorama ("A circumlittoral incised drawing of the entire coastline of Tasmania") combined and condensed the topographical features of the coast drawn from ordinance survey maps ("worked with hand-ground local ochre over letterpress and finished with hand-drawn script") and is inscribed by Palawa terms for country.[28]

The lie of the land[29]

'New Left' cultural politics fragmented from the mid-1980s as the economic, trade and industrial reforms of the Hawke–Keating government dominated mainstream politics, whilst neo-liberal economic doctrines swept aside older traditions of industry (and environmental) regulation. Environmental concerns languished at the fringes of social attention, and the radical art of the masses, the street, forest and community no longer seemed to be politically effective.[30] Many retreated from activist art to understand the theoretical shape of cultural politics in a post-industrial world. The contours of 1980s cultural politics were sketched in academic and gallery contexts; art and working life projects, poster collectives and street performances were perceived to be no longer at the cutting edge of art practice.

An increasingly complex, post-modern visual culture was no place for 'lost world' nostalgia, 'one world' humanism or aesthetic naivety. The call was out for a more critical, post-modern landscape project that would bring "the visual representation of the landscape into a confrontation with the symbolic system of language."[31]

---

[28] Title page, Maddock B, *Terra spiritus...with a darker shade of pale* (1993–98) , National Gallery of Australia Collection.
[29] This sub-title is taken from an exhibition critically deconstructing the colonial ideology of the Australian landscape tradition (Powerhouse Museum, curator Ann Stephen, 1992).
[30] In the North American context, see Smith S, 'Beyond Green', *beyond green: towards a sustainable art*, exhibition catalogue, Smart Museum of Art, Chicago and Independent Curators International, New York, 2006, p. 13.
[31] Holmes J, 'She's a moving place all right: contemporary visual arts in Tasmania", *Studio International*, vol. 196, no. 1002, October 1983, p. 45, also Bann S, 'Art into landscape: the background to contemporary land art', *Praxis M*, Spring 1984, cited

To make audiences think actively about their environment, artists sought to distance or confound the codes of expressive realism and the picturesque landscape. Many looked back to feminist, conceptual and Indigenous art projects of the 1970s that had complicated simplistic nature imagery through use of community research and oral history, photomontage, collage and installation. In the sphere of documentary and landscape photography, for instance, Virginia Coventry's 1979 Biennale of Sydney installation had assembled photographic documents, newspaper clippings and hand-written information: *Whyhalla: not a document* and *Here and there: concerning the nuclear power industry*, (Figure 11.6). Jon Rhodes' photographic series *Just another sunrise?* (1974–6) similarly brought together documentary photography and textual information to chronicle the battle over Nabalco's mining lease in the years immediately preceding the 1976 Northern Territory Land Rights Act. In 1976 Michael Gallagher had relinquished the editorial power of the documentary photographer when invited by Yungngora community elders to document their struggle against Amax's oil drilling program on traditional lands at Nookanbah.[32]

Chips Macinolty, Marie McMahon, Jan Mackay, Michael Callaghan, Ruth Waller and others extended their 1970s activist work with the Earthworks and later Redback Graphix poster workshops in similar community-based projects in regional and remote Australia. Projects like these had framed the landscape within visual, historical, political, economic and legal conflicts of interest. They declared interrogative positions for artist, subject and audience to counter the perceived univocal transmission of documentary information.

Jonathon Holmes, 'Blindspot: regional histories in Australia', *Artlink*, vol. 26, no. 1, 2006, p. 68.
[32] See Hawke S & Gallagher M, *Noonkanbah: whose land, whose law*, Freemantle Arts Centre Press, Perth, 1989.

Figure 11.6 Virginia Coventry, *Here and there: concerning the nuclear power industry*, (1979)

Art Gallery of New South Wales, *Vision and disbelief: Biennale of Sydney* (curator: Bill Wright). Installation of eight collages arranged in two rows of four, each with gelatin silver photographs (some copy photographs) captioned in decal lettering, each with extensive inscriptions, some with collaged photocopied newsprint, with loose photocopies of newspaper stories placed on an adjacent table. Reproduced by permission of VISCOPY Ltd, Sydney, 2007

Collection: National Gallery of Australia, Canberra

Longstanding fine art traditions also came under fire. Franklin campaign veteran Raymond Arnold reflected upon the art historical and colonial origins of his panoramic landscapes, whilst reminding contemporary audiences of other encroachments that human beings have made on the landscape either through mining, forestry or hydro-electric schemes (*Florentine Valley*, 1983).[33] David Stephenson, arriving in Tasmania from

---

[33] Holmes, op. cit., 2006, p. 65.

the United States in 1982, also exploited the virtuosity of 19th century landscape photography in haunting, art-historical visions of paradise lost (Figure 11.7). He works with and against the bravura of the photographic landscape tradition as a visual match for the hubris of Tasmanian hydro-electricity schemes.[34]

Figure 11.7 David Stephenson, *Traveller Above Sea and City* (1985)
Silver gelatin print, 100 x 150cms

Catherine Rogers' photographs similarly prompt the aesthetic contemplation of scientific (ecological, physical, chemical) phenomena related to flooding and clear-felling, packaging nature as an object of language and desire. This post-colonial studio-lore was first road-tested in Ian Burn's sly, painterly proposition: "A landscape is not something you look at but something you look through", etched on

---

[34] ibid, p. 45.

the plexiglass surface of *Homage to Albert ('south through Heavytree Gap')* (1989) and extended in his *Value added landscapes* series of 1995–6.

From the early 1980s, the landscape has been considered as a site where environmental phenomena are registered, rather than as a window on the world. Janet Laurence's *Veil of trees* (1999 with Jisuk Han) was a sculptural, value-added landscape encapsulating many of these ideas. Laurence planted 100 eucalyptus trees along the spine of the Lawson site of Sydney's Domain. Red forest gums, originally on the site, were interspersed with large sheets of glass etched with fragments of writing about trees in Australian literature, and filled with native tree seed, resins, honey and ash. Sue Best describes the work's linearity as akin to a pathway or passage, though its open structure (veils) serves as:

> at once a screen or window through which the landscape passes, and a kind of writing surface, both for the veils and twists of substance, and for the tree poems… The beholder is moved between the panels, and between the literal landscape and the landscape of the imagination, the land imbued with cultural meaning… into the imaginings of landscape that is part of place formation.[35]

With the demise of the open sculpture aesthetic by the late 1970s, the influence of anti-humanist and post-structuralist theory and the lure of electronic technologies, the door shut on the old aesthetic fantasy of 'natura naturans', with its attendant redemptive or reconciliatory artistic gestures and rituals. Nature lurked in the galleries through the 1980s and early 1990s in a repressed state. Spectacular and highly crafted indoor site-machines accented fragility and loss. Robyn Backen's *Sprung* (1991), for instance, transformed the primordial, Edenic garden into a fetishised souvenir. A single, elegant Azolla fern – the lowest order of plant – was 'grown' in the coils of a spare, rusty mattress-spring, barely maintained as a living system through the minimum required light and agonisingly slow droplets of water. Other gallery-based projects by Janet Laurence, Joan Brassil, Joan Grounds and Joyce Hinterding recalled the wonder of the science laboratory, space observatory and natural history museum.

---

[35] Best S, 'Immersion and distraction: the environmental works of Janet Laurence', *Art and Australia*, vol. 38, no. 1, 2000, p. 88.

These artists variously researched a variety of changeable and unstable, non-permanent materials (liquids, rope, lead, chemicals, electricity) as catalysts for chance, alchemical transformations.

Later in the decade, a number of unsustainable, gallery-based garden installations in the United States prompted critics to loudly question the value of bringing nature into the gallery. It was argued that slick packaging wrapped around environmental crises was not necessarily edifying.[36] In Australia, however, this has not been such a big issue. The gallery system remains politically relevant today as a platform for ecological communication largely due to the force of the Aboriginal art revolution. Indigenous curators like Djon Mundine, Hetti Perkins and Brenda Croft maintain an inter-connection between gallery art and the political realm of environmental decision-making. Over the past two decades, they have exploited the aesthetic power of formal gallery installations and the cultural power of the museum sector to publicise, educate and authorise connections between Indigenous art, land and sea claims and customary law. To emphasise their point, Yolngu senior artist Djambawa Marawilli re-stated the claims made by his people's 1963 bark petition, warning audiences at the 2006 Biennale of Sydney to remember that Yirrkala bark paintings have a broader purpose than international gallery artefacts: their status as native title documents in a current battle with the Northern Territory tourist and fishing industries.[37]

The concept of 'country'

Indigenous artworks brought post-colonial frameworks to bear on gallery-based and site-specific eco-art. They showed how European regional landscape traditions have been premised on the invasion and ruination of other peoples' country. These traditions had located Aboriginality in the realm of the natural, as their mythic precondition. The European understanding of culture and nature as mutually exclusive, had prompted radical artists of the 1950s to seek atonement, and those of the 1970s to try to recover a presumed lost connection.

---

[36] Avgikos J, 'Green Peace', *Artforum*, April 1991, pp. 104–110.
[37] Marawili D, artist's statement, *Biennale visitor's handbook*, 2006, p. 21. See related statements in *Saltwater: Yirrkala bark paintings of sea country*, Buku-Larrngay Mulka Centre and Jennifer Isaacs Publishing, Yirrkala, 1999.

Indigenous art and philosophy hastened the rejection of this dualism, and the romantic search for 'harmony between people and nature' was re-cast in the activist framework of social and environmental justice.[38] Much of the art from Indigenous communities of northern Australia and the Pacific islands employ local materials, are community based, activist-oriented and relate to long-held beliefs that everything is inter-related.[39] This work has helped link ecology and art to identity and cultural survival. Conversely, loss of identity is seen to go hand in hand with environmental degradation.[40] This identity remains extremely diverse, for Indigenous artworks express the viewpoints of six hundred or so language groups in Australia, and therefore cannot be reduced to an essentialist art historical concept.

By acknowledging these counter-traditions, the European idea of 'landscape' has broadened to the concept of 'country'. 'Country' is a handy, European term respectful of Indigenous land ownership and custodianship, whilst recognising the potential of non-Indigenous stewardship. It signifies post-colonial relations with the natural world which acknowledge Indigenous, colonial and anti-colonial myths and images, as South Australian arts writer and novelist Stephanie Radok muses, "layered on top of each other to make a richer, deeper place".[41] Canberra-based art historian, Mary Eagle has also observed that in thinking of country:

---

[38] As noted in an international context by US writer Victor Margolin, 'Reflections on art & sustainability', *Beyond green: toward a sustainable art*, Smart Museum of Art, University of Chicago and Independent Curators International, New York, 2006, p. 21.

[39] So said Julie Ewington, then education officer at the Queensland Art Gallery, in her paper 'Installation and environment in South East Asia', Topographies Conference, Centre for Environmental and Ecological Art, Townsville, 5–7 August, 1996, as reported by Chris Downie, 'Topographies', *Periphery*, no. 25, November 1995, p. 10.

[40] This point was made by Perc Tucker Gallery Director Ross Searle in his paper 'The Art of Survival', at the 1996 Topographies Conference. Chris Downie, op. cit. 1995, p. 10 .

[41] Radok S, 'Pip Stokes: Unfolding the night', *Art and Australia*, vol. 39, no. 4, (June-July-Aug 2002) p. 544.

[there is] no divide between representations of land and of people, hence no 'landscape' in the western sense of an abstract scene waiting to be filled … The Aborigines envisioned journeys and represented them in songs and images according to the waterholes, food resources, people, land rights, rites and permissions involved.[42]

In most Aboriginal communities, Indigenous law maintains distinctions between visual representations, dance, ritual, poetry, song and a ritualised use of language, and dictates their use in declaring the central theme of possession, identity and custodianship. Indigenous art has helped others understand how the law codifies and maps obligations to the land.

This has helped raise the standard of Australian 'landliteracy', as Ray Norman terms the ability to read and appreciate the signs of health (and ill-health) in the landscape.[43] A good example is the way Lockhart River painter Samantha Hobson reads the land in environmental, as well as cultural, economic and community terms (*Burn grass season*, 2002). Balkanu's 'Caring for Country' manager Barry Hunter explains traditional agricultural practices that have helped the Top End's potential carbon trade economy:

> "Firestick farming (burning off), is a well-documented technique Aboriginal people used to renew and manage the land … In the north of Australia it is carried out at the beginning of the cool, dry season. Firestick farming serves two main purposes. One is to decrease the chance of a wildfire by reducing the vegetation; this vegetation could be fuel for a major fire. Secondly, fire is used to clear the country and encourage new growth. This new growth attracts wildlife, such as kangaroos and other species, which are drawn to nibble on the soft new shoots sprouting after the fire."[44]

---

[42] Eagle M, 'Traditions of representing the land in Aboriginal art', *Art & Australia*, vol. 37, no. 2, (Dec-Jan-Feb 1999–2000) p. 236.

[43] Norman R, 'Reading the waters', *Artlink*, vol. 21, no. 1, 2001, pp. 10–13.

[44] Hunter B, *Story place: Indigenous art of Cape York and the rainforest*, exhibition catalogue, Cairns Regional Gallery, 2003 p.28. See also Frew W, 'Use Top End to trade in carbon, say scientists', *The Sydney Morning Herald*, 23–24 June, 2007, p. 6.

Peter Debnam notes that Hobson's *Burn grass season*, along with her *Stressed* (2001) and *Bust 'im up* (2000) can also be read:

> as a metaphor for the volatile social conditions that often undermine the community. There is, however, an underlying optimism that 'burning off' also involves purging and cleansing – the growth of fresh grass and new hope.[45]

The concept of country also allows artists to reinterpret useful elements from the western landscape tradition. For instance, the ambiguous, moral discourse of unity, progress and nation afforded by the panoramic vista remains a powerful visual tool. Today, the panorama might still be proprietal and moral; however it is often metaphorically linked with the viewpoint of Walter Benjamin's 'Angel of History', propelled forward into the future whilst looking back, appalled at the environmental and human wreckage of the modern, industrial age. Western Australian photographer Richard Woldendorp's stunning aerial panoramas occasionally stop us in the tracks of this historical viewpoint. Newspaper photo-journalists more regularly return this sorry gaze in panoramic shots of the rural wreckage left by agricultural industrialisation, the cornerstone of Australian modernity. We look out over parched catchment areas and degraded watercourses, the spooky colour coding of bleached coral or salt encrusted soil with a guilty sense of 'proprietal' responsibility.

The intimate landscape's expression of local attachment and productive stewardship also resonates in current projects on agricultural sustainability. Today's intimate bush claims ancestry in both Indigenous bush tucker ceremonies and the English landscape garden tradition. It expresses a dynamic and productive relation between art and nature, where nature aids art, and the artist/gardener aids the creation of future nature.[46] The genre's emotional investment in a corner of nature was the experiential focus of 'Karra: Karrawirraparri Red Gum Forest River' (2000 Adelaide Festival, curator Vivonne Thwaites). Artists Chris de

---

[45] Debnam P, *Story place*, 2003, p. 101.
[46] Instances of art-nature co-productivity range widely, from projects associated with *Waterworks*, SA Country Arts Trust, Adelaide, (curator Catherine Murphy) to the native grasses garden planting at the Casula Powerhouse in Liverpool, South-west Sydney, regularly harvested for community grass-weaving workshops.

Rosa, Agnes Love and Jo Crawford provided a quieter space within the Festival, by installing a bark-scattered, forest bush track in the festival's artspace. The gallery bushwalk implicitly lead outside to the old, gnarled trees along the nearby River Torrens, some pre-dating white settlement, and bearing scars of Aboriginal timber-collecting activities[47]. The settler-landscape themes of 'bush enchantment' and the artisanal knowledge of the artist and crafts worker all resonate with the important Indigenous lesson that ecological communication is both cognate and sensate.

Mary Eagle, writing on Emily Kngwarreye's *Big yam dreaming* (1995) describes how the canvas is worked from the outside in, rendering the yams' journey as they spread underground (Figure 11.8). Kngwarreye painted at arm's reach, demonstrating her knowledge, power and connections with the yam's life force: "Unlike her western counterparts she neither had nor required an encompassing view through looking. She looked at her work from the point of view of a woman digging for yam tubers."[48] Painting as tracing with fingers, Eagle continues, "Her hands understood her subject through a lifetime." The practical philosophy embedded in this artwork educates Australians about tacit knowledge, ownership and responsibility for country.

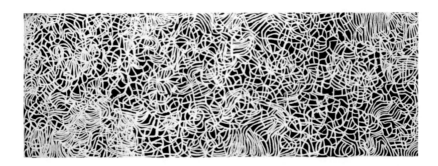

Figure 11.8 Emily Kngwarreye, *Big yam dreaming* (1995)

---

[47] Vivonne Thwaites, 'Karra: Karrawirraparri red gum forest river', *Artlink*, vol. 31, no. 1, March 2001, p. 36.
[48] Mary Eagle, op cit. 1999–2000, p. 236

Acrylic on canvas, 291.1 x 801.8 cm, presented through the Art Foundation of Victoria by Donald and Janet Holt and family, Governors, 1995. National Gallery of Victoria, Melbourne. Copyright Emily Kngwarreye, 1995. Reproduced by permission of VISCOPY Ltd, Sydney, 2007

The inland has come into its own as a positive rather than a negative space. As Hetti Perkins and Hannah Fink noted when introducing the 2000 exhibition, *Papunya: genius and genesis*, marking the centenary of Federation, one (pastoral) landscape tradition (Heidelberg) has given way to another – "an appreciation of the spiritual resonance of the desert".[49] The well-established art centres of the Western Desert helped audiences mentally repopulate the existential void of the modernist heartland.

This opened the space for renewed interest in the anti-colonial, dryland visions of Drysdale, Boyd, Nolan and Namatjira. Tracey Moffatt's photographic series *Up in the sky* (1997) revisited Drysdale's cross-cultural badlands. Her associated 1990 film *Night cries*, which is in part an imaginary sequel to Charles Chauvel's 1955 assimilationist epic *Jedda*, vividly evokes home as heartbeat and prison, mother–daughter relations and stolen generations. It was filmed in a studio set against a Namatjira-style backdrop (*Jedda's* opening credits were themselves projected against a generic 'Namatjira' watercolour).

Susan Norrie has also often evoked a Drysdale-esque orchestration of natural disaster and human menace. Her 2006 video *Black wind* is an elegiac tribute to the Aboriginal Tent Embassy haunting Canberra's parliamentary triangle, and also to memories of nuclear testing at Maralinga, with its legacies of dispersal, blindness and sickness (Figure11.9). The camera slowly rolls out an extended drive-by dolly-shot of the wind-swept campsite, stopping, starting up again, moving in and around tents and washing-lines to again circle the beltway in an eddy of movement, like wind moving across country. Norrie's 2003 video installation *UNDERTOW* similarly surrounds the spectator with slow-moving, ominous imagery of wonderous and ominous environmental phenomena (tempests, bubbling mud pools, dust storms, cherry

---

[49] Perkins H & Fink H, 'Covering ground: the corporeality of landscape', *Art & Australia*, vol. 38, no. 1 (Sept-Oct-Nov 2000), p. 75. See also Langton M, 'Sacred geography', in Perkins H & Fink H, *Papunya Tula: genesis and genius*, Art Gallery of New South Wales, Sydney, 2000, pp. 258–267.

blossoms, environmental disasters) and equally inexplicable scientific experiments.[50] Neither seem to hook up – a theme that Norrie has developed over a decade of investigating environmental phenomena and human prediction. *HAVOC*, her video installation at the Australian Pavilion for the 2007 Venice Biennale, continues to explore our dreadfully dislocated environmental times. As the artist explains of the Venice project, "I continue to deal with my ongoing interest in thermodynamics, which is an indicator of disorder within our times. This project is located in the region of the 'ring of fire' – a glimpse into worlds which are both geologically and politically volatile ... Indonesia acts as a microcosm for the broader condition of the world."[51]

[50] Norrie S, *UNDERTOW*, Art Gallery of New South Wales Contemporary Art Projects, Art Gallery of New South Wales, Sydney, 2003.
[51] Norrie S, *HAVOC*, Artist's Statement, Au3 Venice Biennale 2007, Australia Council www.australiavenicebiennale.com.au/content/view/68/115/, accessed 13 June 2007.

Figure 11.9 Susan Norrie, *Black wind* (2006)
DVD installation, Mori Gallery, Sydney

An aesthetic green audit?

Concern for the environmental impact of artworks, processes and objects has prompted informal green audits, re-igniting and extending the 1980s industrial health and safety campaigns of the state-based Artworkers' Unions. Studio residencies now screen pets, the use and disposal of toxic materials and the removal or alteration of flora. "What's wrong with tying this artwork to this tree?" or "What do you normally do with the waste toxic resins you use in your work?" are now common questions.[52]

Could we also make a metaphoric green audit of art writing? At the very least, critics are starting to ascertain whether an artwork is simply a passive object or an active force. Is it something that is simply created, or is it something that creates? A renewed emphasis on creation leads to viewing the panoply of eco-art projects with a more creative aesthetic response than one derived solely from traditional curatorial and critical frameworks.

In the field of public art, for instance, David Cranswick observes a shift from 'plonk art' (object-in-the-space) to art as restoration ecology. This shift has dovetailed with the emerging eco disciplines that are also concerned with the study of relationships, supplanting outmoded ideas about humans being dominant and separate from the places in which they live. Artists now share knowledge within collaborative, interdisciplinary teams for ecological restoration.[53]

For instance, Jennifer Turpin and Michaelie Crawford's 1996 *The memory line* called upon local residents to help plant a 270- by 4-metre expanse of rye-corn grass meandering along what was the original course of a creek in Fairfield, a suburb of south west Sydney (Figure 11.10). This early stage of Fairfield City Council's 'Restoring the Waters'

---

[52] Grant P, op cit. 2005, p. 39.
[53] Cranswick D, 'Bridging art and ecology', *Artlink*, vol. 21, no. 1, March 2001.

environmental rehabilitation project aimed to get the locals involved, and the grass line was the first stage in the removal of a concrete storm water drain and restoration of a sustainable creek line.[54] The community planting successfully reversed local cultural and environmental amnesia, and highlighted the vulnerability of the urban landscape. Such projects are evaluated for the strength of their inter-related environmental and aesthetic dimensions. It is difficult, however, to formalise imaginative resources for evaluating art as ecological communication. As United States art historian Victor Margolin argues:

> We will need a new aesthetic to embrace the three categories of object, participation, and action without privileging the conventional formal characteristics of objects. In this aesthetic, the distinctions between art, design, and architecture will blur as critics discover new relations between the value of form and the value of use.[55]

This aesthetic is necessarily contingent, and could never be a singular category embracing all objects or participatory actions. Nor can it be set down in advance; rather, like feminist aesthetics, it develops a descriptive, evaluative and analytic purchase in tandem with specific art projects, audiences and contexts. It would be silly, for instance, to set out *a priori* aesthetic frameworks for projects that welcome the potential loss of control over medium and message that comes with working in public, as in the unscripted, interactive processes of Squatspace's popular anti-development *Tours of beauty* (2004–6) through the backstreets, community centres and housing commission apartments of inner-Sydney Redfern and Waterloo.[56]

---

[54] Lynn V, 'Jennifer Turpin and Michaelie Crawford: The choreography of time, light and water', *Art & Australia*, vol. 39, no. 2, Dec 2001-Jan/Feb 2002, pp. 238–247.

[55] Margolin V, 'Reflections on art and sustainability', in *Beyond green: toward a sustainable art*, Smart Museum of Art, University of Chicago and Independent Curators International, New York, 2006, p. 29.

[56] Ihlein L, 'Art as situated experience', *If you see something, say something*, (ed. de Souza K & Begg Z), exhibition project documentation and catalogue, Sydney/Melbourne, January-February 2007, p. 9. For a broader appraisal of related activist projects see Dean B, 'Seeing what we need to see', *realtime*, no. 78, April-May 2007, p. 46.

Figure 11.10 Jennifer Turpin and Michaelie Crawford, *The memory line* (1996)

Corn grass, 270 x 4 x 1 m. Clear Paddock Creek, Fairfield, Sydney. For the Australian conservation and 'Restoring the Waters' Project' with Schaffer Barnsley Landscape Architects. Photo: Ian Hobbs.

Compositional unity, dynamic symmetry, aesthetic emotion, truth to materials, sculptural presence and the tonal nuances of the zone system are among the many criteria used to discuss modern art. Eco-aesthetics introduces values like sustainability, biodiversity, environmental activism and Indigenous community protocols, although the critical and art historical language for these seemingly instrumental outcomes have yet to be developed beyond their use as simple descriptors.[57] Undoubtedly, our critical language will broaden as authors, subjects, objects and processes change. Bush tucker, salinity, tidal patterns and rainfall are now common artistic motifs. Artistic processes have expanded to include direct seeding, hand-planting, feral pest control and water sampling.[58] Adelaide artist Gavin Malone proposes a common view:

> It is easy to consider a sculptural form to be a river valley, paint strokes to be the planting of trees, shrubs and grasses, the grubbing of fennel and poisoning of blackberry to be the editing of superfluous content. But bring in others – collaboration with engineers, architects, urban planners, landscape planners – those who influence the form of our public space and infrastructure. Then another layer – ecologists, botanists, cultural planners, and importantly, artists ... To manipulate an urban, rural, or remote landscape, to change its aesthetic from degraded to sustainable, to mediate and act on the way people understand and live in the bio-physical world, can be and is art. [59]

Many of the projects discussed here share a speculative, working framework of environmental forces or elements. Given the space available, let us elaborate how just one of these elements could be used to help frame a 'green aesthetics'. No doubt the most important element in Australia at present is water. Stephanie Radok has already conveyed the poetic force of water as an important motif in contemporary art:

> Art that concerns itself with some manifestation of water demonstrates what can be considered a new phase in Australian art about the land. After Mabo, ... after the Aboriginal art that makes known the daily patterns of almost every region of Australia, this land can never be seen in the same way again. Aboriginal land, occupied land, land covered with stories, births and deaths, it is yet ready to receive more

[57] The positive value of critical description has, however, been ably argued by New Zealand art critic Justin Paton in 'The shadow economy', *Art Monthly Australia*, no. 200, June 2007, pp. 9–11.
[58] Radok S & Malone G, 'Remediation as art', *Artlink*, vol. 25, no. 4, 2005, p. 47.
[59] Malone G, 'The Ecology of Art or Art as Ecology', *Broadsheet*, vol. 27, no. 7, Summer 1998, p. 5.

living and to deepen our understanding of what was and may still be. Our understanding of this history makes both bitter and sweet our current occupation. Each of us arguably comes from river people, or plains people, book people or boat people, people of the night, of the fish, of the mountains or of the sea. Many of us do not know what kind of people are ours or where we belong but perhaps we can, by listening to our intuitions and feelings, understand where we fit in and take responsibility for the effects on the world produced by our actions and ways of thinking.[60]

Saltwater

Radok implies that water is a productive, scarce, sacred and contested element.[61] Beyond that, we can make no easy generalities. Yolgnu artists, for instance, relate the poetics of water to specific actions on land and sea rights in their region. A case in point is the 1999-2001 travelling exhibition *Saltwater: Yirrkala bark paintings of sea and country*, which was prompted by Garranali custodian Wäka Munungurr's discovery of an illegal barramundi fishing camp hidden amongst the mangroves near the homeland community of Bäniyala (Figure 11.11). As Andrew Blake, art coordinator at Yirrkala's Buku-Larrngay Mulka Centre explains:

> This apparently small incident began the monumental story of the production of 80 bark paintings – set against the backdrop of a national legal and political maelstrom. While these barks were being painted, we saw the historic recognition of Native Title in the sea by the Federal Court one day … and its extinguishment by the Parliament literally two days later. Through all this, the events set in train by Wäka's discovery continued as inexorably as an incoming tide. These works and this catalogue have been brought in by that tide.[62]

---

[60] Radok S, 'A water or a light', *Artlink*, vol. 21, no. 1, March 2001, p. 47.
[61] See also Langton M, 'Waterscapes: the social and spiritual construction of water in Aboriginal societies' In David B, Barker B and McNiven I J (eds.) *The social archaeology of indigenous societies*, Aboriginal Studies Press, Canberra, 2006.
[62] Blake A, 'Preface', *Saltwater: Yirrkala bark paintings of sea country*, Buku-Larrngay Mulka Centre and Jennifer Isaacs Publishing, Yirrkala, 1999, p. 6.

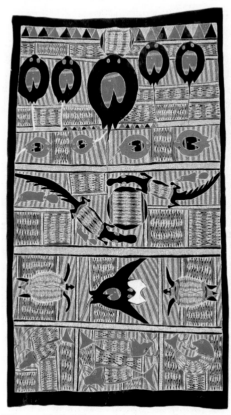

Figure 11.11 Miniyawany Yunupinu, From Biranybirany (c. 1996–1997)

Painted stringybark, 178 x 107cms, reproduced in the exhibition catalogue *Saltwater: Yirrkala Bark Paintings of Sea Country*, Buku-Larrngay Mulka Centre and Jennifer Isaacs Publishing, Yirrkala, 1999

Floating an exhibition of bark paintings about Sea Rights on an incoming political tide is a powerful ecological aesthetic platform. The image of estuarine ebb and flow provides a poetic, cross-cultural metaphor for reconciliation and extends the concept of Native Title to the sea. Curator Djon Mundine explains how

> The Yolngu use water as a tool, a model for philosophising. The estuarine area of a river has different plant species along its bank. The constant renewal where fresh and salt mix and

return is known as ganma. This is used as a metaphor to describe a different kind of mixing: mixing Balanda thought from overseas (saltwater) and indigenous wisdom from the land (fresh water) to create new life and ways of thinking.[63]

The image of eddying, converging or blending philosophical currents carries political implications in other coastal waters. In the metropolitan context of super-marina real estate, Sydney artist Nicole Ellis images the ocean as a conduit "for ideas and bodies, history & knowledge ... How does water carry the memories of those who lived on its shores and even on the water and below the waterline ... ?"[64] Ellis worked with James McGrath to digitally tabulate the contentious submarine spaces of Sydney Harbour for the 'Green Olympics' Arts Festival. *Tidal vectors: 2000* mapped the congested patterns of boat hulls, bordered by more streamlined underwater currents moving around landforms and the contours of harbour inlets and channels (Figures 11.12a & 11.12b).

On the Tasmanian coast, the laissez-faire mixing of seawater and introduced material angers artist Jane Quon, a self-proclaimed 'boat person'. Quon projects digitalised photographic images on industrial structures to communicate the threat to Tasmania's marine environment from dumped ship ballast. Her 2000 installation *Ballast exchange* was developed from a combination of phenomenological and scientific research on coastal ecology gained through her work as a diver (Figure 11.13). Geographer Pete Hay writes:

> ... she has seen the inshore ravaged by proliferating Pacific starfish (Asterias amurensis), the European green crab (Carcinus maenas), a Japanese seaweed (Underia pinnatifida), and toxic dinoflagellates, all introduced per the agency of dumped ballast water. Islands are especially vulnerable to the perturbation wrought by invasive species, diversity being typically lower and ecological relationships less resilient than on continental landmasses."[65]

[63] Mundine D, 'Saltwater', *Saltwater: Yirrkala Bark Paintings of Sea Country,* 1999, p. 20.
[64] Radok S, op. cit., 2001, p. 49.
[65] *Ballast Exchange* was devised for the Bass Strait Forum in Launceston, December 2000. See Peter Hay, 'Dinoflagellates, and Art: Jane Quon's Marine Installations', *Artlink,* vol. 21, no. 1, March 2001, p. 19 Jane Quon, 'Phenomenology and artistic

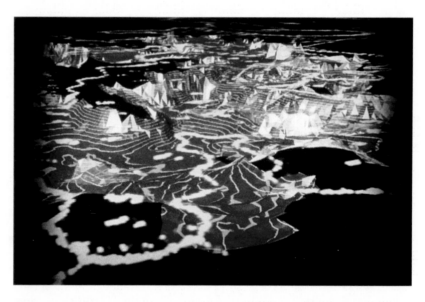

(a)

(b)

Figure 11.12a and 11.12b Nicole Ellis (with James McGrath), *Tidal vectors: 2000*

Digital installation, Museum of Sydney, Olympic Arts Festival, image courtesy of the artists and dLux media/arts 2000. Permission by Viscopy Ltd, Sydney, 2007

praxis: an application to marine ecological communication', *Leonardo*, vol. 38, no. 3, 2005, pp. 185–191.

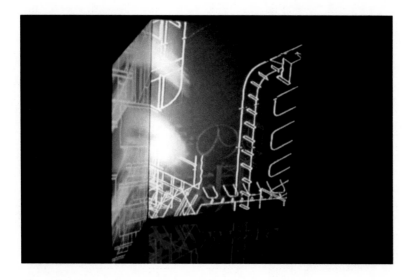

Figure 11.13 Jane Quon, *Ballast exchange* (detail), 2000

Mixed media installation of polystyrene, aluminium, steel cable and fittings, glass, video, slide projection, sound, 240 x 240 x 420 cm

From the Top End to the Southern Ocean, fluid metaphors describe processes of marine pollution, historical flotsam and more productive mixing of thought, information and action. Saltwater might also be used to evoke the generative mix of interdisciplinary and cross-cultural knowledge embodied in the production and reception of these works. Incoming political and cultural tides bear these projects through gallery spaces and arts festivals to bob up against our scientific and political institutions. As the Yirrkala artists suggest, politicians are starting to acknowledge the cultural authority of their internationally-recognised artworks. Tasmanian arts writer David Cranswick admits, however, that the scientific community is still backward in according due authority to art and to indigenous knowledge when it comes to ecological sustainability – a residue of scientific dominance in the history of modernism.[66] There remains a minority scientist or wildlife ranger perception of 'surely the natural world can speak for itself', a legacy of the old nature/culture opposition, and a reluctance to understand how art adds another side to the conservation story.

Freshwater

Our river systems, the proverbial lifeblood of Australian economic history, have become as stressed and depleted as the agricultural cliché itself. Art projects feed the system as backwaters, creeks, waterholes and tributaries, carrying provisional images of subjectivity, customary and tacit environmental knowledge to come up against the mainstream current of Australian history. There is no easy or abundant flow in a badly regulated and overdrawn system. Art projects can remind us of historical moments when it could have been otherwise, and champion overlooked local knowledge of water management.

For her ten-year project *The Darling* (2000), Ruby Davies decorated the walls of the gallery with photographic prints, explorers' observations written in river mud, and included stories and songs on compact disc (Figure 11.14). Tracing the passage of Charles Sturt and Thomas Mitchell over the Darling River in the 1830s, Davies returned to her childhood home at Wilcannia in far western New South Wales to explore different viewpoints – colonial, pastoral, Indigenous – of the landscape. These images are soaked in the photographic history of Charles Bayliss's 1886 photographic drift down the flooded Darling River. Davies uses a pinhole camera, which requires extended exposures, giving her time to look around for the "shell middens, campfires, canoe trees and flints" of the Bakandji people along the river banks and alluvial flood plain. The pinhole camera gives a vignette-like blur around the periphery and a central focal point for each image, offering a clarity of vision which stretches to infinity.

---

[66] Cranswick D, op cit. 2001, p. 47. Cranswick cites an important exception in the employment of indigenous artist Tex Skulthorpe as a senior consultant to the Murray Darling Basin Commission in the late 1990s. Skulthorpe was given significant respect and authority at senior levels of integrated planning, and his paintings about the land "were accepted as a complete state of the environment report for the Murray River."

Figure 11.14 Ruby Davies '…stories (detail)', from *The Darling* (2000)
Silver gelatin pinhole photograph, 63.5 x 80cm

Historical and political clarity is granted through recognition of the intimate landscape photography that has framed the river from the early trade in views to the 20th century photogenic stockmen who drove their cattle across the pages of popular illustrated magazines like *Walkabout*. *Walkabout's* regular feature, 'Our cameraman's walkabout' tailored the picturesque, the curious and the conversational for armchair travellers. Davies' sweeping river gums recall the earlier narrative style and pay tribute to these photographic backblocks. The later work rewrites earlier travelogues. Davies alerts us to the changes that have taken place to the river, and includes recorded local narratives about irrigation, drought and dispossession. Radok discusses Davis' work in relation to the cotton industry, with its impact on the river, "… breathing life into the human populations of places such as Bourke while tragically setting back the health of the river and its flora and fauna".[67] Davis looks over the shoulders of the *Walkabout* cattlemen and beyond her own, brief childhood memories, to discover the enduring connection the Bakandji feel with the river, as they have celebrated in image and song: "We are the people of the river"; "My people are Bakandji, the river knows who we are".[68]

Figure 11.15 Michael Riley, *Untitled (Locust)* (2000), from the Cloud series

Inkjet print on banner paper, reproduced by permission of VISCOPY Ltd, Sydney, 2007

Wiradjuri/Kamilaroi artist Michael Riley's *Cloud* series (2000) is also a poetic catalogue of iconic objects recalled from the artist's childhood on the Macquarie River at Dubbo, north western New South Wales (Figure 11.15). Curator Djon Mundine lists them: "A floating feather, a

[67] Stephanie Radok, op cit 2001, pp. 47–48.
[68] As sung by Bakandji Children's Choir, St Therese Community School, Wilcannia. Compact disc accompanying Davies' series 'The Darling'.

sweeping wing, a vigilant angel and the cows from the mission farm. A single Australian plague locust in flight, referring to the cyclical swarms of locusts, a comforting bible and a graceful emblematic returning boomerang".[69] Each isolated object is floated against an expanse of blue sky and cirrus cloud, redolent with conflicting memories of human occupation and dispossession, sweet pain, productivity and degradation. Riley's images probe the sights glossed or overlooked on whitefella walkabouts, and Mundine's accompanying commentary recounts stories left out of pastoralist and travellers' tales: the Breelong Massacre in 1900; John Oxley's surveying of the area; the setting up of the Talbragar Mission under the Aboriginal Protection Board around 1900; and the important first meetings of the Aboriginal Progressive Association in the 1930s. Murray-Darling photographers like Riley and Davies offer the postcolonial flipside of agricultural landscape photography and modern travel writing. The well-known painter Margaret Preston was one such artist–traveller. She journeyed up the Darling River in 1942 to paint its tributary, the Warrego River, at Cunnamulla and Charleville.[70] The resulting paintings haunt Davies' carefully composed photographs of river banks and over-arching, elegant gums (barnara or, as the Bakandji call it, the 'main tree on the river').[71] Davies lingers to remember, whereas Preston travelled smartly, in a hurry to spot and describe the next picturesque watering-hole, which was always:

> A short motor drive away. Brewarrina, one of these, looks a thrifty, up-to-date place on the Barwon, nee Darling. This river has aboriginal fisheries close to the town. They consist of stones, big and little, placed about the river to catch the fish as they come down. Brewarrina has had many aborigines, but they are now drifting to Bourke, much to the latter's annoyance.[72]

Brewarrina photographer Mervyn Bishop also set Preston's unwitting racism to rights in his return trip up the Darling River. His 2004 slide

[69] Mundine D, 'On a wing and a prayer' in *Michael Riley: Cloud*, exhibition catalogue, Australian Centre for Photography, Sydney, 2000, p. 3.
[70] Preston M, 'Hunting the Warrengo', *Australia Weekend Book*, no. 2, 1942, Ure Smith, Sydney, pp. 170–74.
[71] Butcher M, Bakandji educator, cited *The Darling*, 2000.
[72] Preston, op. cit, 1942, pp. 171–72.

and video monologue, *Flash blak*, describes how far-flung river communities from all over were unwillingly brought from their country to Brewarrina. With fellow photographer William Yang, Bishop drove back home to see the ruins of the old mission, now reduced to a pile of building rubble and a solitary road-sign. He made a wide-angled, photographic monument of the bridge over Hospital Creek, a local massacre site. Bishop is no slick presenter, however; these beautifully framed images are singularly reticent. The memories are too painful for easy words and images, and the often difficult lives of Brewarrina's present Indigenous communities are briefly noted with 'blak' humour or veiled sadness. Bishop is far more fulsome in naming every niece and nephew, aunt and uncle, grandmother, father and neighbouring child featured in each picture. Brewarrina seems filled with Indigenous families and community histories, if only Margaret Preston knew. These photographs add personal, aesthetic, political and historical arguments to our environmental consideration of the Murray-Darling basin. The work of these photographers re-imagines the history of occupation, exploration and depiction along the Darling River to help us think through issues of ownership, development and regulation of the river system.

Water Table

Downstream in Sunraysia, water is everything. It is now common knowledge that the Murray-Darling River is on the 'top ten' list of endangered rivers of the world, along with the Nile, the Yangtze, the Rio Grande and Danube. The raising of the water table and increasing salinity in soil is cause for common alarm, as salinity audits predict ten million tons per year moving through the landscape by 2100. The Sunraysia Irrigation Scheme was Australia's earliest large-scale regulation of the Murray River. Deakin visited California in 1885, and subsequently pushed irrigation legislation through the Victorian parliament. Sunraysia's pumping stations and irrigation channels were in place by the turn of century, forming the backbone of South-Eastern Australia's agriculture. Artist Megan Jones created a series of digitally-manipulated photographs of the scheme's history for the Mildura Alfred Deakin Centre in 2000–01. She researched and manipulated local, historical photographs to give a historical snapshot of this artificial landscape, along with satellite images and panoramic photographs. We note the progressive degradation of the river system and acknowledge sporadic, recent efforts for more efficient and less wasteful water use, more extensive soil surveys, increased drainage and monitoring of groundwater – all part of the regional Salinity Management Plan. Malcolm MacKinnon notes that:

> Dwell long enough within it, and it's possible to lose sight of the multiple layers of intervention which have created the place. It's the same illusion as that practised in the neo-Arcadian parks and gardens of Palladian England, or romantic landscape paintings from the 18th and 19th centuries.[73]

Megan Jones makes this layering of intervention visible, through photographing derelict or outdated pumping station equipment, and by digitally piecing together 360-degree panoramas to guide the viewer through interconnected sites. Her interactive window display orchestrates images and sounds to simulate the controlled flow of water and salt through a constructed environment.

Figure 11.16 Alex Kershaw, *A lake without water* (2006) (detail) Mixed media installation, Artspace, Sydney 2006

---

[73] McKinnon M, 'Simulating the flow', *Artlink*, vol. 21, no. 1, March 2001, p. 57.

A lake without water was a community-based project that also concerned itself with related environmental, aesthetic, social and economic legacies of poor land management (Illustration 16). Coordinated by artist Alex Kershaw (with sound artist Gail Priest), this elegant multi-screen video installation (Artspace, Sydney 2006) involved local residents from Weereewa, a dry lake in the Southern Tablelands of New South Wales. An auctioneer calls an imaginary land auction for what is becoming Sydney sea-changer real-estate. A race-caller scans the desolate lake bed and calls an imaginary race. Two surveyors in Akubras run down a mossy hill, scattering 'planning' paper at their feet. They then slowly trudge back up the hill, cleaning up the mess, to the surprisingly violent, amplified sound of scrunching paper. An adjacent screen shows a dry, sandy riverbed being re-planted by Landcare labour. "Like an overzealous gesture towards reforestation, the trees are placed where even weeds couldn't grow", thought reviewer Bec Dean.[74] In the distance, a young musician from the local brass band plays a trumpet in a large, empty concrete water-tank. Her melancholy tune underscores the race-call and auctioneer's chant, bouncing around the gallery walls is if it were also an empty tank. Google Earth aerial shots of the area are projected on tables in the centre of the room: "From the air, farms look like geometric abstractions, punctuated here and there by the appearance of white-rimmed, black welts of salt that have risen to the surface of the earth." Nearby Goulburn residents were the first to vote for recycling their drinking water and Canberra's Cotter Dam was at a historic low as the community art project took form. Dean's review accurately noted how this project offered regional and metropolitan Sydney audiences a "timely meditation on propriety, planning, speculation and the mythopoeia of struggle in the Australian landscape".[75]

Catchment

River systems closer to regional and metropolitan centres are more commonly considered as water catchment areas, and are subsequently highly regulated through scientific, town planning, engineering and economic overview. This level of interest and control provides a suggestive, interdisciplinary metaphor for environmentally-based

---

[74] Dean B, "A desolation too real', *Realtime*, online, April 2007.
[75] ibid

curatorial strategies, particularly in regard to public art projects. Increased local government sponsorship of restorative projects require artists to frame recreational sites, provide imaginative and protective points of access to wetlands or sites of historical, cultural and ecological significance. These community-based, local government projects can sometimes prove to be locally popular, but illustrative, tendentious and visually unexciting. More often than not, these problems result from a weak curatorial selection framework or a flawed commissioning process, and an unimaginative aesthetic response to art and environment. As a basic measure, Alan Cruickshank argues, pointing to Adelaide's woeful environmentally-based public art, the so-called public – town planners, councillors, mayors, council architects and general 'public opinion' ("more often than not, private-opinion-as-public-interest") – should be kept out of the commissioning and implementation loop.[76]

More successful restoration commissions have given curators and artists creative control. Strong curatorial strategies are particularly important when blurring the traditional distinction between practical and discursive arts, as when art, community and economic development combine with landcare and employment programs, as in 'best practice' community-based arts centres like Yirrkala, Ernabella and Hermannsberg. In regional and metropolitan areas, the primacy of discourse in artistic practice, and the fact that artists need not be accountable, as designers are, to produce something useful, has given artworks special status in a museum or gallery.[77] This opens the possibility for gallery-based art to be a platform for ecological activism, and for community and campaign materials to claim a discursive power usually granted to 'disinterested' images and objects. *Grounded: art, activism, environment* (Campbelltown Art Gallery, 2007, curators Lisa Havilah and Jo Holder) brought together artists and community activists from south-west Sydney to reflect on the compromised state and reckless development of their local environment. An eclectic installation wove historical connections between fine arts, crafts and resident actions to highlight the Iemma government's poor

---

[76] Cruickshank A, 'Tyranny of consensus: who put 'public' in public art', and why do "they" think they own it?', *Broadsheet*, vol. 32, no. 2, (June, July & August 2003), pp. 12–15.

[77] Margolin, op cit, 2006, pp. 24–25.

performance on over-development, water and energy resources management in the lead-up to the 2007 state election.

A Google Earth map helpfully pin-pointed areas of interest from the ocean (disputed luxury developments at Sandon Point on the Illawarra coast) where local painters reprise traditional pictorial conventions of the intimate landscape to convey local attachment. Alongside, a frayed and burnt Aboriginal flag was draped alongside photographs of the Sandon Point Aboriginal Tent. The escarpment meets the sea at the nearby historic Bulli coal seam, acknowledged with miners' union reliquary objects and Sydney artist Deborah Vaughan's video loop of coal trains weaving through the escarpment tunnels to the Kembla Grange BHP steelworks. Up the Bulli Pass, the Appin long-wall colliery has a less illustrious history of unsuitable technology, inadequate regulation and resultant devastation of the Avon and Nepean River systems. A video documentary by the Save Our Rivers group links the southern coalfields with similar riverbed collapses in the Upper Hunter.

On the Cumberland Plains, local botanical drawings by Sonia Bennett and John Riley are sold to help fund the protest against the Australian Defence site sell-off, a significant remnant of urban bush with high levels of biodiversity, including roaming mobs of emu. The exhibition then traces Sydney's fast-sprawling growth corridor upstream to the Nepean River headwaters, the Wingecarribee wetlands and Warragamba Dam. These are mediated by Alison Clouston playing Huckleberry Finn in a sculptural boat-ride down the Nepean River, accompanied by aerial maps, a taxonomy of endangered local birds and the sound of an increasing volume of water trickling, burbling then running and crashing out to sea. Nearby Toni Warburton's *Wall chronology: transactions to catchment* (1990–2007) poses a large, sculptural figure of a boy facing a wall, arms upraised in the act of drinking a beaker of water. He seems to look through the bottom of his upturned glass like binoculars to read the poetic wall-text describing the sheer, sensual pleasure of his drink. Alongside, an elegant wall installation of ceramic, glass and hand-made artist's books relate the beaker form to sedge, wetlands and the natural science of water filtration (Figure 11.17)

Figure 11.17 Toni Warburton *Wall chronology: transactions to catchment* (1990–2007). Photo: Jo Holder
Courtesy the artist and Mori Gallery

Elegant banner slogans by Sydney conceptual artist Ruark Lewis punctuated the show with poetic reminders of the potential for grass-roots action. The exhibition of historical campaign materials provided an activist context for studio-based artworks, which in turn invite audiences to appreciate inventive graphics and complex historical, aesthetic and emotional connections on display. The aesthetic formality of the installation and artworks, alongside the documentation of local town planning and conservation battles, moves between discourse and action.

The orchestration of art, ecology and action responds to the aesthetic activism of many works discussed in this chapter. It is a creative institutional response to local environmental issues that is shared by a few independent commercial galleries, artist-run initiatives and regional art centres. Well-curated public and gallery-based projects make fruitful links between the art industry and other agencies, and support a pluralistic approach to producing, viewing and participating art as a platform for ecological communication.

This chapter has charted some of the ways that Australian artists, curators and art institutions have shifted their aesthetic focus from topographical views of the landscape to phenomenological perceptions of the country's environmental forces. Both the western landscape tradition and Indigenous art have helped us develop all our senses, overturning the old divisions between mind and body, subject and object, self and nature. 'Perception through the senses', the original meaning of the term aesthetics, can be understood as a precondition and correlate of ecological activism. In Australia, the landscape tradition has been thoroughly modified by the forces of Indigenous knowledge, scientific research and environmental activism. In turn, art continues to make us grasp the fact that we are ourselves part of a threatened nature.[78]

---

[78] Roberts D, 'Aura and aesthetics of nature', *Thesis Eleven*, no. 36, 1993, Massachusetts Institute of Technology, p. 128.

12

Framing the debate: an analysis of the Australian Government's 2006 nuclear energy campaign

Gabrielle Higgins, Catherine Maggs, Mathew McKenzie, Eike Christian Meuter and Erin Semon

Abstract

Nuclear energy has recently experienced a global renaissance. It is considered by many as one possible way to reduce the human contribution to climate change. Australia, with its lengthy anti-nuclear history, has seen revived debate during the years 2006 and 2007, on whether the country should embrace nuclear power given its vast uranium reserves and the significant greenhouse gas emissions by existing fossil fuel energy sources. This chapter examines the issue of nuclear energy in Australia from a public relations perspective and within a framework of political communication theory. From research conducted in 2006, we argue that, well before announcing a potential PR campaign on nuclear energy in May 2007, the federal government was already conducting such a campaign, with a view to presenting a nuclear energy policy proposal to the Australian electorate.

Introduction

On 30 May 2007, the following exchange took place during question time in the Australian Commonwealth Parliament's House of Representatives:

Mr Rudd: Can the Prime Minister... confirm that the government is now also planning a taxpayer-funded public education campaign to increase community support for an Australian nuclear industry?

Mr Howard: We think that providing information to the Australian public about the energy challenges of this country is important ... If it does go ahead, it would be entirely appropriate and defensible.[1]

A strategic communication campaign on the nuclear issue was, in fact, underway a year before this interchange. In 2006, the Australian Government created and commenced a political public relations campaign around the issue of nuclear energy, with a view to presenting a nuclear energy policy proposal to the Australian electorate. This chapter investigates the public relations strategies used by the federal government during its campaign and is based around the specific timeframe of the Uranium Mining, Processing and Nuclear Energy taskforce. The taskforce was established by Cabinet on 6 June 2006, and released its findings in December 2006, in a report entitled, *Uranium mining, processing and nuclear energy – opportunities for Australia?*

Nuclear energy is a controversial issue and because of Australia's lengthy anti-nuclear history, it is a significantly risky policy to pursue. Wherever it has been introduced, from the United States to South Africa, from Argentina to Germany, it has ignited numerous activities calling for its abandonment. Earlier attempts to introduce nuclear energy in Australia have proved unsuccessful and the contentious[2] nature of this issue demands particular attention to all aspects of political communication.

This study analyses a representative selection of publicly available government documents and media reports, within a framework of political communication theory. The primary research and analysis was conducted between July and October 2006, with consideration given to some later events.

---

[1] Commonwealth of Australia, House of Representatives, Votes and Proceedings, Hansard, Wednesday, 30 May 2007, p. 42. http://www.aph.gov.au/hansard/reps/dailys/dr300507.pdf.
[2] Refer to Appendix A for a list of stakeholders.

Political communication is strategic and campaigning is structured into discrete stages and tactics, which build upon and inform each other. The public phase of this campaign began in May 2006 when the Prime Minister, John Howard, returned home after travelling to Ottawa and Washington announcing plans to investigate both nuclear energy and uranium. During the campaign, Mr Howard continued to assert he was facilitating an open-minded public debate of the issue.

History of nuclear energy

An Australian perspective

Nuclear energy is a multi-faceted issue with historic implications. The issue has become increasingly contentious in a contemporary international environment. This is due to the dichotomous fears of nuclear proliferation and the need for sustainable energy alternatives in the face of the growing awareness of the detrimental effects of global warming. Nuclear energy is not a new concept in Australia. Current investigation into the potential value of nuclear energy has roots in historical debates.

In 1975, amid growing public concern regarding the implications of expanding the nuclear industry in Australia, the federal Labor Government established The Fox Inquiry or Ranger Uranium Inquiry – a public federal investigation into aspects of the nuclear industry. Prior to publication of the results of the inquiry, the Labor Government lost office and was replaced by the Coalition Government led by Malcolm Fraser with the current Prime Minister, John Howard, as Treasurer. [3]

The Fox Report concluded that placement of stringent regulation and controls were sufficient to override the hazards of uranium mining, milling and the routine operations of nuclear power reactors. In addition, all export recipients of uranium must have ratified the Nuclear

---

[3] 'Nuclear chronology', *Four Corners*, ABC TV, 22 August 2005. Source: http://www.abc.net.au/4corners/content/2005/20050822_nuclear/nuclear-chronology.htm.

Non-Proliferation Treaty.[4] In 1976, on the basis of the report's findings, the government gave conditional approval for the Ranger, Olympic Dam/Roxby Downs and Narbarlek uranium mines to proceed. The Labour Party resumed office in 1983 and enacted the Three Named Uranium Mines policy, with a view to the eventual cessation of uranium mining. Thirteen years later, the Coalition won government and discarded the three mines policy.[5]

The discovery and exploitation of large reserves of domestic fossil fuels in the 20th century[6] has enabled Australia to be less pragmatic about the use of nuclear energy than other countries. The damage resulting from the melting of nuclear fuel rods at the Three Mile Island Reactor in 1979 and the nuclear disaster at Chernobyl seven years later cultivated the Australian public's view that nuclear energy is dirty, dangerous and avoidable. In 1998, the media obtained a leaked proposal by Pangea Resources to establish a nuclear waste facility in Western Australia to store one fifth of global spent fuel and weapons. The proposal was publicly condemned and abandoned.[7]

Contemporary developments

Turmoil in the Middle East, the rapidly expanding and energy ravenous economies of China and India and the robust scientific evidence of carbon's significant contribution to global warming have intensified Australia's concerns and opportunities regarding energy security in the 21st century and reopened the debate on nuclear energy.

---

[4] *The agreements, treaties and negotiated settlements*, Ranger Uranium Environment Inquiry (1976–1977). Source: http://www.atns.net.au/biogs/A001270b.htm.
[5] 'Nuclear chronology', *Four Corners*, ABC TV, 22 August 2005. Source: http://www.abc.net.au/4corners/content/2005/20050822_nuclear/nuclearchronol ogy.htm.
[6] 'A chronology of Australian mining', Ready-Ed Publications. Source: http://www.readyed.com.au/Sites/minehist.htm.
[7] Parliament of Australia, Parliamentary Library, Politics and Public Administration Group, *Chronology of radioactive waste and spent nuclear fuel management in Australia*, 1 January 2006. Source: http://www.aph.gov.au/library/pubs/online/Radioactive Waste.htm.

In May 2006, Mr Howard announced plans to investigate both nuclear energy and uranium mining. The nuclear debate is of paramount interest for Australia as the nation holds close to 40 per cent of the world's known uranium reserves, but has yet to embrace nuclear power. The Prime Minister appointed Dr. Ziggy Switkowski, nuclear physicist and former head of Telstra, as chairperson of a ministerial taskforce to research nuclear power and the role it could have in Australia's future. Debate and criticism followed the announcement of the taskforce, as Mr Howard was labelled pro-nuclear, calling into question the objectivity of his goals.[8] The six taskforce officials – particularly the appointment to the chair of Dr Switkowski, who was himself seen to be pro-nuclear – compounded this criticism.[9] We will return later to the importance of the nuclear energy taskforce and its appointed members.

Several factors influence current government decisions to revive the nuclear debate. First is the Australian mining industry's recognition of the potential for increased profit and global status because of increasing world energy demands. The Australian mining industry was guaranteed these things when the Labor party overturned its 23-year-old Three Named Uranium Mines Policy at its national conference in April 2007, allowing Australia to increase uranium exports worldwide.[10] Second, global concerns over pollution and climate change have brought energy debates to the forefront of international talks.

Greenhouse gas emissions from burning fossil fuels such as coal – which accounts for nearly 80 per cent of energy in Australia – are on the rise.[11] Nuclear energy could provide a viable alternative to coal-burning power plants and would bring Australia into the same arena as Europe, the United States and many other nations. There are, according to the

---

[8] Peake R., 'Nuclear inquiry still biased, say detractors', *Canberra Times*, 9 June 2006.

[9] Murphy K Khadem N & Smiles S, 'Nuclear body has trouble in fusion', *The Age*, 8 June 2006.

[10] Wilkinson M, 'Power for the people', *The Sydney Morning Herald*, 19 May 2007.

[11] Australian Uranium Association, *Sustainable Energy*, Nuclear Issues Briefing Paper no. 54, November 2005. Source: http://www.uic.com.au/nip54.htm.

International Atomic Energy Agency, approximately 435 nuclear power reactors in operation in 31 countries around the world.[12]

The recent surge of interest in nuclear energy has been propelled by US President G W Bush's announcement of a 'nuclear renaissance', which presents benefits to political and business agencies throughout Australia. 'Nuclear renaissance' combines two polar ideals, one of destruction and one of rebirth, the irony of which has not been lost. As part of President Bush's Advanced Energy Initiative, the Global Nuclear Energy Partnership (GNEP) seeks to develop worldwide consensus on enabling expanded use of economical, carbon-free nuclear energy to meet growing electricity demand. It will use a nuclear fuel cycle that enhances energy security, while promoting non-proliferation.[13] President Bush is adamant that his new energy plan incorporates the global market – inviting all nations to participate.

The GNEP ensures that stable governments produce energy using nuclear technologies and store the waste by-product of nuclear power plants.[14] Australia is in a unique position as a supplier country – a nation that mines uranium but is not an active user of nuclear energy technologies. Apart from the Lucas Heights research reactor in Sydney, Australia does not currently have an operational nuclear power plant. The GNEP inferred that Australia might have to accept nuclear waste from other countries, reprocess the nuclear waste in accordance with non-proliferation guidelines and store the reprocessed nuclear waste for an indeterminate amount of time.

---

[12] International Atomic Energy Agency, *Nuclear Power Plant Information*, Number of Reactors in Operation Worldwide (as of 13 of June 2007). Source: http://www.iaea.org/cgi-bin/db.page.pl/pris.oprconst.htm.

[13] U.S. Department of Energy, *The Global Nuclear Energy Partnership*. Source: http://www.gnep.energy.gov/gnepprogram.html

[14] Transcript of Clay Sell, Deputy Secretary of Energy; Robert Joseph, Under Secretary of State for Arms Control and International Security, Foreign Press Center Briefing, Washington, DC, 16 February 2006. Source: http://fpc.state.gov/fpc/61808.htm.

Figure 12.1 UN Non-Proliferation Treaty

The NPT is a landmark international treaty whose objective is to prevent the spread of nuclear weapons and weapons technology, to promote co-operation in the peaceful uses of nuclear energy and to further the goal of achieving nuclear disarmament and general and complete disarmament. The Treaty represents the only binding commitment in a multilateral treaty to the goal of disarmament by the nuclear-weapon States. Opened for signature in 1968, the Treaty entered into force in 1970. A total of 187 parties have joined the Treaty, including the five nuclear-weapon States. More countries have ratified the NPT than any other arms limitation and disarmament agreement, a testament to the Treaty's significance.

Source: UN Department for Disarmament Affairs

The GNEP will persuade countries that are not signatory members of the UN Non-Proliferation Treaty (see Figure 12.1) into signing, by providing them with safe and secure methods of disposing of their nuclear waste. Also, by having countries like Australia, and possibly Canada, accept and process nuclear waste, it ensures the potential for proliferation is kept at a minimum. GNEP is an initiative by the United States and President Bush to press other nations to increase their civilian nuclear technologies, and perhaps, in the process, decrease the availability of non-civilian nuclear supplies, such as plutonium.[15]

India and China are poised to control the fate of global nuclear energy campaigns. China is set to increase its nuclear power five-fold by 2020, and India is planning twenty to thirty new reactors by 2020.[16] The globalisation of nuclear energy technologies – through a mechanism such as the GNEP – facilitates China and India's expansion of nuclear

---

[15] Weitz R, *Chinese-US Deals Opens Opportunities for Nuclear Cooperation,* 4 January 2007. Source: http://www.worldpoliticsreview.com/article.aspx?id=453.
[16] World Nuclear Association, *The nuclear renaissance,* May 2007. Source://www.world-nuclear.org/info/inf104.html.

energy reactors. Without uranium to power the new reactors, China and India will have sought the technology in vain, which is why the decisions about nuclear energy in Australia become so crucial.

A Newspoll conducted in May 2006 found that 51 per cent of Australians were against "nuclear power stations being built in Australia" and 38 per cent were in favour.[17] One month later a Roy Morgan poll found that that 49 per cent of participants approved of the introduction of "nuclear power plants replacing coal, oil, and gas power plants to reduce greenhouse gas emissions" and 37 per cent disapproved.[18]

Influence and strategic communication

Communication often involves the transfer of information in a one-way flow. Information can then be presented strategically to persuade the audience toward certain beliefs or actions. The normative model for communication in Australian politics is the information model, which stipulates a one-way flow of communication from the government and disseminated to the public through the media.[19] The Australian Government, during this campaign, employed informative and persuasive strategies. Due to the framing of the issues, however, much of the information represented as informative and facilitating an unbiased public debate on the issue, actually operated more persuasively, integrating the public within a defined worldview.

By creating a worldview and interpolating themselves into it, politicians create a framework for their communication with the public. Their goal is to have the public accept the framework presented as reality. Several frameworks were constructed for the nuclear campaign until a strategic fit was found (refer to Figure 12.2 for an illustration of strategic communication).

---

[17] Newspoll, 'Australian Attitude on Uranium and Nuclear Power', May 2006. Source: http://www.newspoll.com.au/cgi-bin/polling/display_poll_data.pl
[18] Roy Morgan poll, Finding 4032, 10 June 2006. Source: http://www.roymorgan.com/news/polls/2006/4032/
[19] Stanton, R. (2006), Masters Program, Political Public Relations Seminar, 1 August, University of Sydney.

To understand the process of political communication, it is necessary to comprehend the environment in which it operates and the ways in which political information is presented and processed. Democracy requires that people have access to information on which to base their political choices. Governments' require the consent of people to legitimise their offices and successfully implement policy.

Figure 12.2 The contextual frame

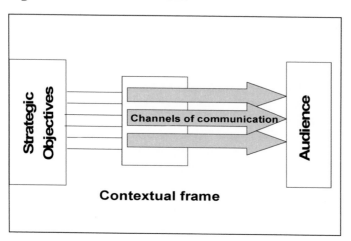

Political communication is designed to produce an effect on the actions and beliefs of individual citizens and the society as a whole.[20] In the dual processes of decision-making and legitimation there are: 'insiders' who are privy to policy debates and involved in decision-making; 'semi-insiders', who are aware of the decision-making going on by the elites, but are observers, rather than participants; and 'political outsiders', the public who consume the mass media disseminated hype.[21] Two political spheres emerge in this process; the sphere of elite politics, with an emphasis on policy making and the sphere of mass politics, with an emphasis on 'steering voters'.[22] The Australian Government's nuclear

[20] Graber D, 'Political communication faces the 21st century', *Journal of Communication*, September 2005, p. 479.
[21] Louw E, *The Media and Political Process*, Sage Publications, London, 2005, pp. 17–18.
[22] ibid, p. 22.

campaign can be seen as operating in both spheres. In the elite politics sphere, the campaign developed earlier than in the campaign being undertaken in the sphere of mass politics.

As policy goals are established, persuasive methods are employed to steer public opinion. This is a form of hegemony building. Hegemony involves developing consent and legitimacy, so that the population accepts as 'natural' the decisions and discourses of the dominant. It also involves organising alliances amongst the elite.[23] The shaping of public opinion can be described as manufacturing consent, which can be achieved by strategic planning in a political public relations campaign. The increase in mediated politics has necessitated the incorporation of professional communicators into the political process. A symbiotic relationship has developed between politicians, communicators and the media. Politicians rely on publicity and journalists often rely on information supplied from political communicators.

Opportunities arise for communicators to present information in a particular frame, which can direct the public's attention and affect the way issues are considered. The mass media, therefore, becomes implicit in the strategic construction of publics and public opinions. The outcome is a public that perceives that it participates in the decision making process, however, in reality it is distanced and obstructed from substantive politics.[24] The incorporation of modern media techniques appropriated from the public relations industry is argued to have de-emphasised party ideology, causing the decision making process to move away from party level and the public space of parliament to the private offices of the leader and senior ministers. [25]

Political players remain extremely influential in deciding which worldviews "become hegemonic," as politicians endorse certain ideologies, while rejecting others. The popularisation of worldviews is not an issue of simple production of "appropriate knowledge", but an

[23] Gramsci A in Louw, p. 19.
[24] Louw, op.cit., pp. 143–171.
[25] Kavanagh,D, 'New campaign communications: consequences for British political parties', *Press/Politics*, vol. 1, no. 3, 1996, p. 73.

issue of information dissemination[26] – indicative of a symbiotic relationship between the media, professional communicators and politicians.[27]

Campaign staging and development

Analysis of political communication has concentrated on the process of election campaigning. While various stakeholders may be peculiar to a particular campaign, the principle groups involved in election campaigning – politicians, media and citizens – remain the same in an issue campaign. Election and issue campaigns are about informing, persuading and mobilising stakeholder groups and the broad strategies used to develop and direct an effective election campaign are similar to those involved in an issue campaign. It is important to remember that a government's primary goal, regardless of any other campaign being conducted, is the retention of an electoral majority.[28]

A political campaign like any public relations campaign has a distinct starting and finishing point. A successful campaign will have a clearly defined goal, well-formulated and measurable objectives with aligned tactics. Campaign objectives are designed to provide information and to effect attitudinal and behavioural change. Objectives are directed towards specific stakeholder groups, while tactics are the visible elements devised and implemented to achieve the objectives.

There are different models for structuring a campaign. While a campaign should have a linear direction, the strategy may require modification to ensure achievement of the goal. Strategy can be defined in terms of gaining a competitive advantage over an opponent and is influenced by the skill of the political player and the available financial and technological resources. Most models emphasise the importance of preliminary and continuing research, setting objectives, enacting tactics and evaluating the results. The importance of a well-calculated strategy and the employment of reasonable tactics is the foremost task for

---

[26] Louw, op. cit., pp. 202–203.

[27] ibid, p. 1.

[28] Stanton R, Masters Program, Political Public Relations Seminar, 22 August 2006, University of Sydney.

political campaign teams and a well-constructed campaign will have an alignment of all these elements.

The model used in this chapter to analyse the Australian Government's nuclear energy campaign has been adapted from a model that originated to evaluate political campaigning in US elections.[29] There are five stages in the adapted model: (1) preliminary, (2) nomination, (3) attack, (4) regroup, and (5) deliver.

Although the stages are discrete and contain particular communicative functions, each stage informs the other and any analysis of the effectiveness of the campaign must include all stages and the relationships that exist between them, which will be discussed below. Because the campaign had not reached a conclusion during the course of our research, our analysis focuses on the first three stages – preliminary, nomination, and attack.

The government's nuclear energy campaign

The prelude

In March 2005, the Australian Government announced an inquiry into the uranium industry and a possible expansion of the country's three mines.[30] Three months later the Prime Minister was reported as saying that many would think it odd, given the vast supplies of uranium that we would not allow a debate on nuclear power.[31] In August 2005, the Federal Government exercised its Commonwealth powers and assumed control of the Northern Territory's uranium mining to guarantee certainty to the industry and ensure the expansion of exports.[32]

---

[29] Trent J S & Friedenberg R V (2004), *Political campaign communication: principles & practices* 5th ed, Rowan & Littlefield Publishers, Inc., Oxford.

[30] ABC News Online, 'MacFarlane talks down uranium boom risks', 18 March 2005. Source: http://www.abc.net.au/news/newsitems/200536/s1326711.htm.

[31] ABC News Online, 'PM encourages nuclear power debate', 9 June 2005. Source: http://www.abc.net.au/news/newsitems/200506/s1388563.htm.

[32] Wilson A & Murphy K, 'Howard seizes NT uranium', *The Australian*, 5 August 2005.

In November 2005, Federal Science Minister, Brendan Nelson and Federal Industry Minister, Ian MacFarlane lodged a submission with the Prime Minister for an inquiry into the benefits and impact of Australia developing a domestic nuclear power industry. Dr Nelson was careful to state that a possible inquiry was a matter for the Prime Minister and the Government.[33]

The preliminary stage

Developing the platform

Speaking in Ottawa on 19 May 2006 ahead of meetings with the Canadian Government and the US Government, the Prime Minister told Southern Cross Radio that nuclear power was closer "than some people would have thought a short while ago" and he hoped "that we have an intense debate on the subject over the months ahead".[34] Three months earlier, the Prime Minister had told Southern Cross Radio, "If the economics of energy lead us to embracing nuclear power, then we should be willing to do so".[35] In the 19 May interview, he restated the governing economic considerations; however, he extended the frame of the issue to include the "environmental advantages of nuclear power".[36] Indeed, the Prime Minister's language regarding nuclear energy on the trip to North America marked a overtly positive stance on the issue. The following week on 26 May 2006, the government's Australian Nuclear Science and Technology Organisation (ANSTO) released a report to the Federal Science Minister, Julie Bishop, concluding that electricity generation from nuclear power would be competitive with coal.[37]

With these comments and the release of the ANSTO report, the Prime Minister was developing the platform of the campaign and framing the issue of nuclear energy as one with possible economic and

---

[33] ABC News Online, 'Nelson seeks Aust nuclear power inquiry', 27 November 2005. Source: http://www.abc.net.au/news/newsitems/200511/s1517596.htm.

[34] 'Nuclear power inevitable, says PM', *The Age*, 19 May 2006.

[35] ABC News Online, 'Don't rule out nuclear future: PM', 24 February 2006. Source: http://www.abc.net.au/news/newsitems/20060602/s1577452.htm.

[36] 'Nuclear power inevitable, says PM', *The Age*, 19 May 2006.

[37] ABC News Online, 'Nuclear power economically viable: ANSTO', 26 May 2006. Source: http://www.abc.net.au/news/newsitems/200605/s1648257.htm

environmental advantages. Economic considerations are at the core of the predictive model of political communication and are powerful determinants of voting patterns.[38] The Prime Minister's success in retaining office has been attributed to the economic prosperity of Australia over the last decade.[39] If stakeholders perceive the Prime Minister as a responsible and successful economic manager and trust his economic qualifications, then a contentious issue such as nuclear power may become acceptable within an economic frame because, "Without trust there is no persuasion".[40] The leader of any campaign, and in our case the Prime Minister, is an integral part of the process. As a campaign gains momentum, a complex network of communication and perception is woven together intricately by the media and the government.

Researching the issue and modifying models

A function of the preliminary stage, research, was realised when the Prime Minister announced on 6 June 2006 that Cabinet had approved the establishment of a Prime Ministerial taskforce – the Uranium Mining Processing and Nuclear Energy Review (UMPNER) – to examine uranium mining, processing and nuclear energy in Australia.[41] As mentioned previously, Dr Switkowski, a nuclear physicist and former CEO of Telstra, was appointed as chairperson. Some weeks later, Dr Switkowski resigned as a director of ANSTO amidst accusations of a conflict of interest.[42]

The taskforce invited submissions and a draft report was released publicly in November 2006. Inviting the public to participate in the process fulfils a function of the nomination stage and is bound to the ideology of democracy. The invitation was not widely publicised;

---

[38] Jamieson K H, *Everything you think you know about politics: and why you're wrong*, Basic Books, London, 2000, p. 6.

[39] O'Brien K, 'John Howard: 10 years at the top', *The 7:30 report*, ABCTV, 2 March 2006. Source: http://www.abc.net.au/7.30/content/2006/s1582730.htm.

[40] Lupia A & McCubbins M, cited in Graber D A op. cit, p. 490.

[41] Transcript of the Prime Minister The Hon John Howard MP, press conference, Parliament House, Canberra, 6 June 2006. Source: http://www.pm.gov.au/news/interviews/Interview1966.html.

[42] ABC News Online, 'Nuclear review chief quits ANSTO board', 8 June 2006. Source: http://www.abc.net.au/news/stories/2006/06/08/1657943.htm.

however, it is the appearance of inviting participation that is, perhaps, more important in political communication. Public participation can be troublesome for governments because it disrupts the business of governing, implementing policy, directing resources and creating legislation.[43] Additionally, perceived time and resource constraints may have restricted the mass public's ability to lodge submissions. The taskforce, however, did identify supportive and oppositional stakeholders, with the intention of inviting their submissions.[44]

Campaigning for an issue such as nuclear energy requires the issue be deemed fit for political consideration so it can be placed within the popular political dialogue. The Prime Minister successfully integrated the issue of nuclear energy into the political dialogue and validated the reasoning behind its inclusion by creating a taskforce. The introduction of the taskforce established the seriousness of the issue, confirmed that nuclear energy was a viable competitor to other energy sources, such as fossil fuels, and placed the debate in the public forum. For an issue to gain traction, it must gain visibility, particularly in the media.[45] The establishment of the taskforce was the Prime Minister's way of declaring the beginning of the campaign.

Appointing independent experts to the taskforce[46] in the fields of nuclear science, economics and the energy sector, allowed the government to be perceived as being concerned and seeking the 'truth' and providing an objective assessment of the issue. In fact, the Department of Prime Minster and Cabinet conceived of the terms of reference, which would direct the inquiry's review and the Prime Minister chose the taskforce members on advice from the Department.[47]

---

[43] Louw, op. cit., p. 145.
[44] Murphy K, 'Nuclear debate picks up with show of British energy', *The Age*, 5 July 2006.
[45] Trent & Friedenberg, op.cit., p. 27.
[46] The six-member taskforce was chaired by former Telstra CEO and nuclear physicist, Ziggy Switkowski and included eminent economist, Warwick McKibbin, three additional nuclear physicists and a senior energy sector executive who replaced Sylvia Kidziak.
[47] 'Senate Standing Committee on Finance and Public Administration Estimates (Supplementary Budget Estimates)', Proof Committee Hansard, Commonwealth of Australia, 30 October 2006, Canberra, p. 62.

In seeking to control communication flows, the government instructed the taskforce members to route any requests for interviews through the review's secretariat.[48] The issues paper,[49] provided by the government and attached to the review, reinforced the predominant economic frame. The paper contained 86 questions regarding economic issues, nine questions regarding environmental issues and 23 questions regarding health, safety and proliferation issues.

It is significant for the analysis of the campaign that the Prime Minister himself appeared to be the person who initiated dialogue surrounding the issue. The taskforce was established in the Department of the Prime Minister and Cabinet and only in rare instances did ministers other than Mr Howard discuss the issue in the media. There is, therefore, a centralised information system for prime-ministerial public relations.[50] The fact that Dr Switkowski, a well-known and high-profile business personality, headed the taskforce is another important element of the campaign. Both these circumstances lead to the question as to what extent celebrity plays a role in the current campaign.

Celebrity has been described as a phenomenon "tied to the rise of visual mass media", invented by the Hollywood studios' system to promote their actors through images and "a powerful tool for steering mass publics".[51] In terms of political communication, John Howard has been identified as one of the leaders whose character has been scripted by spin-doctors to create a celebrity politician "with the sorts of 'ordinary' features voters could identify with".[52] For the purposes of the campaign, the appointment of Dr Switkowski appears to be as close as one could get to celebrity-status without losing credibility. He has a very useful mix of qualities, which includes expert knowledge on the science of nuclear energy, knowledge of political processes and extensive media experience.

[48] Kerr J, 'Green firm dumps N-probe expert', *The Australian*, 16 June 2006.
[49] Australian Government, 'Issues paper', *Uranium mining, processing and nuclear energy review*, June 2006. Source: http://www.dpmc.gov.au/umpner/paper.cfm.
[50] McNair B, *An introduction to political communication*, Routledge, London, 2003, p. 161.
[51] Louw, op. cit., p. 174.
[52] ibid, p. 176.

The taskforce creation can be seen as a primary instrument of the routine processes of politics and can thereby legitimise possible further action. In this sense, it can be interpreted as a pseudo-event, whose creation is another strategy of incumbents.[53] If one assumes the decision to extend uranium mining and introduce nuclear power was made before the campaign commenced, the taskforce would only serve to add more credibility to this decision. Indeed, shortly before the taskforce reported, the Prime Minister endorsed the development of a nuclear industry in Australia.

Another function of the preliminary stage is the modification of conflicting existing models. The Government's 2004 white paper on energy policy, *Securing Australia's energy future*, stated that fossil fuels will "meet the bulk of the nation's energy needs".[54] Nuclear energy was tabled as a "reserve" energy technology – one where Australia has less of a strategic interest – behind Australia's market leading and fast-following technologies such as coal, hot dry rocks, natural gas and wind. Even hydrogen – another reserve energy technology – was considered more likely than nuclear to potentially deliver low-emissions energy.[55] The policy was updated in July 2006 and states, "There is significant potential for Australia to increase and add value to our uranium extraction and exports"[56] and "[to invest] in leading-edge, clean energy technology while being pragmatic about what technologies help Australia achieve its economic, energy and environmental goals".[57] The use of the word *pragmatic* is interesting and one could infer from its use that nuclear energy, while perhaps not the most popular choice for clean energy technology, is nonetheless, the most practical.

---

[53] Trent & Friedenberg, op. cit., p. 82.
[54] Australian Government, *Securing Australia's Energy Future,* June 2004, p. 4. Source: http://www.pmc.gov.au/publications/energy_future/docs/energy.pdf.
[55] ibid, p. 32.
[56] Australian Government, *Securing Australia's Energy Future: July 2006 Update*, p. 5. Source: http://www.pmc.gov.au/energy_reform/docs/energy_update_july2006.rtf.
[57] ibid, p. 1.

Rhetoric and Persuasion

The employment of rhetorical devices serves to reinforce existing beliefs and values and to introduce and embed an issue within a framework of those beliefs and values, thereby legitimising and popularising the issue. The Prime Minister has steered the debate on nuclear energy by employing the rhetorical device of comparing our failure to exploit uranium processing as analogous to Australia's historical experience of having our wool processed overseas to the country's economic disadvantage.[58]

In his address to the Committee for Economic Development of Australia on 18 July 2006, the Prime Minister said Australia has "global responsibilities including environmental stewardship" and "a growing number of environmentalists now recognise that nuclear energy has significant environmental advantages". In the same address, the Prime Minster claimed Australia has "the makings of an energy superpower", if we grasp the opportunities that globalisation offers by exporting to an expanding energy market.[59] The symbol of Australia as a 'superpower' is a powerful instrument of persuasion. He concluded the nuclear component of his speech by saying, "…if we sacrifice rational discussion on the altar of anti-nuclear theology and political opportunism, we will pay a price. Maybe not today or tomorrow, but in 10, 15 or 20 years Australia will surely pay a price".

Both the Prime Minister and the Foreign Minister have suggested there has been a shift in attitudes towards nuclear energy. During the press conference to announce the establishment of the taskforce, the Prime Minister said, "My mind remains open. I am not persuaded as yet, although in my bones I think there has been a fundamental change."[60] The Foreign Minister told *The Advertiser*, "My take on where the public is at is that there has been a quantum shift in public opinion on this issue

---

[58] Transcript of the Prime Minister The Hon John Howard MP, press conference, Parliament House, Canberra, 6 June 2006.
[59] Howard J, Address to the Committee for Economic Development of Australia, Sydney Convention & Exhibition Centre, 18 July 2006.
[60] Transcript of the Prime Minister The Hon John Howard MP, press conference, Parliament House, Canberra, 6 June 2006.

in the last ten years".[61] These types of agenda-setting comments can create a "spiral of silence",[62] where people whose views diverge from the perceived norm refrain from debating issues that exclude them from the popular majority.

The Nomination Stage

Nurturing the Stakeholders [63]

Fulfilling one of the central functions of the nomination stage – to nurture stakeholder groups – can entail making promises. The issue of storing spent nuclear fuel rods was raised early in the campaign when the government confirmed Australia would store France's spent fuel from its uranium exports.[64] Following private discussions between the Prime Minister and US officials in May 2006 regarding Australia's potential role in the US created GNEP, speculation ensued regarding the possibility of Australia becoming a global repository for spent fuel if an enrichment industry was to proceed.[65]

The Prime Minister told the Nine Network in July 2006, that Australia has a responsibility to dispose of nuclear waste from its exports and that it is a "Nimby head in the sand attitude", to export uranium and refuse to store the waste.[66] The unsavoury image of Australia as a radioactive waste dump, however, prompted the Prime Minister to alleviate public concern and tell ABC Radio less than one month later, "I am not going to have this country used as some kind of repository for other people's

---

[61] Russell C, Starick P & England E, 'Cure or killer – the nuclear future', *The Advertiser*, 29 August 2006.

[62] Noelle-Neumann E, *The spiral of silence: public opinion–our social skin*, The University of Chicago Press, Chicago, 1984.

[63] Refer to Appendix A for a list of stakeholders.

[64] Crowe D, 'Spent nuclear fuel back in five years', *Australian Financial Review*, 19 June 2006.

[65] Baker R, 'Secrecy on Howard's nuclear trip', *The Age*, 29 June 2006.

[66] Howard J, Interview with Laurie Oakes on *Sunday*, Nine Network, 18 June 2006. Source:http://sunday.ninemsn.com.au/sunday/political_transcripts/article_2009.asp
.

nuclear problems ... waste problems".[67] But within the Australian Parliament, policy changes had already been implemented. The ANSTO Amendment Bill 2006 was passed on 20 June 2006 to provide more flexibility – particularly in terms of nuclear waste storage – by allowing the incorporation of waste "not exclusively from ANSTO's reactors".[68]

Dr John White chairs the Australian waste company, Global Renewables and the federal government's Uranium Industry Framework steering committee: a committee that has been meeting since August 2005 to advise the Government on uranium policy. While visiting the US in November 2006, White discussed with *New Matilda*, his and Australia's potential leadership role in nuclear fuel leasing, which includes the return to Australia and storage of nuclear waste. Apart from the considerable economic benefits, White stressed the diplomatic benefits in a display of demagoguery:

> If we agree to do this for America, we will never again have to put young Australians in the line of fire. We will never have to prove our loyalty to the US by sending our soldiers to fight in their wars, because a project like this would settle the question of our loyalty once and for all.[69]

This demonstrates that the operation of the Australian Government's nuclear campaign has been progressing strategically in very different ways at the elite and mass levels.

The major existing fossil fuel energy providers – the coal and gas industries – have received some reassurance from the government that they will continue to provide base-load energy to the electricity grid. The Industry, Tourism and Resources Minister Ian Macfarlane said on 16 October 2006, "We will not turn our backs on Australia's traditional

---

[67] Frew W, 'PM blows cold on nuclear dumping', *The Sydney Morning Herald*, 7 July 2006.
[68] Parliament of Australia, Department of Parliamentary Services, Australian Nuclear Science and Technology Organisation Amendment Bill 2006, Parliamentary Library Bills Digest, 20 June 2006, no. 153, 2005–06, ISSN 1328-809.
[69] Macken J, 'Nuclear Debate: Part One: The Plan', *New Matilda*, 8 November 2006. Source:http://www.newmatilda.com./home/articledetailmagazine.asp?ArticleID=1913&HomepageID=168.

energy sources – like coal and gas".[70] In an address to the Energy Networks Association (ENA) on 11 September 2006, the Minister spoke of the gas industry as "one of the foundation stones of the Australian economy"[71] and of the solid prospects for its future growth.

Changing the frame – the need for a strategic shift

One of the difficulties the campaign has encountered is public assertions, by important business leaders in the uranium industry, which question the economic viability of developing uranium processing and a domestic fuel cycle. These statements implicitly refute the Prime Minister's positive economic framing of the issue. Rio Tinto and the French company, AREVA, argued that developing uranium processing in Australia has no demonstrated economic benefits, due to the current and immediate future market saturation.[72] In its submission to the taskforce, BHP Billiton stated its belief that uranium conversion, enrichment and fuel leasing is economically unviable, as is nuclear power in the absence of significant carbon taxing.[73] However, Dr Switkowski told ABC Radio on 5 October 2006 that nuclear power generation could be competitive with conventional sources.[74]

---

[70] Macfarlane I, Speech to the *15th Pacific Basin Nuclear Conference*, 16 October 2006. Source:http://minister.industry.gov.au/index.cfm?event=object.showContent&obje ctID=4ECF4EE3-CDB6-D660-70446A89BBAA72ED.

[71] Macfarlane I, Address to the *Energy Networks Association* (ENA) Gas Speak Colloquium, 11 September 2006. Source: http://minister.industry.gov.au/index.cfm? event=object.showContent&objectID=9BC6946C-CFFD-463B8837B15F93C2A 58E

[72] AREVA, Submission to the uranium mining, processing and nuclear power review, September 2006. Source: http://www.pmc.gov.au/umpner/submissions/ 72_lowres_sub_umpner.pdf. Rio Tinto, Submission to the uranium mining, processing and nuclear power review, September 2006. Source: http://www. pmc.gov.au/umpner/submissions/197_sub_umpner.pdf. Kerin J, 'Miners cool on enrichment', Australian Financial Review, 1 September 2006.

[73] BHP Billiton, *Submission to the uranium mining, processing and nuclear power review*, September 2006. Source: http://www.dpmc.gov.au/umpner/submissions/223_ sub_umpner.pdf.

[74] ABC News Online, 'Nuclear energy panel considers Chernobyl', 5 October 2006. Source: www.abc.net.au/news/newsitems/200610/s1755907.htm.

For the past two decades, nuclear energy has been the most heavily subsidised energy industry in the world.[75] During this campaign, the Prime Minister refused to confirm whether the government would subsidise the industry and remained staunchly opposed to carbon trading.[76] During the press conference to announce the taskforce he stated, "[sic] Our general policy is that we don't normally start an industry up with government support that is our general policy".[77] As the Prime Minister has continued to frame the issue as one with great economic benefits, it may have been damaging to admit to the need for government subsidies. Between May and October 2006, the Finance Minister, Nick Minchin, repeated his belief that a domestic nuclear industry in Australia is economically unfeasible in the short-term.[78] These are interesting comments from a Cabinet minister. At the time, it could have been questioned whether he was asserting an independent view or if it was a strategic manoeuvre to prime the public for the possibility of government subsidies or carbon pricing to assist the development of a nuclear industry.

At any rate, with the public's escalating and widespread concern about the consequences of global warming,[79] opportunities arose for a strategic shift in focus to the environmental advantages of nuclear power. It was evident that climate change would probably become an important election issue and the government has been criticized about its late

---

[75] *Energy Subsidies and External Costs*, UIC Nuclear Issues Briefing Paper no. 71, February 2007, Uranium Information Centre. Source: http://www.uic.com.au/nip71.htm.
[76] Transcript of the Prime Minister The Hon John Howard MP, press conference with The Hon Peter McGauran MP, Minster for Agriculture, Fisheries and Forestry, Parliament House, Canberra, 17 October 2006. Source: http://www.pm.gov.au/news/interviews/Interview2184.html.
[77] Transcript of the Prime Minister The Hon John Howard MP, press conference, Parliament House, Canberra, 6 June 2006.
[78] Crouch B & Farr M, 'No nuke plant in 100 years Liberal leaders at odds', *Sunday Mail*, 21 May 2006. ABC News Online, 'Minchin downplays Macfarlane's nuclear energy comments', 17 October 2006 source: http://www.abc.net.au/news/stories/2006/10/17/1767227.htm.
[79] The Chicago Council on Global Affairs, *Global Views* 2006, Source: http://www.lowyinstitute.org/Publication.asp?pid=470.

acknowledgement of climate change and its refusal to seriously address the issue.[80]

The government had grasped opportunities to align itself with credible environmental prolocutors – spokespeople – to promote the 'environmental advantages' of nuclear energy and to allay concerns regarding waste disposal and reactor safety. There was the last-minute and failed attempt to procure Greg Bourne – former president of BP Australia and current CEO of conservation group WWF Australia – as a member of the taskforce.[81] In early May 2006, Bourne publicly accepted that Australia would continue mining and exporting uranium to an increasing world market.[82] In June 2006, the Prime Minister enlisted the credentials of Tim Flannery, scientist, environmentalist and 2006 Australian of The Year in an ABC Radio interview. Flannery had given circumspect endorsement to nuclear power as an option for addressing global climate change.[83] On 8 May 2006, the environmental movement in Australia united and released a joint media statement opposing all aspects of the nuclear industry.

The media's role

The nuclear debate remained relevant throughout July and August 2006 in the media, with stories of nuclear controversy; everything from the Nuclear Non-Proliferation Treaty to the anniversary of the Hiroshima bombings entered the public domain. Coverage, however, was limited until the submissions made to the taskforce were released in September 2006. Furthermore, the Prime Minister provided fewer spectacles and speeches, which lessened the number of tangible events on which to report. Tim Flannery, however, became a target amidst scrutiny for his perceived endorsement of nuclear power. Flannery countered with an interview with WWF Australia.[84] In the interview, he includes uranium

---

[80] Silkstone D, 'Forget about left or right, I'm just the weatherman', *The Age*, 26 August 2006.

[81] Murphy K, 'Nuclear body has trouble in fusion', *The Age*, 8 June 2006.

[82] Hodge A, 'Green group accepts U-mines', *The Australian*, 4 May 2006.

[83] Doherty B, 'Nuclear way to go: Flannery', *The Age*, 5 August 2006.

[84] This was made available to the public in print on the organisation's website in addition to a podcast available through Apple ITunes (Flannery, personal interview). Source: http://wwf.org.au/articles/interview-with-tim-flannery.

as an energy alternative. However, he also indicts Australia as "the most backward nation on the planet" in terms of how political and industry leaders address both global warming and the debate surrounding alternative energies.

An article in *The Age* on 26 August 2006 entitled 'Forget about left or right, I'm just the weatherman', asserts that Flannery's "position on nuclear energy has been misrepresented".[85] The article depicts Flannery as not anti-nuclear power; however, Flannery argues against the use of 'dirty' fuels, such as coal and gas. He instead points to alternative renewables, such as solar and wind power, which he argued appeared to be less of a priority for the federal government. He described the government as "the worst of the worst", with regard to seriously addressing climate change and was "incredulous" at being made a target of "the far left and far right".

On *Enough rope with Andrew Denton* on 11 September 2006, former US Vice-President Al Gore called the United States and Australia the "Bonnie and Clyde of the global community" for their continued resistance to the Kyoto protocol. He furthermore pointed to Mr Howard's policy as in need of change. *The Australian* ran two stories on the same day. First, an article entitled 'Australia could show China the way: Gore',[86] offered commentary with specific reference to Mr Gore, who voiced concern regarding proliferation. Mr Gore was also quoted as saying, "It's no secret that the Prime Minister and I disagree on the issue, but I think he's a smart man with a generally open mind when new evidence is available". Second, *The Australian* published an interview with the Prime Minister under the headline 'Documentary films don't guide my environment policy'.[87] In the interview, Mr Howard once again rejected the Kyoto protocol as acting against the economic interests of the country and presented accusations of 'alarmist' views specifically regarding global warming, which ironically he employs as a backdrop for the 'rational debate' on nuclear energy.

---

[85] Silkstone, op. cit.
[86] Bodey M & Warren M, 'Australia could show China the way: Gore', *The Australian*, 12 September 2006.
[87] 'Documentary films don't guide my environment policy', *The Australian*, 12 September 2006.

Steering the debate: a tactical bid for control

The Foreign Minister stated in a speech on 11 October 2006 that the main reason for Australia to commence generating nuclear power would be to reduce greenhouse emissions and not for energy security and "we don't need Al Gore to tell us that the growth in carbon emissions from fossil fuels is a major global challenge that must be confronted".[88] Six days later in an address to the 15th Pacific Basin Nuclear Conference in Sydney, Ian MacFarlane asserted that nuclear energy could be "a major part of the global strategy to curb greenhouse emissions" and "the issue of uranium and nuclear power is as much about lowering greenhouse gas emissions as it is about the supply of energy".[89] On the same day, the Prime Minister asserted, "I believe very strongly that nuclear power is part of the response to global warming, it is clean green".[90] Statements of belief such as this are more difficult to counter than statements of fact because beliefs tend to exist as 'givens'[91] and are less subject to scrutiny than policies.

The day after the 15th Pacific Basin Nuclear Conference, the Prime Minister publicly endorsed the domestic use of nuclear power for the first time. He stated, "I just think that if we're serious about having a debate about global warming, particularly as the holder of some of the largest uranium reserves in the world, we have got to be willing to consider the nuclear option". His promotion of nuclear power came almost a month before the results of the taskforce's inquiry were to be released and just over a week after the effects of North Korea's nuclear detonation were being considered both domestically and internationally.

---

[88] Downer A, Speech to a symposium organised by *the Australian Institute of International Affairs* & the *Australian Homeland Security Research*, 11 October 2006. Source: http://www.foreignminister.gov.au/speeches/2006/061011_es.html. Al Gore visited Australia in October 2006 to promote the film 'An Inconvenient Truth', about the consequences of global warming.

[89] Macfarlane I, Speech to the 15th Pacific Basin Nuclear Conference, 16 October 2006.

[90] Transcript of the Prime Minister The Hon John Howard MP, press conference with The Hon Peter McGauran MP, Minster for Agriculture, Fisheries and Forestry, Parliament House, Canberra, 17 October 2006.

[91] Louw, op.cit., p. 207.

In response, the then federal Opposition leader, Kim Beazley, contended that Australia's future is, "renewables not reactors" and "there will be no nuclear power in Australia under a Beazley Labor Government".[92] Martin Ferguson, the federal Opposition's energy spokesperson, accused the government of "diversion"[93] by promoting the nuclear debate ahead of the pressing need to act on clean coal technology and renewable energy sources.

The following week the Federal Treasurer, Peter Costello and Ian MacFarlane announced a $75 million grant to build a large-scale solar concentrator in Victoria and $50 million for a brown coal drying and post-combustion carbon dioxide capture and storage project. Further announcements regarding the Government's $500 million Low Emissions Technology Demonstration Fund (LETDF) followed in the ensuing weeks.[94] While the fund was established in July 2006, the timing of this announcement appeared to be a strategically placed response to Mr Beazley's and Mr Ferguson's comments.

The attack stage

The appropriation of funds for grants is a powerful, pragmatic strategy of the incumbent as is the establishment of taskforces to investigate issues of public concern.[95] By allocating grants, the government sought to develop and maintain mutually beneficial relationships with the renewable energy and fossil fuel industries, while at the same time appearing to be genuinely concerned about and responsive to the issue of global warming. The announcement partially countered criticism that the government was deliberately neglecting, and perhaps even sabotaging, the renewable energy sector by refusing to increase Australia's Mandatory Renewable Energy Target (MRET), thereby

---

[92] Warren M, 'Nuclear plants in a decade', *The Australian*, 17 October 2006.
[93] ABC News Online, 'Nuclear debate a diversionary tactic: ALP', 17 October 2006. Source: http://www.abc.net.au/news/newsitems/200610/s1766287.htm.
[94] '$125M Towards a Lower Emission Future', joint media release, Treasurer & The Minister for Industry, Tourism and Resources, 25 October 2006.
Source: http://minister.industry.gov.au/index.cfm?event=object.showContent& objectID=7CEB92AC-E9AA-9CC1-1B8D4EC6D15F0D4B.
[95] Trent & Friedenberg, op.cit., p. 82.

dissuading investment.[96] The promise of further grant allocations provided opportunities for pseudo-events to attract media attention and to capitalise on that attention by directing the issue.

Aside from shifting attention from the economic focus of the nuclear debate, it also enabled the Government to attack vigorously opponents of nuclear energy. The Prime Minister declared people who oppose nuclear energy, but demand solutions to climate change to be "unreal" and that many "rabid environmentalists"[97] have realised the benefits of nuclear energy. The converging issues of climate change and nuclear energy may benefit the Government's election strategy by dividing the federal opposition, which remains ideologically opposed to the domestic use of nuclear energy and uranium enrichment, but was at that time considering amending the Three Named Uranium Mines policy in the presence of the nuclear debate.[98] The Prime Minister warned that the Opposition would attempt to run a 'fear campaign', but the public was ready for a mature debate.[99] The implication was that the Labor Party was attempting to manipulate the Australian public with emotive appeals.

Much of an elected representative's time is invested in providing educative mechanisms to the public. When the policies being promoted are in line with public opinion, a straightforward informational model of communication can be employed. When the public is likely to resist the elite policy decisions, more persuasive methods are needed. Hegemonically, this can be viewed as the policy elite maintaining the compliance of the masses.[100]

---

[96] Rollins A, 'Call to put more energy into renewables', *Australian Financial Review*, 15 August 2006.
Frew W, 'It's an ill wind', *The Sydney Morning Herald*, 19 May 2006.
[97] Transcript of the Prime Minister The Hon John Howard MP, press conference with The Hon Peter McGauran MP, Minster for Agriculture, Fisheries and Forestry, Parliament House, Canberra, 17 October 2006.
[98] Wilson N & Salusinszky I, 'Beazley to win on uranium', *The Australian*, 26 July 2006.
[99] Transcript of the Prime Minister The Hon John Howard MP, press conference, Parliament House, Canberra, 6 June 2006.
[100] Bennett W in Louw, op.cit., p. 257.

Because communication is contextual, strategists need to be aware of the environment in which the communication will take place, when developing political campaigns. The matching of campaign to environment is known as the search for 'strategic fit'.[101]

Taskforce findings and the continuing campaign

On 21 November 2006, the taskforce released its findings in a draft report that was followed by the final version on 12 December.[102] Dr Switkowski, who was appointed chairperson of ANSTO in March 2007, and the other taskforce members asserted that under certain conditions it would be probable that Australia could introduce nuclear power in the medium-term. According to their estimations, the first plant could be operational in about ten years: "The review sees nuclear power as a practical option for part of Australia's electricity production."[103]

The findings of the report reflected the reframing that has taken place during the campaign – nuclear energy was again very much seen against the background of climate change. In fact, in an interview on ABC's *Lateline* on the day of the draft report's release, Dr Switkowski said that, at the beginning of the inquiry, climate change was an issue they had hoped to keep separate from their discussion. But fuelled by strong community interest in climate change the connection had to be made as to how the adoption of alternative energy sources could help the country lower its greenhouse gas emissions.[104]

While the taskforce emphasised that nuclear power would be around 30–50 per cent more costly than energy from coal-fuelled power plants, it was seen as a potential part of the solution to tackle climate change:

---

[101] Stanton op.cit.

[102] Australian Government, *Uranium mining, processing and nuclear energy – opportunities for Australia*, Report to the Prime Minister by the Uranium Mining, Processing and Nuclear Energy Review Taskforce, December 2006. Source: http://www.dpmc.gov.au/umpner/docs/nuclear_report.pdf.

[103] ibid, p. 5.

[104] 'Ziggy Switkowski discussed new nuclear report', *Lateline*, ABCTV, 21 November 2006. Source: http://www.abc.net.au/lateline/content/2006/s1794281.htm.

Nuclear power is an option that Australia would need to consider seriously among the range of practical options to meet its growing energy demand and to reduce its greenhouse gas signature.[105]

However, to make nuclear energy competitive a form of emission pricing would be required. Dr Switkowski made this clear when he said that investment in nuclear power could and should proceed only if a cost on carbon emissions be imposed.[106]

Two weeks after the findings of the taskforce were made public, Mr Howard announced that a joint government/business Prime Ministerial Task Group to investigate carbon trading would be formed. In his announcement he made no specific reference to the finding by Dr Switkowski that emissions pricing would be a condition to making nuclear energy competitive.

The task group presented its findings on 31 May 2007 and recommended that Australia establish a carbon trading system by the year 2012 with gradual emissions reductions through a cap and trade model. It did not name a specific target in its final report saying a "long-term aspirational goal"[107] could be announced in 2008. The task group also suggested winding up the Mandatory Renewable Energy Target (MRET).[108]

While the task group on emission trading was still in the process of gathering relevant data, the Prime Minister made a further important decision on 28 April 2007. On the same day, during its national conference, the Labor party, against strong internal opposition, voted to overturn its 25-year-old 'no new uranium mines' policy, while emphasising its opposition to the domestic use of nuclear energy. Mr

---

[105] Australian Government, op.cit., p. 13.
[106] Peatling S, 'Build 25 nuclear reactors', *The Sydney Morning Herald*, 22 November 2006.
[107] Australian Government, *Report of the Task Group on Emissions Trading*, May 2007, p. 13. Source: http://www.dpmc.gov.au/publications/emissions/docs/emissions_trading_report.pdf.
[108] Australian Government, op.cit., p. 137.

Howard in turn, in a speech to the Victorian Liberal Party conference announced further support for a possible nuclear future by announcing a "strategy to increase uranium exports and to prepare for a possible expansion of the nuclear industry in Australia".[109] Part of this effort would be the removal of legislative bans to construct nuclear power stations in Australia, namely the *Environment Protection and Biodiversity Conservation Act* and the *Australian Radiation Protection and Nuclear Safety Act*.

According to the Prime Minister, the country would also apply for membership of the Generation IV International Forum, a group of 13 countries collaborating on the development of the fourth generation of nuclear reactors. In addition, four work maps in relation to nuclear energy are to be developed by the federal government with areas including: a nuclear energy regulatory regime; skills and technical training; enhanced research and development; and "communication strategies so that all Australians and other stakeholders can clearly understand what needs to be done and why".[110]

Communication with the wider public is of particular importance – given what we have ascertained concerning the campaign between June and October 2006. In fact, the taskforce itself acknowledged this is a deciding factor for a possible nuclear future in Australia:

> "Community acceptance would be the first requirement for nuclear power to operate successfully in Australia. This would require informed discussion of the issues involved, including the potential costs and benefits of nuclear power."[111]

In a statement on the day of Mr Howard's April 2007 announcement, Ian MacFarlane said funds would need to be allocated to educate the

---

[109] Howard J, Media Release, 'Uranium Mining and Nuclear Energy: A Way Forward for Australia', 28 April 2007.   Source: http://www.pm.gov.au/media/Release/2007/Media_Release24284.cfm.

[110] ibid.

[111] Australian Government, op.cit., p. 13.

public about the value of nuclear power.[112] A uranium industry-commissioned poll from May 2007 suggests a slight majority of 51 per cent is in favour of nuclear power generally,[113] but two-thirds of Australians say they were opposed to nuclear power stations being built in their area.[114]

At the end of May 2007, *The Sydney Morning Herald* revealed that the federal government was planning to spend $23 million on a public information campaign on its climate change strategy. Proposed measures for the campaign include television, radio and newspaper advertising, as well as a booklet on energy saving that would be sent to seven million households.[115] Whether this initiative would run parallel to a public awareness campaign on nuclear power or both issues would be integrated into one single climate change campaign frame was not yet clear.

Conclusion

Incredible amounts of time are spent planning campaigns by political communicators. Implementation, however, is a much more difficult and intimidating undertaking.[116] As a result, communicative strategies are most often minimalist in nature and feature asymmetrical, or one-way flows of communication. This is apparent through tactics such as speeches, which are most effective when supported by other tactics also communicated asymmetrically, for example, media releases. Advances in technology have developed an increased ability to produce and disseminate these tactics, through vehicles like the internet and television. Visible tactics by the government were apparent, concluding the existence of an issues-based campaign surrounding nuclear energy. It

---

[112] ABC News Online, 'MacFarlane outlines Govt's nuclear industry plans', 28 April 2007. Source: http://www.abc.net.au/news/newsitems/200704/s1908836.htm.

[113] Australian Uranium Association, 'Australian's Support Uranium Mining', 14 May 2007. Source: http://aua.greenbanana.com.au/page.php?pid=14&category=1.

[114] Wilkinson M, 'Power for the people', *The Sydney Morning Herald*, 19 May 2007.

[115] Wilkinson M, '$23m ad blitz to save planet – and the PM', *The Sydney Morning Herald*, 25 May 2007.

[116] Stanton, op.cit.

must be assumed that because a campaign exists, the tactics comprise an element of an overall goal-oriented strategy.

Initially, the strategic frame adopted by the government was predominantly economic. The fact that this frame appeared to have receded in importance as the campaign progressed indicated that there was a search, in the preliminary stages, for a strategic fit. Acknowledging that the Australian public had a strong, historical negative reaction to the nuclear issue, meant that the government had to move carefully so as not to inflame existing negative opinions. The government used prolocutors, such as Tim Flannery, to present a 'clean green' image of nuclear energy.

Once the 'clean green' message had been established, the Prime Minister could interpellate[117] himself in the established worldview, without the suspicion that the claim may have received if being communicated solely from a government position. With the linking of nuclear energy as a solution to global warming, the federal government has found a strong strategic fit that also frames itself as environmentally responsible, an important consideration given the priority the public is placing on environmental concerns in the lead up to the next federal election.

Acknowledgements

The authors would like to thank Dr Richard Stanton (School of Letters, Art, and Media, the University of Sydney) whose work forms the basis of this study, for his guidance and support.

---

[117] Althusser L, *Lenin and philosophy, and other essays.* Translated from the French by Ben Brewster. New York, Monthly Review Press, 1972.

Appendix A

Stakeholder group	Function / position
The nuclear industry	Is extremely important in the campaign. The Government requires the industry's support for the policy to ensure economic viability. The industry includes mining, e.g. BHP Billiton, Rio Tinto, Silex and domestic and overseas investors and energy distributors e.g. Energy Networks Association's members and the Nuclear Fuel Leasing Group.
Existing energy providers	Potentially oppositional if the government is seen to disregard their interests e.g. coal, gas and oil industries.
Media	As a communication channel for the information flow from the government to citizens. As agenda setters and opinion leaders, the media is able to influence and direct public opinion on the issue.
Federal backbenchers	Potentially supportive or oppositional. Their position relies, largely, on the reaction in their electorates, e.g. if their electorate gains economically or if their electorate may be a proposed site for a nuclear reactor. From monitoring the Hansard database, Liberal backbenchers in the lower house appear to be supportive of the debate; however, concerned if there is real possibility of a nuclear reactor in their electorate. It is possible the Prime Minister and Cabinet have targeted this group through a direct mail campaign to generate support and allay any concerns.
The federal opposition	Changed its Three Mines policy in April 2007, however, it remains opposed to the domestic use of nuclear energy and enrichment.
Non-government-organisations (NGOs)	1. Opponents of nuclear energy, e.g. Australian Conservation Foundation (ACF), Greenpeace Australia and anti-nuclear organisations. 2. Supporters of nuclear energy e.g. Uranium Information Centre (UIC), Australian Institute of Nuclear Science and Engineering, Australian Nuclear Association, Minerals Council of Australia. Undecided – do not have a decisive position. Their position is dependent on the Government's proposed policy e.g. Australian Strategic Policy Institute.
Customers	Current customers e.g. USA, Japan, South Korea, EU, China potential customers include India. India is not a signatory to the Nuclear Non-Proliferation Treaty. The Prime Minister has alluded to the possibility of selling uranium to India.
Citizens	Have the power to remove the government from office at the next federal election.
Renewable energy sector	E.g. wind, geothermal and solar. This sector has criticised the government for its failure to increase the mandatory renewable energy target (MRET).